D1029698

Infrared Spectra of Inorganic and Coordination Compounds

Infrared Spectra of Inorganic and Coordination Compounds

KAZUO NAKAMOTO

Associate Professor of Chemistry
Illinois Institute of Technology

JOHN WILEY & SONS, INC., NEW YORK · LONDON

Copyright © 1963 by John Wiley & Sons, Inc.

All Rights Reserved. This book or any part thereof must not be reproduced in any form without the written permission of the publisher.

Library of Congress Catalog Card Number: 63–8057

Printed in the United States of America

QH
535.842
N163i
104197

Dedicated to the memory of
Professor Ryutaro Tsuchida
who first stimulated my interest in
inorganic and coordination chemistry

PREFACE

Since 1945, the volume of literature on the infrared spectra of inorganic and coordination compounds has grown with ever-increasing rapidity. As a result, it is becoming more and more difficult for any one individual to read all pertinent articles. Excellent books on the theory of vibrational spectra and on the infrared spectra of organic compounds have been published, but relatively few comprehenisve reviews of the vibrational spectra of inorganic or coordination compounds are available. This situation has prompted me to write this book.

In reviewing the literature, I have attempted to interpret the experimental results in terms of normal vibrations, as far as it is possible. Consequently, I have been most interested in normal coordinate analysis, in fundamental frequencies, in band assignments and in structural considerations, while omitting any consideration of band intensities or rotational fine structure. The experimental aspects of vibrational spectra have also been omitted.

Part I is devoted to the minimum amount of theory necessary for an understanding of the concept of the normal vibration and of the method of normal coordinate analysis. For a more detailed discussion of the theory, the reader may consult the references cited in Part I. An application of the method of normal coordinate analysis to a complex system is given in detail in Appendix III. In Parts II and III, the observed fundamental vibrational frequencies of molecules are discussed in terms of their relation to molecular structure. Although most of the data are from infrared spectra, Raman spectral data have been quoted wherever pertinent or necessary. This volume is intended as a critical review of the infrared spectra of inorganic and coordination compounds; but it was clearly impossible to refer to all work which has been reported in these fields. I have, however, tried to give a broad and reasonably complete coverage of the fields. But in the discussion I have had to select examples which I considered more illustrative, more important or more interesting. Although this book is intended to cover all inorganic and coordination compounds, the border line between these and organic compounds is a difficult one to draw. Therefore I have chosen to omit most of the metallo-organic compounds.

I wish to express my sincere thanks to Professor Arthur E. Martell whose discussions inspired me to begin this book. A special word of gratitude is due to Professors S. Mizushima, T. Shimanouchi and

I. Nakagawa whose publications and personal communications have greatly helped me in writing on normal coordinate analysis. I am also deeply indebted to Dr. J. L. Bethune, Rev. Paul J. McCarthy, S.J., and Sister M. Paulita, C.S.J., who read the whole manuscript and gave many valuable comments. Thanks are also due to Dr. Junnosuke Fujita and Mr. Yukiyoshi Morimoto, who assisted in the preparation of this book, and to Mrs. Helen Kwan and Mrs. Jeannette Lynch, who typed the manuscript.

KAZUO NAKAMOTO

Chicago, Illinois
December, 1962

NOTES ON FIGURES, TABLES AND REFERENCES

Most of the infrared spectra illustrated in this book were obtained by the author using a Perkin-Elmer Model 21 double-bean infrared spectrophotometer equipped with NaCl and CsBr optics. The KBr pellet technique and the nujol mull method were employed for the preparation of the sample in the NaCl and CsBr regions, respectively. References are given for spectra taken from the literature.

Vibrational frequencies given in the tables are those observed. Calculated values are in parentheses. Some frequency values given in the literature were rounded off to preserve uniformity in the tables. If more than one reference is cited for a compound, the data listed in the table were taken from the first reference in the reference column. In some tables, it is not indicated whether the data are from infrared spectra or from Raman spectra.

The following abbreviations and symbols are used in the tables: IR, infrared; R, Raman; *p*, polarized; *dp*, depolarized; ν, stretching; δ, deformation; ρ_w, wagging; ρ_r, rocking; ρ_t, twisting; π, out-of-plane bending; *as*, antisymmetric; *s*, symmetric; *d*, degenerate; GVF, generalized valence force field; UBF, Urey-Bradley force field.

References are found at the end of each part. A reference number I-12, for example, indicates reference 12 of Part I. If no Part number (I, II or III) precedes the reference number, the reference is to be found at the end of the part in which it is cited.

CONTENTS

Theory of the Normal Vibration

Part I

I-1. ORIGIN OF MOLECULAR SPECTRA

As a first approximation, it is possible to separate the energy of a molecule as three additive components associated with (1) the rotation of the molecule as a whole, (2) the vibrations of the constituent atoms and (3) the motion of the electrons in the molecule.† The translational energy of the molecule may be ignored in this discussion. The basis for this separation lies in the fact that the velocity of electrons is much greater than the vibrational velocity of nuclei, which is again much greater than the velocity of molecular rotation. If a molecule is placed in an electromagnetic field (e.g., light), a transfer of energy from the field to the molecule will occur only when Bohr's frequency condition is satisfied:

$$\Delta E = h\nu \tag{1.1}$$

where ΔE is the difference in energy between two quantized states, h is Planck's constant, and ν is the frequency of the light.‡ If

$$\Delta E = E'' - E' \tag{1.2}$$

where E'' is a quantized state of higher energy than E', the molecule *absorbs* radiation when it is excited from E' to E'' and *emits* radiation of the same frequency as given by Eq. 1.1 when it reverts from E'' to E'.

† Hereafter, the word *molecule* may also represent an *ion*.

‡ The frequency, ν, is converted to the wave number, $\tilde{\nu}$, or wavelength, λ_w, through the relation

$$\nu = c\tilde{\nu} = c/\lambda_w$$

where c is the velocity of light. For theoretical discussion, ν and $\tilde{\nu}$ are more convenient than λ_w since they are proportional to the energy of radiation. More explicit relations between these three units are given below for the region in which vibrational spectra occur.

Frequency (sec^{-1})	Wave Number (cm^{-1})	Wavelength (μ)
$3 \cdot 10^{14}$	10^4	1
$3 \cdot 10^{13}$	10^3	10
$3 \cdot 10^{12}$	10^2	10^2

Although the dimensions of ν and $\tilde{\nu}$ differ from one another, it is conventional to express the frequency by the wave number unit. For example, a phrase such as "a frequency shift of 25 cm^{-1}" is often employed. All the spectral data in this book are given in terms of $\tilde{\nu}$ (cm^{-1}). For convenience, a conversion table for $\tilde{\nu}$ (cm^{-1}) and λ_w (μ) is given in Appendix IV.

Because rotational levels are relatively close to each other, transitions between these levels occur at low frequencies (long wavelengths). In fact, pure rotational spectra appear in the range between 1 cm^{-1} (10^4 μ) and 10^2 cm^{-1} (10^2 μ). The separation of vibrational energy levels is greater, and the transitions occur at higher frequencies (shorter wavelengths) than do the rotational transitions. As a result, pure vibrational spectra are observed in the range between 10^2 cm^{-1} (10^2 μ) and 10^4 cm^{-1} (1 μ). Finally, electronic energy levels are usually far apart, and electronic spectra are observed in the range between 10^4 cm^{-1} (1 μ) and 10^5 cm^{-1} (10^{-1} μ). Thus pure rotational, vibrational and electronic spectra are usually observed in the microwave and far infrared, the infrared, and the visible and ultraviolet regions, respectively. This division into three regions, however, is to some extent arbitrary, for pure rotational spectra may appear in the near infrared region ($1.5 \sim 0.5 \times 10^4$ cm^{-1}) if transitions to higher excited states are involved, and pure electronic transitions may appear in the near infrared region if the levels are closely spaced.

Figure I-1 illustrates transitions of the three types mentioned for a diatomic molecule. As the figure shows, rotational intervals tend to increase as the rotational quantum number J increases, whereas vibrational intervals tend to decrease as the vibrational quantum number v increases. The dotted line below each electronic level indicates the zero point energy which exists even at a temperature of absolute zero as a result of nuclear vibration. It should be emphasized that not all transitions between these levels are possible. In order to see whether the transition is *allowed* or *forbidden*, the relevant selection rule must be examined. This, in turn, is determined by the symmetry of the molecule. As will be seen later, vibrational problems like those mentioned above can be solved for polyatomic molecules in an elegant manner by the use of group theory.

Since this book is concerned only with vibrational spectra, no description of electronic and rotational spectra is given. Although vibrational spectra are observed experimentally as infrared or Raman spectra, the physical origins of these two types of spectra are different. Infrared spectra originate in transitions between two vibrational levels of the molecule in the electronic ground state and are usually observed as *absorption spectra* in the infrared region. On the other hand, Raman spectra originate in the electronic polarization caused by ultraviolet or visible light. If a molecule is irradiated by monochromatic light of frequency ν,† then, because of electronic polarization induced in the molecule by this incident light, light of frequency ν (Rayleigh scattering) as well as of $\nu \pm \nu_i$ (Raman

† In principle, light of any frequency can be used unless the incident light is absorbed by the molecule.

scattering) is emitted (ν_i represents a vibrational frequency). Thus the vibrational frequencies are observed as *Raman shifts* from the incident frequency ν in the ultraviolet or visible region.

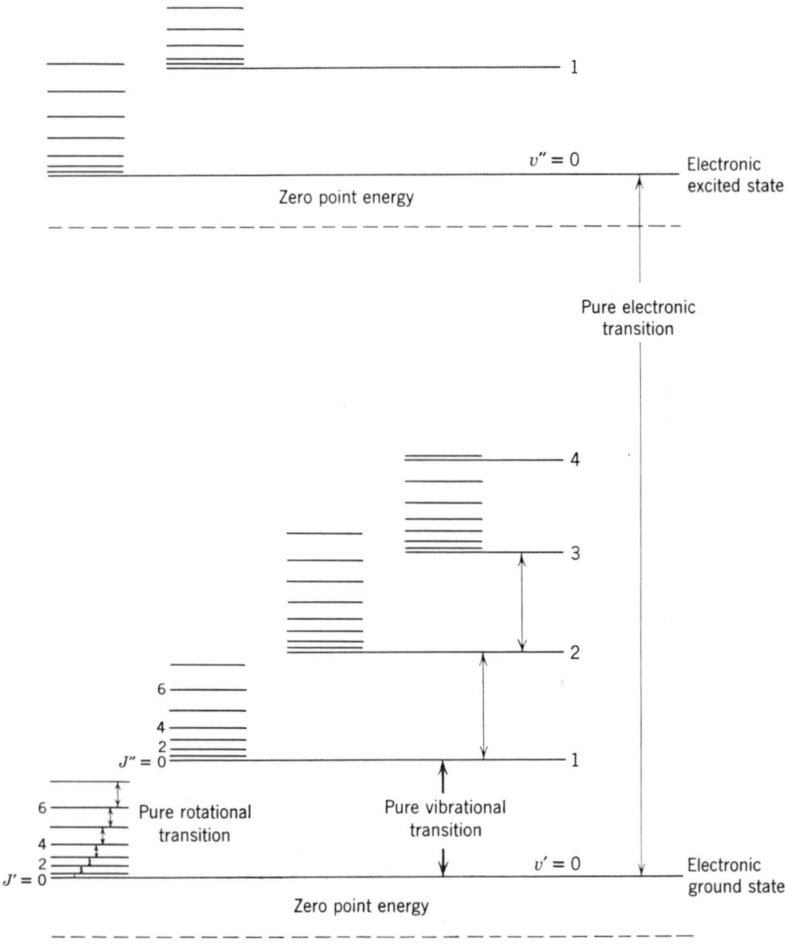

Fig. I-1. Energy levels of a diatomic molecule (the actual spacings of electronic levels are much larger and those of rotational levels are much smaller than those shown in the figure).

It is to be expected, from Fig. I-1, that vibrational spectra will be relatively complex because they are accompanied by rotational transitions. In fact, simple molecules such as ammonia exhibit rotational fine structure in the gaseous state; see Fig. I-2. In polyatomic molecules, however, such

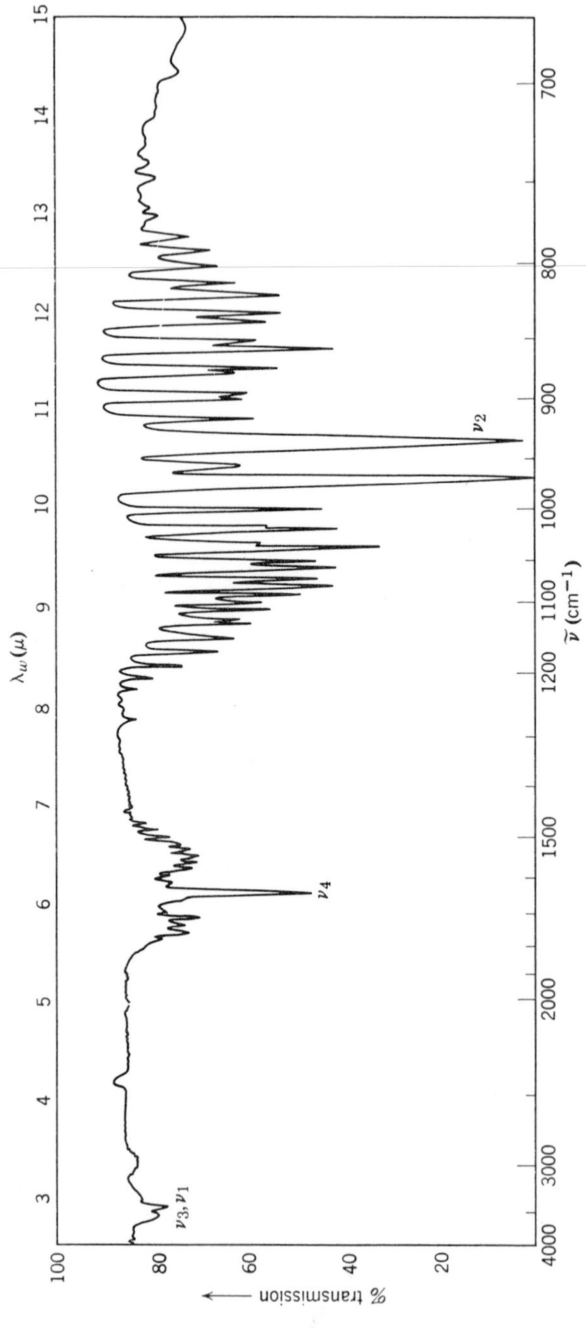

Fig. I-2. Rotational fine structures of gaseous NH_3.

rotational fine structure is not observed because of the relatively close spacing of the rotational levels.

According to the selection rule for the harmonic oscillator, any transitions corresponding to $\Delta v = \pm 1$ are allowed (Sec. I-2). Under ordinary conditions, however, only the *fundamentals* which originate in the transition from $v = 0$ to $v = 1$ in the electronic ground state can be observed. This is due to the fact that most of the transitions have $v = 0$ in the initial state, for at room temperature the number of molecules in this state is exceedingly large compared with that in the excited states (*Maxwell-Boltzmann distribution law*). In addition to the selection rule for the harmonic oscillator, another restriction results from the symmetry of the molecule (Sec. I-9). Thus the number of allowed transitions in polyatomic molecules is greatly reduced. The *overtones and combination bands*† of these fundamentals are forbidden by the selection rule of the harmonic oscillator. However, they are weakly observed in the spectrum because of the anharmonicity of the vibration (Sec. I-2). Since they are less important than the fundamentals, they will be discussed only when necessary.

I-2. VIBRATION OF A DIATOMIC MOLECULE

Through quantum mechanical considerations,[1–4] the vibration of two nuclei in a diatomic molecule can be reduced to the motion of a single particule of mass μ, whose displacement q from its equilibrium position is equal to the change of the internuclear distance. μ is called the *reduced mass* and is represented by

$$\frac{1}{\mu} = \frac{1}{m_1} + \frac{1}{m_2} \tag{2.1}$$

where m_1 and m_2 are the masses of the two nuclei. The kinetic energy is then

$$T = \tfrac{1}{2}\mu\dot{q}^2 = \frac{1}{2\mu}\,p^2 \tag{2.2}$$

where p is the conjugate momentum, $\mu\dot{q}$. If a simple parabolic potential function such as that shown in Fig. I-3 is assumed, the system represents a *harmonic oscillator*, and the potential energy is simply given by

$$V = \tfrac{1}{2}Kq^2 \tag{2.3}$$

Here K is the force constant for the vibration. Then the Schrödinger wave equation becomes

$$\frac{d^2\psi}{dq^2} + \frac{8\pi^2\mu}{h^2}(E - \tfrac{1}{2}Kq^2)\psi = 0 \tag{2.4}$$

† Overtones represent multiples of some fundamental, whereas combination bands arise from the sum or difference of two different fundamentals.

If this equation is solved with the condition that ψ must be a *well-behaved function*,[3] the eigenvalues are

$$E_v = h\nu(v + \tfrac{1}{2}) = hc\tilde{\nu}(v + \tfrac{1}{2}) \tag{2.5}$$

with the frequency of vibration

$$\nu = \frac{1}{2\pi}\sqrt{\frac{K}{\mu}} \quad \text{or} \quad \tilde{\nu} = \frac{1}{2\pi c}\sqrt{\frac{K}{\mu}} \tag{2.6}$$

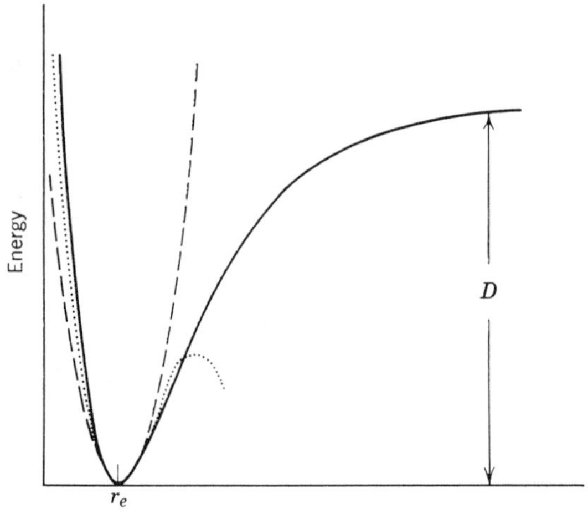

Fig. I-3. Potential curve for a diatomic molecule. Actual potential, solid line; parabola, broken line; cubic parabola, dotted line.

Here v is the vibrational quantum number, and it can have the values 0, 1, 2, 3, ...

The corresponding eigenfunctions are[1–4]

$$\psi_v = \frac{(\alpha/\pi)^{1/4}}{\sqrt{2^v v!}}\, e^{-\alpha q^2/2} H_v(\sqrt{\alpha}\, q) \tag{2.7}$$

where $\alpha = 2\pi\sqrt{\mu K}/h = 4\pi^2\mu\nu/h$, and $H_v(\sqrt{\alpha}\, q)$ is a Hermite polynomial of the vth degree. Thus the eigenvalues and the corresponding eigenfunctions are

$$\begin{array}{ll} E_0 = \tfrac{1}{2}h\nu & \psi_0 = (\alpha/\pi)^{1/4} e^{-\alpha q^2/2} \\ E_1 = \tfrac{3}{2}h\nu & \psi_1 = (\alpha/\pi)^{1/4} 2^{1/2} q e^{-\alpha q^2/2} \\ \cdots\cdots & \cdots\cdots\cdots\cdots \\ \cdots\cdots & \cdots\cdots\cdots\cdots \end{array} \tag{2.8}$$

As Fig. I-3 shows, actual potential curves can be approximated more exactly by adding a cubic term:[4]

$$V = \tfrac{1}{2}Kq^2 - Gq^3 \qquad (K \gg G) \tag{2.9}$$

Then the eigenvalues are

$$E_v = hc\omega_e(v + \tfrac{1}{2}) - hc\omega_e x_e(v + \tfrac{1}{2})^2 + \cdots \tag{2.10}$$

where ω_e is the wave number corrected for *anharmonicity*, and $\omega_e x_e$ indicates the magnitude of anharmonicity. Table II-1 of Part II indicates the observed wave numbers and ω_e values for a number of diatomic molecules. Equation 2.10 shows that the energy levels of the anharmonic oscillator are not equidistant, and the separation decreases slowly as v increases. This anharmonicity is responsible for the appearance of overtones and combination vibrations which are forbidden in the harmonic oscillator.[4] Since the anharmonicity correction has not been made for most polyatomic molecules, in large part because of the complexity of the calculation, the frequencies given in Parts II and III are not corrected for anharmonicity (except for those given in Table II-1).

According to Eq. 2.6, the frequency of the vibration in a diatomic molecule is proportional to the square root of K/μ. If K is approximately the same for a series of diatomic molecules, the frequency is inversely proportional to the square root of μ. This point is illustrated by the series H_2, HD and D_2 shown in Table II-1 (Part II). If μ is approximately the same for a series of diatomic molecules, the frequency is proportional to the square root of K. This point is illustrated by the series HF, HCl, HBr and HI. These simple rules, obtained for a diatomic molecule, are helpful to the understanding of the vibrational spectra of polyatomic molecules.

Figure I-4 indicates the relation between the force constant K, calculated from Eq. 2.6, and the dissociation energy in a series of hydrogen halides. Evidently, the bond becomes stronger as the force constant becomes larger. It should be noted, however, that a theoretical relation between these two quantities is difficult to derive even for a diatomic molecule.† The force constant is a measure of the curvature of the potential well near the equilibrium position:

$$K = \left(\frac{d^2V}{dq^2}\right)_{q\to 0} \tag{2.11}$$

whereas the dissociation energy D is given by the depth of the potential

† Quantum mechanical expression of the potential function involves a Coulomb integral, an exchange integral and an overlap integral.[1–5] Calculation of K from Eq. 2.11, therefore, is extremely difficult.

energy curve (Fig. I-3). Thus a large force constant means sharp curvature of the potential well near the bottom but does not necessarily indicate a deep potential well. Usually, however, a larger force constant is interpreted as an indication of a stronger bond, although no theoretical justification is available at the present time.

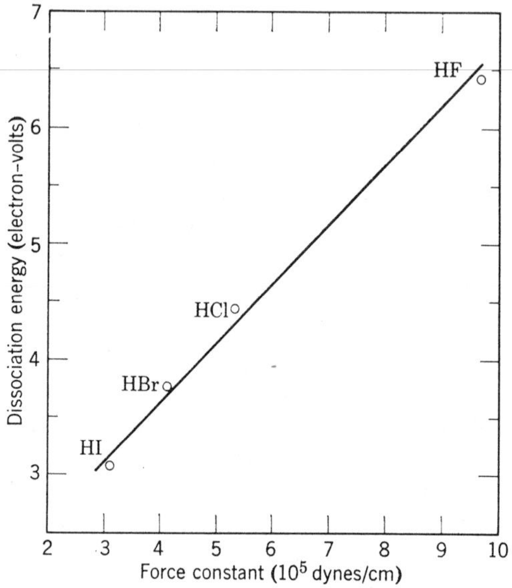

Fig. I-4. Relation between force constant and dissociation energy in hydrogen halides.

I-3. NORMAL COORDINATES AND NORMAL VIBRATIONS

In diatomic molecules, the vibration of the nuclei occurs only along the line connecting two nuclei. In polyatomic molecules, however, the situation is much more complicated because all the nuclei perform their own harmonic oscillations. It can be shown, however, that any of these extremely complicated vibrations of the molecule may be represented as a superposition of a number of *normal vibrations*.

Let the displacement of each nucleus be expressed in terms of rectangular coordinate systems with the origin of each system at the equilibrium position of each nucleus. Then the kinetic energy of an N-atom molecule would be expressed as

$$T = \frac{1}{2}\sum_N m_N\left[\left(\frac{d\,\Delta x_N}{dt}\right)^2 + \left(\frac{d\,\Delta y_N}{dt}\right)^2 + \left(\frac{d\,\Delta z_N}{dt}\right)^2\right] \tag{3.1}$$

If generalized coordinates such as

$$q_1 = \sqrt{m_1}\,\Delta x_1, \quad q_2 = \sqrt{m_1}\,\Delta y_1, \quad q_3 = \sqrt{m_1}\,\Delta z_1, \quad q_4 = \sqrt{m_2}\,\Delta x_2, \quad \ldots \tag{3.2}$$

are used, the kinetic energy is simply written

$$T = \frac{1}{2}\sum_i^{3N} \dot{q}_i^{\,2} \tag{3.3}$$

The potential energy of the system is a complex function of all the coordinates involved. For small values of the displacements, it may be expanded in a Taylor's series as

$$V(q_1, q_2, \ldots, q_{3N}) = V_0 + \sum_i^{3N}\left(\frac{\partial V}{\partial q_i}\right)_0 q_i + \frac{1}{2}\sum_{i,j}^{3N}\left(\frac{\partial^2 V}{\partial q_i\,\partial q_j}\right)_0 q_i q_j + \cdots \tag{3.4}$$

where the derivatives are evaluated at $q_i = 0$, the equilibrium position. The constant term V_0 can be taken as zero if the potential energy at $q_i = 0$ is taken as a standard. The $(\partial V/\partial q_i)_0$ terms also become zero since V must be a minimum at $q_i = 0$. Thus V may be represented by

$$V = \frac{1}{2}\sum_{i,j}^{3N}\left(\frac{\partial^2 V}{\partial q_i\,\partial q_j}\right)_0 q_i q_j = \frac{1}{2}\sum_{i,j}^{3N} b_{ij} q_i q_j \tag{3.5}$$

neglecting higher order terms.

If the potential energy given by Eq. 3.5 did not include any cross products such as $q_i q_j$, the problem could be solved directly by using Newton's equation:

$$\frac{d}{dt}\left(\frac{\partial T}{\partial \dot{q}_i}\right) + \frac{\partial V}{\partial q_i} = 0 \qquad i = 1, 2, \ldots, 3N \tag{3.6}$$

From Eqs. 3.3 and 3.5, Eq. 3.6 is written

$$\ddot{q}_i + \sum_j b_{ij} q_j = 0 \qquad j = 1, 2, \ldots, 3N \tag{3.7}$$

If $b_{ij} = 0$ for $i \neq j$, Eq. 3.7 becomes

$$\ddot{q}_i + b_{ii} q_i = 0 \tag{3.8}$$

and the solution is given by

$$q_i = q_i^0 \sin(\sqrt{b_{ii}}\,t + \delta_i) \tag{3.9}$$

where q_i^0 and δ_i are the amplitude and the phase constant, respectively. Furthermore, b_{ii} in this equation corresponds to K/μ of Eq. 2.6 for diatomic molecules.

Since, in general, this simplification is not applicable, the coordinates

q_i must be transformed into a set of new coordinates Q_i through the relations

$$
\begin{aligned}
q_1 &= \sum_i B_{1i} Q_i \\
q_2 &= \sum_i B_{2i} Q_i \\
&\cdots\cdots \\
q_k &= \sum_i B_{ki} Q_i
\end{aligned}
\tag{3.10}
$$

The Q_i are called *normal coordinates* for the system. By appropriate choice of the coefficients B_{ki}, both the potential and the kinetic energies can be written

$$T = \tfrac{1}{2} \sum_i \dot{Q}_i^2 \tag{3.11}$$

$$V = \tfrac{1}{2} \sum_i \lambda_i Q_i^2 \tag{3.12}$$

without any cross products.

If Eqs. 3.11 and 3.12 are combined with Newton's equation (3.6), there results

$$\ddot{Q}_i + \lambda_i Q_i = 0 \tag{3.13}$$

The solution of this equation is given by

$$Q_i = Q_i^0 \sin (\sqrt{\lambda_i}\, t + \delta_i) \tag{3.14}$$

and the frequency is

$$\nu_i = \frac{1}{2\pi} \sqrt{\lambda_i} \tag{3.15}$$

Such a vibration is called a *normal vibration*.

For the general N-atom molecule, it is obvious that the number of the normal vibrations is only $3N - 6$ since 6 coordinates are required to describe the translational and rotational motion of the molecule as a whole. Linear molecules have $3N - 5$ normal vibrations as no rotational freedom exists around the molecular axis. Thus the general form of the molecular vibration is a superposition of the $3N - 6$ (or $3N - 5$) normal vibrations given by Eq. 3.14.

The physical meaning of the normal vibration may be demonstrated in the following way. As shown in Eq. 3.10, the original displacement coordinate is related to the normal coordinate by

$$q_k = \sum_i B_{ki} Q_i \tag{3.10}$$

Since all the normal vibrations are independent of each other, consideration may be limited to a special case in which only one normal vibration, subscripted by 1, is excited (i.e., $Q_1{}^0 \neq 0$, $Q_2{}^0 = Q_3{}^0 = \cdots = 0$). Then it follows from Eqs. 3.10 and 3.14 that

$$\begin{aligned} q_k = B_{k1}Q_1 &= B_{k1}Q_1{}^0 \sin(\sqrt{\lambda_1}\, t + \delta_1) \\ &= A_{k1} \sin(\sqrt{\lambda_1}\, t + \delta_1) \end{aligned} \tag{3.16}$$

This relation holds for all k. Thus it is seen that the excitation of one normal vibration of the system causes vibrations, given by Eq. 3.16, of all the nuclei in the system. In other words, in the normal vibration, all the nuclei move with the same frequency and in phase.

This is true for any other normal vibration. Thus Eq. 3.16 may be written in the more general form

$$q_k = A_k \sin(\sqrt{\lambda}\, t + \delta) \tag{3.17}$$

If Eq. 3.17 is combined with Eq. 3.7, there results

$$-\lambda A_k + \sum_j b_{kj} A_j = 0 \tag{3.18}$$

This is a system of first order simultaneous equations with respect to A. In order for all the A's to be non-zero,

$$\begin{vmatrix} b_{11} - \lambda & b_{12} & b_{13} & \cdots \\ b_{21} & b_{22} - \lambda & b_{23} & \cdots \\ b_{31} & b_{32} & b_{33} - \lambda & \cdots \\ \cdot & \cdot & \cdot & \\ \cdot & \cdot & \cdot & \\ \cdot & \cdot & \cdot & \end{vmatrix} = 0 \tag{3.19}$$

The order of this secular equation is equal to the number of normal vibrations. Suppose one root, λ_1, is found for Eq. 3.19. If it is inserted in Eq. 3.18, A_{k1}, A_{k2}, . . . are obtained for all the nuclei. The same is true for the other roots of Eq. 3.19. Thus the most general solution may be written as a superposition of all the normal vibrations:

$$q_k = \sum_l B_{kl} Q_l{}^0 \sin(\sqrt{\lambda_l}\, t + \delta_l) \tag{3.20}$$

By using these normal coordinates, the Schrödinger wave equation for the system can be written

$$\sum_i \frac{\partial^2 \psi_n}{\partial Q_i{}^2} + \frac{8\pi^2}{h^2}\left(E - \tfrac{1}{2}\sum_i \lambda_i Q_i{}^2\right)\psi_n = 0 \tag{3.21}$$

Separation of the variables can be made by means of the substitution

$$\psi_n = \psi_1(Q_1) \cdot \psi_2(Q_2) \cdots \tag{3.22}$$

If Eq. 3.22 is substituted in Eq. 3.21, there results

$$\frac{d^2\psi_i}{dQ_i^2} + \frac{8\pi^2}{h^2}(E_i - \tfrac{1}{2}\lambda_i Q_i^2)\psi_i = 0 \tag{3.23}$$

where

$$E = E_1 + E_2 + \cdots$$

with

$$E_i = h\nu_i(v_i + \tfrac{1}{2})$$

$$\nu_i = \frac{1}{2\pi}\sqrt{\lambda_i} \tag{3.24}$$

I-4. SYMMETRY ELEMENTS AND POINT GROUPS

As noted before, polyatomic molecules have $3N - 6$ or, if linear, $3N - 5$ normal vibrations. For any given molecule, however, only those vibrations which are permitted by the selection rule for that molecule appear in the infrared and Raman spectra. Since the selection rule is determined by the symmetry of the molecule, this must first be studied.

The spatial geometrical arrangement of the nuclei constituting the molecule determines the symmetry of the molecule. If a coordinate transformation (a reflection or a rotation or a combination of both) produces a configuration of the nuclei indistinguishable from the original one, this transformation is called a *symmetry operation*, and the molecule is said to have a corresponding *symmetry element*. Molecules may have the following symmetry elements, corresponding to the symmetry operations.

(1) Identity, *I*

This is a symmetry element possessed by every molecule no matter how unsymmetrical it is, the corresponding operation being to leave the molecule unchanged. The inclusion of this element is necessitated by mathematical reasons which will be discussed later.

(2) A Plane of Symmetry, σ

If reflection of a molecule with respect to some plane produces a configuration indistinguishable from the original one, the plane is called a plane of symmetry.

(3) A Center of Symmetry, *i*

If reflection at the center, i.e., inversion, produces a configuration indistinguishable from the original one, the center is called a center of symmetry. This operation changes the signs of all the coordinates involved, i.e., $x_i \rightarrow -x_i$, $y_i \rightarrow -y_i$, $z_i \rightarrow -z_i$.

(4) A *p*-fold Axis of Symmetry, C_p

If rotation through an angle $360°/p$ about an axis produces a configuration indistinguishable from the original one, the axis is called a *p*-fold axis of symmetry, C_p. For example, a two-fold axis, C_2, implies that a rotation of 180° about the axis reproduces the original configuration. Molecules may have a two-, three-, four-, five- or six-fold or higher axis. Linear molecules have an infinite-fold (denoted by ∞-fold) axis of symmetry since a rotation of $360°/\infty$, i.e., an infinitely small angle, transforms the molecule into one indistinguishable from the original.

(5) A *p*-fold Rotation-Reflection Axis, S_p

If rotation by $360°/p$ about the axis followed by reflection at a plane perpendicular to the axis produces a configuration indistinguishable from the original one, the axis is called a *p*-fold rotation-reflection axis. Molecules may have a two-, three-, four-, five- or six-fold or higher rotation-reflection axis. Symmetrical linear molecules have an S_∞ axis.

A molecule may have more than one of these symmetry elements. Combination of more and more of these elements produces systems of higher and higher symmetry. Not all combinations of symmetry elements, however, are possible. For example, it is highly improbable that a molecule will have a C_3 and C_4 axis in the same direction because this requires the existence of a twelve-fold axis in the molecule. It should also be noted that the presence of some symmetry elements often implies the presence of other elements. For example, if a molecule has two σ planes at right angles to each other, the line of intersection of these two planes must be a C_2 axis. A possible combination of symmetry operations whose axes intersect at a point is called a *point group*.† It can be shown theoretically[8] that only a limited number of such point groups exist. Figure I-5 illustrates the symmetry elements of the point groups which appear frequently in this book.‡

I-5. SYMMETRY OF NORMAL VIBRATIONS AND SELECTION RULES

Figure I-6 indicates the normal modes of vibration in CO_2 and H_2O molecules. In each normal vibration, the individual nuclei carry out a simple harmonic motion in the direction indicated by the arrow, and all the nuclei have the same frequency of oscillation (i.e., the frequency of the normal vibration) and are moving in the same phase. Furthermore, the

† In this respect, point groups differ from space groups, which involve translations and rotations about non-intersecting axes.

‡ For other point groups, see Refs. 5, 8 and 12.

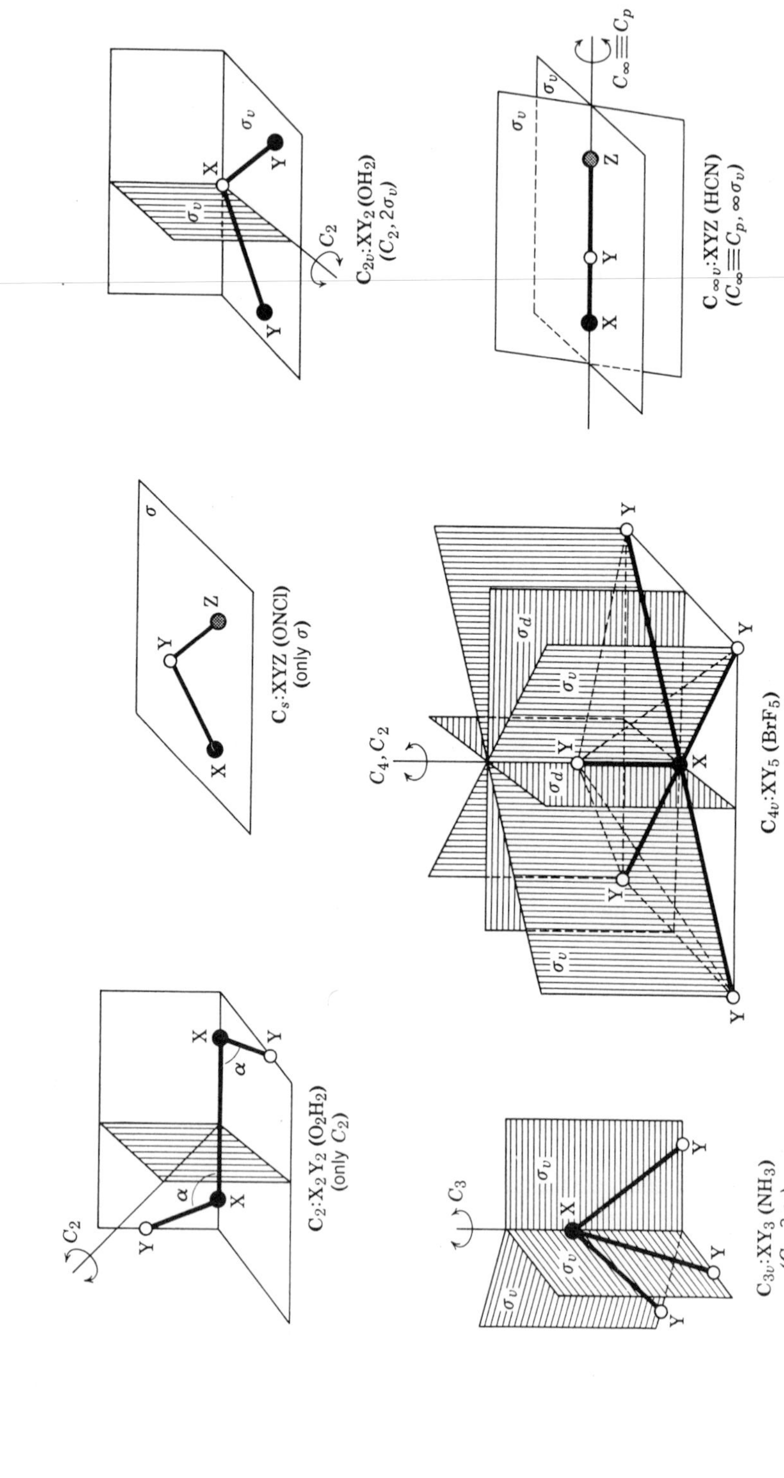
C_2
Y
X
α
X
Y
C_2:X_2Y_2 (O_2H_2)
(only C_2)
X
Y
Z
σ
C_s:XYZ (ONCl)
(only σ)
C_2
σ_v
X
Y
Y
σ_v
C_{2v}:XY_2 (OH_2)
(C_2, $2\sigma_v$)
C_3
X
σ_v
σ_v
σ_v
Y
Y
Y
C_{3v}:XY_3 (NH_3)
(C_3, $3\sigma_v$)
C_4, C_2
σ_v
σ_d
σ_v
σ_d
X
Y
Y
Y
Y
Y
C_{4v}:XY_5 (BrF_5)
($C_4 \gtrsim C_2$, $2\sigma_v$, $2\sigma_d$)
σ_v
σ_v
X
Y
Z
$C_\infty \equiv C_p$
$C_{\infty v}$:XYZ (HCN)
($C_\infty \equiv C_p$, $\infty\sigma_v$)

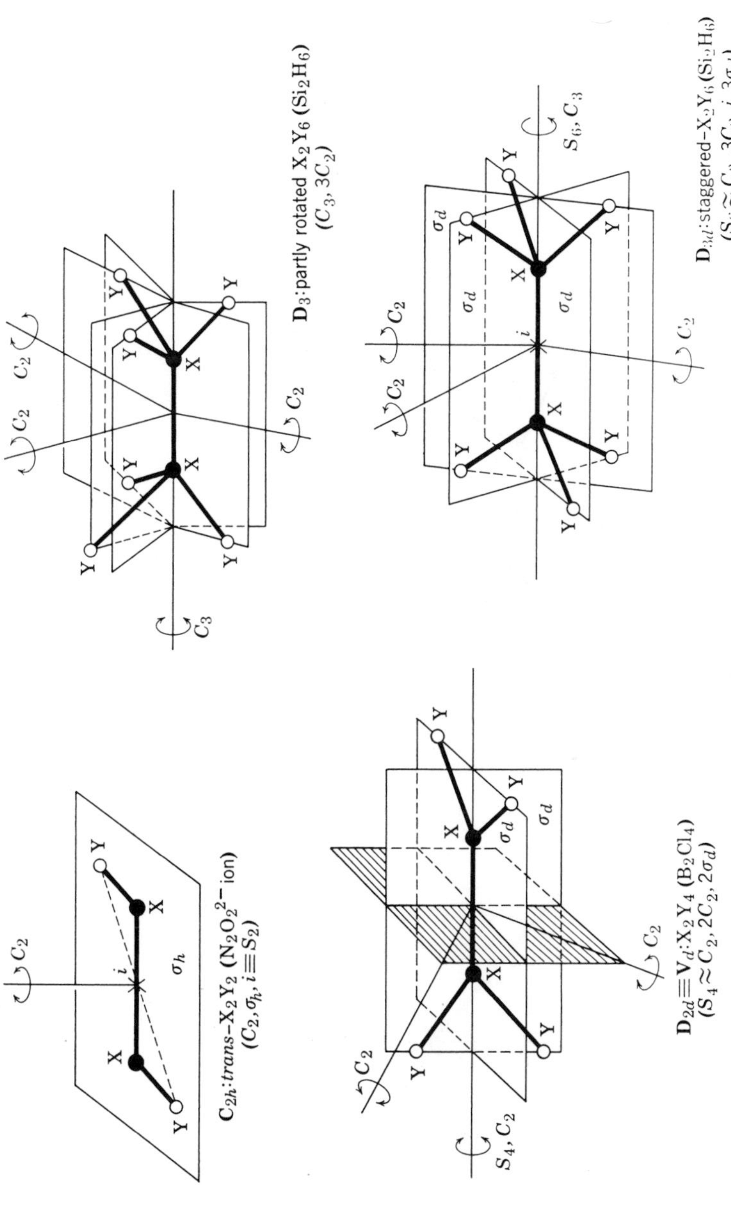

Fig. I-5. Symmetry elements of various point groups (σ_v, σ_h and σ_d denote *vertical*, *horizontal* and *diagonal* planes of symmetry respectively).

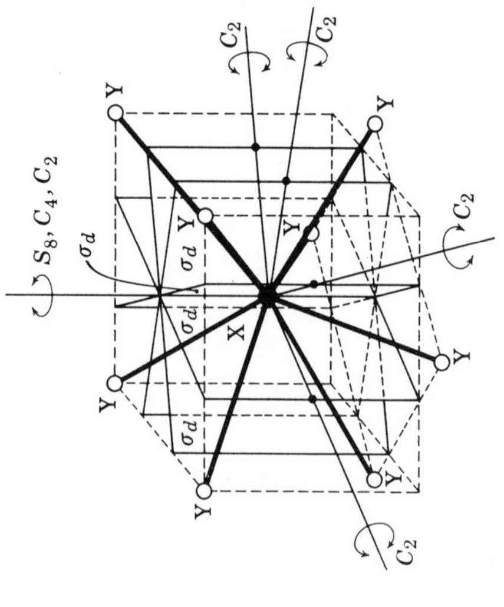

$\mathbf{D}_{4d}$: staggered-XY_8 (TaF_8^{3-} ion)
($S_8 \simeq C_4 \simeq C_2, 4C_2, 4\sigma_d$)

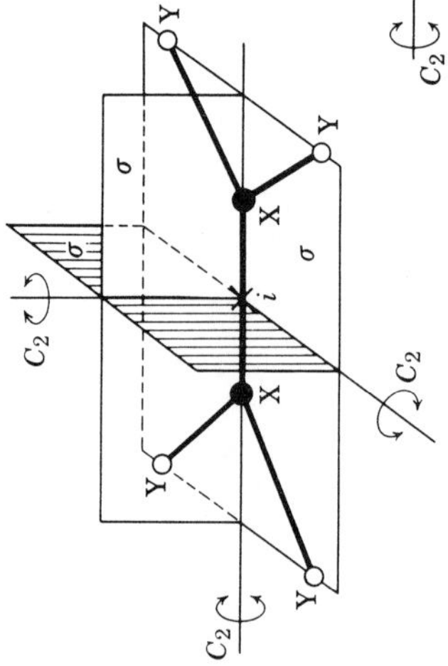

$\mathbf{D}_{2h} \equiv \mathbf{V}_h$: X_2Y_4 ($C_2O_4^{2-}$ ion)
($3C_2, 3\sigma, i$)

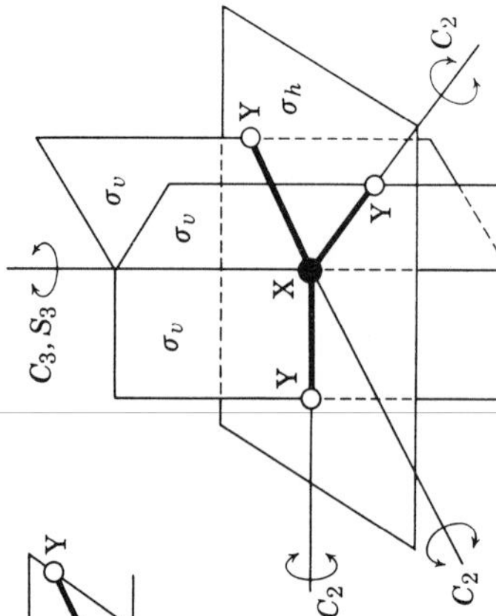

$\mathbf{D}_{3h}$: XY_3 (CO_3^{2-} ion)
($C_3 \simeq S_3, 3C_2, 3\sigma_v, \sigma_h$)

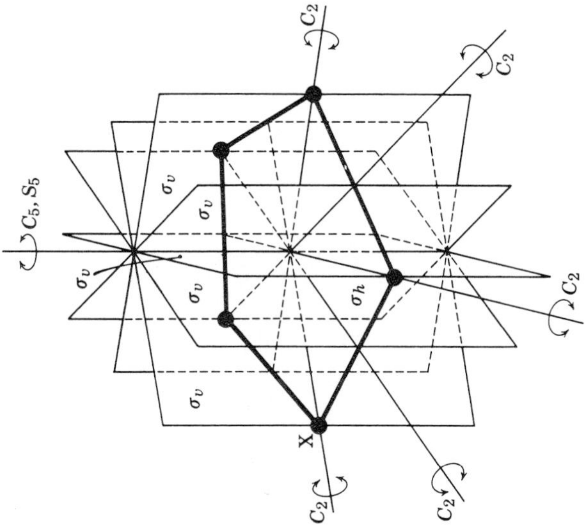

$\mathbf{D}_{5h}$: X_5Y_5 ($C_5H_5^-$ ion) only X atoms shown
($C_5 \approx S_5, 5C_2, 5\sigma_v, \sigma_h$)

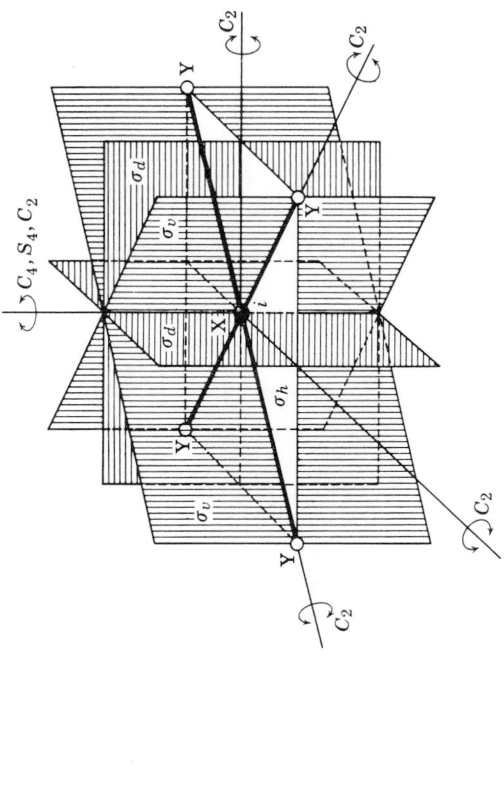

$\mathbf{D}_{4h}$: XY_4 ($PtCl_4^{2-}$ ion)
($C_4 \approx S_4 \approx C_2, 4C_2, 4\sigma, \sigma_h, i$)

Fig. I-5 (Continued).

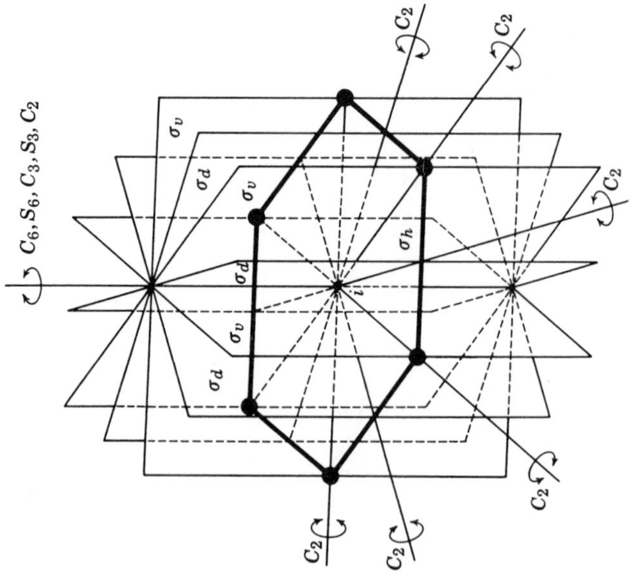

D_{6h}:X_6Y_6 (C_6H_6), only **X** atoms shown
($C_6 \approx S_6 \approx C_3 \approx S_3 \approx C_2, 6C_2, 6\sigma, \sigma_h, i$)

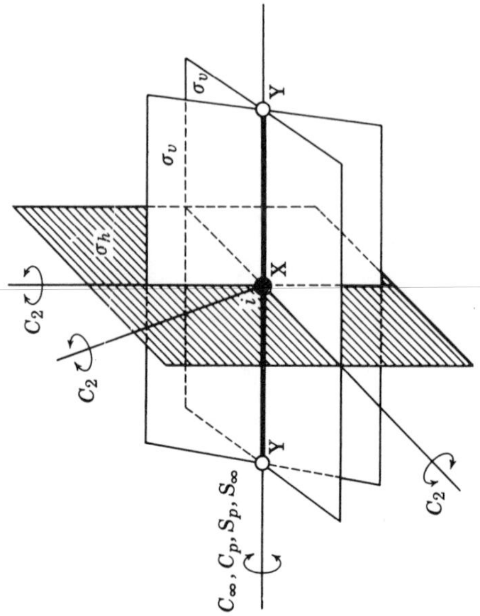

$D_{\infty h}$:XY_2 (CO_2)
($S_\infty \approx C_\infty \approx C_p \approx S_p, \infty C_2, \infty\sigma_v, \sigma_h, i$)

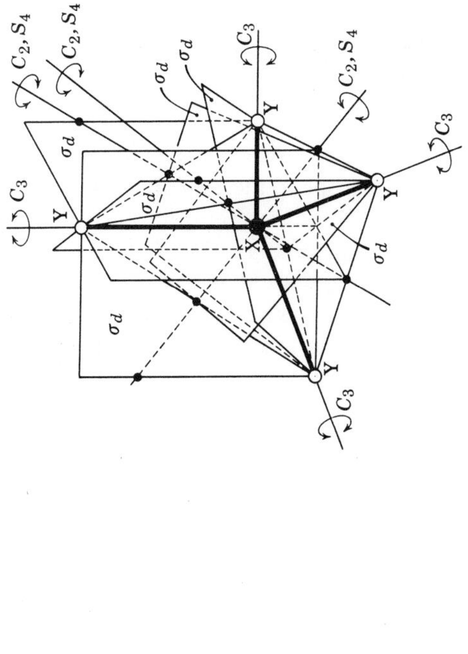

T_d:XY_4 (SO_4^{2-} ion)
($4C_3, 3C_2 \approx S_4, 6\sigma_d$)

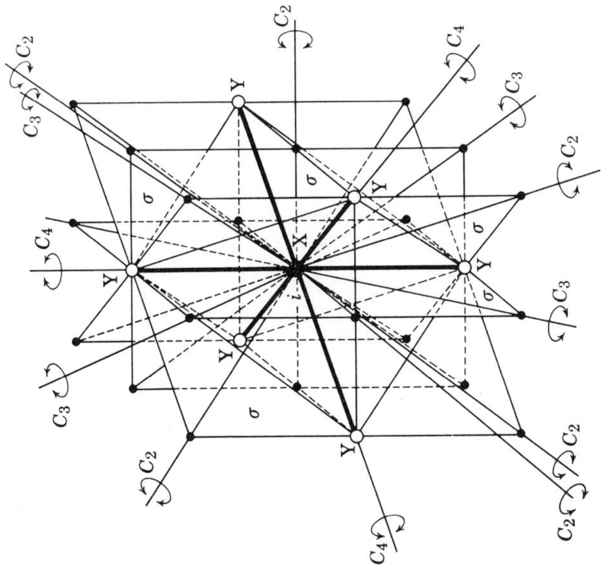

O_h:XY_6 (UF_6)
($3C_4 \approx S_4 \approx C_2, 4C_3 \approx S_6, 6C_2, 9\sigma, i$)

Fig. I-5 (Continued).

relative lengths of the arrows indicate the relative velocities and the amplitudes for each nucleus.† The ν_2 vibrations in CO_2 are worth comment since they differ from the others in that two vibrations (ν_{2a} and ν_{2b}) have exactly the same frequency. Apparently, there are an infinite number of normal vibrations of this type which differ only in their directions perpendicular to the molecular axis. Any of them, however, can

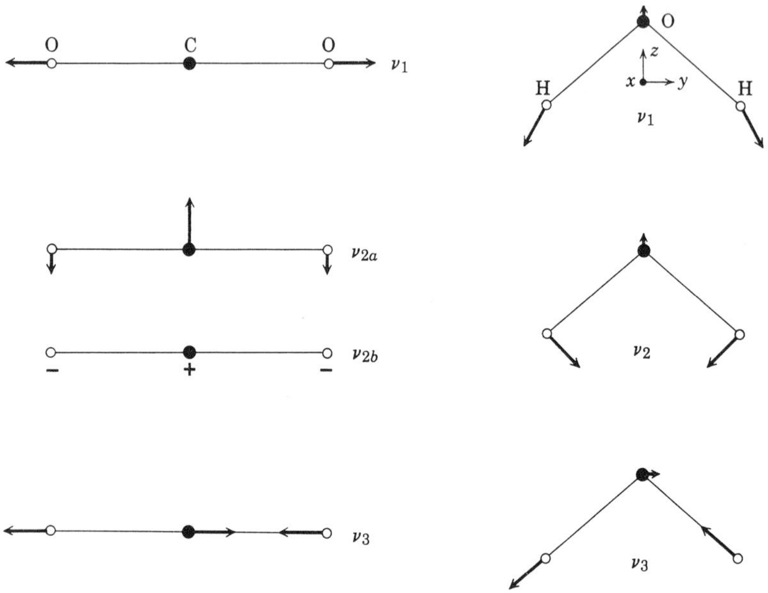

Fig. I-6. Normal modes of vibration in CO_2 and H_2O molecules (+ and − denote the vibrations going upward and downward, respectively, in the direction perpendicular to the paper plane).

be resolved into two vibrations such as ν_{2a} and ν_{2b} which are perpendicular to each other. In this respect, the ν_2 vibrations in CO_2 are called *doubly degenerate vibrations*. Doubly degenerate vibrations occur only when a molecule has an axis higher than C_2. *Triply degenerate vibrations* also occur in molecules having more than one C_3 axis.

In order to determine the symmetry of a normal vibration, it is necessary to begin by considering the kinetic and potential energies of the system. These have already been discussed in Sec. I-3.

$$T = \frac{1}{2} \sum_i \dot{Q}_i^2 \tag{3.11}$$

$$V = \frac{1}{2} \sum_i \lambda_i Q_i^2 \tag{3.12}$$

† In this respect, all the normal modes of vibration shown in this book are only approximate.

Let some symmetry operation which changes Q_i into Q_i' be applied. The kinetic and potential energies are not changed by such a symmetry operation. λ_i does not change, since b_{ij} in Eq. 3.19 does not change. Then, if λ_i is not degenerate, i.e., if no other λ is equal to λ_i,

$$Q_i^2 = Q_i'^2 \quad \text{or} \quad Q_i = \pm Q_i' \tag{5.1}$$

Thus the normal coordinate must change either into itself or its negative. If $Q_i = Q_i'$, the vibration is said to be *symmetric*. If $Q_i = -Q_i'$, it is said to be *antisymmetric*. If Q_i is doubly degenerate, i.e., if, for example, $\lambda_{i1} = \lambda_{i2}$, a relation such as

$$Q_{i1}^2 + Q_{i2}^2 = Q_{i1}'^2 + Q_{i2}'^2 \tag{5.2}$$

holds. In any case, the normal vibration must be either symmetric or antisymmetric or degenerate for each symmetry operation.

The symmetry properties of the normal vibrations of the H_2O molecule shown in Fig. I-5 are classified as indicated in Table I-1. Here, +1 and −1 denote symmetric and antisymmetric, respectively. In the ν_1 and ν_2

TABLE I-1

$\mathbf{C}_{2v}$	I	$C_2(z)$	$\sigma_v(xz)$	$\sigma_v(yz)$
Q_1, Q_2	+1	+1	+1	+1
Q_3	+1	−1	−1	+1

vibrations, all the symmetry properties are preserved during the vibration. Therefore they are *symmetric vibrations* and are called, in particular, *totally symmetric vibrations*. In the ν_3 vibration, however, symmetry elements such as C_2 and $\sigma(xz)$ are lost. Thus it is called a *non-symmetric vibration*. If a molecule has a number of symmetry elements, the normal vibrations are classified as various species according to the number and the kind of symmetry elements preserved during the vibration.

In order to determine the activity of the vibrations in the infrared and Raman spectra, the selection rule must be applied to each normal vibration. From a quantum mechanical point of view,[1–4] *a vibration is active in the infrared spectrum if the dipole moment of the molecule is changed during the vibration, and it is active in the Raman spectrum if the polarizability of the molecule is changed during the vibration.* Changes in the dipole moment or polarizability are not immediately obvious from consideration of the normal modes of vibration in polyatomic molecules. As will be shown later, the application of group theory gives a clear-cut solution in this case.

In simple molecules, however, the activity of a vibration may be determined by inspection of the normal mode. For example, it is obvious that the vibration in a homopolar diatomic molecule is not infrared active but is Raman active, whereas the vibration in a heteropolar diatomic molecule is both infrared and Raman active. It is also evident from Fig. I-6 that all the vibrations in H_2O and CO_2 molecules are infrared active (except the ν_1 vibration of the latter), since they result in a change in the dipole moment during the vibration. On the other hand, all the vibrations of H_2O and the ν_1 vibration of CO_2 are Raman active because they result in a change in the polarizability. The ν_2 and ν_3 vibrations of CO_2 are not Raman active because, as Fig. I-7 indicates, the two states of vibration

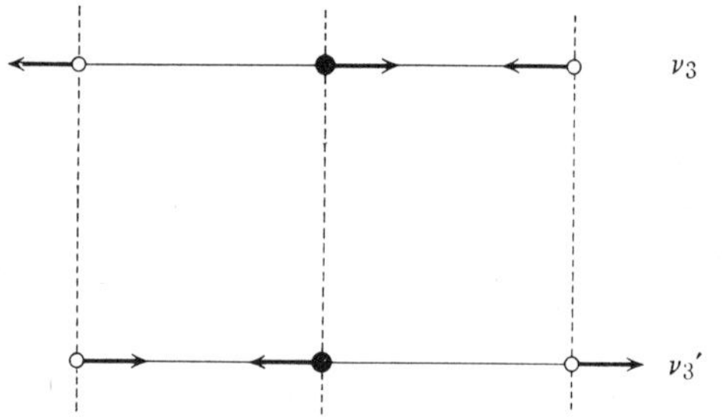

Fig. I-7.

before and after the nuclei pass through their equilibrium positions are completely superimposable if the molecule is rotated by 180°. In other words, there is no change in the polarizability during the vibration.

It should be noted that in CO_2 the vibration symmetric with respect to the center of symmetry (ν_1) is Raman active and not infrared active, whereas the vibrations antisymmetric with respect to the center of symmetry (ν_2 and ν_3) are infrared active but not Raman active. In a polyatomic molecule having a center of symmetry, the vibrations symmetric with respect to the center of symmetry (*g* vibrations†) are Raman active and not infrared active, but the vibrations antisymmetric with respect to the center of symmetry (*u* vibrations†) are infrared active and not Raman active. This rule is called the *mutual exclusion rule*. It should be noted, however, that in polyatomic molecules having several symmetry elements besides the center of symmetry, the vibrations which should be active according to this rule may not necessarily be active, because of the presence of other symmetry elements. An example is seen in a square-planar XY_4 type of molecule of $\mathbf{D}_{4h}$ symmetry where the A_{2g} vibrations are not Raman active

† *g* and *u* stand for "gerade" and "ungerade" in German, respectively.

and the A_{1u}, B_{1u} and B_{2u} vibrations are not infrared active (see Sec. II-8(3) and Appendix I).

I-6. INTRODUCTION TO GROUP THEORY

In Sec. I-4, the symmetry and the point group allocation of a given molecule were discussed. In order to understand the symmetry and selection rules of normal vibrations in polyatomic molecules, however, a knowledge of group theory is required. The minimum amount of group theory needed for this purpose is given here.†

Consider a pyramidal XY_3 molecule (Fig. I-8) which has I, C_3^+, C_3^-, σ_1, σ_2 and σ_3 as its symmetry elements. Here C_3^+ and C_3^- denote rotation

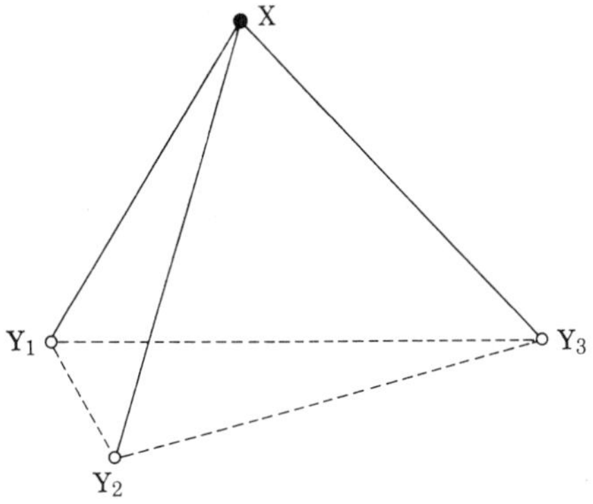

Fig. I-8.

through 120° in the clockwise and counterclockwise directions, respectively, and σ_1, σ_2 and σ_3 indicate the symmetry planes which pass through X and Y_1, X and Y_2, and X and Y_3, respectively. For simplicity, let these symmetry elements be denoted by I, A, B, C, D and E, respectively. Other symmetry operations are possible, but they are all equivalent to some one of the operations mentioned. For instance, a clockwise rotation through 240° is identical with operation B. It may also be shown that two successive applications of any one of these operations is equivalent to some single operation of the group mentioned. Let operation C be applied to the original figure. This interchanges Y_2 and Y_3. If operation A is applied to the resulting figure, the net result is the same as application of the single operation D to the original figure. This is written $AC = D$. If all the possible multiplicative combinations are made, there is obtained Table I-2, in which the operation applied first is written across the top of the table.

† For details on group theory and matrix theory, see Refs. 2 and 6–10.

This is called the *multiplication table* of the group.

TABLE I-2

	I	*A*	*B*	*C*	*D*	*E*
I	*I*	*A*	*B*	*C*	*D*	*E*
A	*A*	*B*	*I*	*D*	*E*	*C*
B	*B*	*I*	*A*	*E*	*C*	*D*
C	*C*	*E*	*D*	*I*	*B*	*A*
D	*D*	*C*	*E*	*A*	*I*	*B*
E	*E*	*D*	*C*	*B*	*A*	*I*

It is seen that a group consisting of the elements *I*, *A*, *B*, *C*, *D* and *E* satisfies the following conditions:

1. The product of any two elements in the set is another element in the set.
2. The set contains the identity operation which satisfies the relation $IP = PI = P$, where P is any element in the set.
3. The associative law holds for all the elements in the set; that is, $(CB)A = C(BA)$, for example.
4. Every element in the set has its reciprocal X which satisfies the relation, $XP = PX = I$, where P is any element in the set. This reciprocal is usually denoted by P^{-1}.

These are necessary and sufficient conditions for a set of elements to form a *group*. It is evident that the operations *I*, *A*, *B*, *C*, *D* and *E* form a group in this sense. It should be noted that the commutative law of multiplication does not necessarily hold. For example, Table I-2 shows that $CD \neq DC$.

The six symmetry elements can be classified into three types of operations: the identity operation, I; the rotations, C_3^+ and C_3^-; and the reflections, σ_1, σ_2 and σ_3. Each of these sets of operations is said to form a *class*. More precisely, two operations, P and Q, which satisfy the relation $X^{-1}PX = P$ or Q, where X is any operation of the group and X^{-1} is its reciprocal, are said to belong to the same class. It can easily be shown that C_3^+ and C_3^-, for example, satisfy the relation. Thus the six elements of the point group $\mathbf{C}_{3v}$ are usually abbreviated I, $2C_3$ and $3\sigma_v$.

The relations between the elements of the group are shown in the multiplication table in Table I-2. Such a tabulation of a group is, however, awkward to handle. The essential features of the table may be abstracted by replacing the elements by some analytical function which reproduces the multiplication table. Such an analytical expression may be composed of a simple integer, an exponential function or a matrix. Any set of such expressions which satisfies the relations given by the multiplication table is called a *representation* of the group and is designated by Γ. The representations of the point group $\mathbf{C}_{3v}$ discussed above are indicated in Table I-3. It is easily proved that each representation in the table satisfies the multiplication table.

TABLE I-3

$\mathbf{C}_{3v}$	I	A	B	C	D	E
$A_1(\Gamma_1)$	1	1	1	1	1	1
$A_2(\Gamma_2)$	1	1	1	-1	-1	-1
$E(\Gamma_3)$	$\begin{pmatrix} 1 & 0 \\ 0 & 1 \end{pmatrix}$	$\begin{pmatrix} -\frac{1}{2} & \frac{\sqrt{3}}{2} \\ -\frac{\sqrt{3}}{2} & -\frac{1}{2} \end{pmatrix}$	$\begin{pmatrix} -\frac{1}{2} & -\frac{\sqrt{3}}{2} \\ \frac{\sqrt{3}}{2} & -\frac{1}{2} \end{pmatrix}$	$\begin{pmatrix} -1 & 0 \\ 0 & 1 \end{pmatrix}$	$\begin{pmatrix} \frac{1}{2} & -\frac{\sqrt{3}}{2} \\ -\frac{\sqrt{3}}{2} & -\frac{1}{2} \end{pmatrix}$	$\begin{pmatrix} \frac{1}{2} & \frac{\sqrt{3}}{2} \\ \frac{\sqrt{3}}{2} & -\frac{1}{2} \end{pmatrix}$

Besides the three representations in Table I-3, it is possible to write an infinite number of other representations of the group. If a set of six matrices of the type $S^{-1}R(K)S$ is chosen where $R(K)$ is a representation of the element K given in Table I-3, S ($|S| \neq 0$) is any matrix of the same order as R, and S^{-1} is the reciprocal of S; this set also satisfies the relations given by the multiplication table. The reason is obvious from the relation

$$S^{-1}R(K)SS^{-1}R(L)S = S^{-1}R(K)R(L)S = S^{-1}R(KL)S$$

Such a transformation is called a *similarity transformation*. Thus it is possible to make an infinite number of representations by similarity transformations.

On the other hand, this statement suggests that a given representation may be broken into simpler ones. If each representation of the symmetry element K is transformed into the form

$$R(K) = \begin{vmatrix} Q_1(K) & 0 & 0 & 0 \\ 0 & Q_2(K) & 0 & 0 \\ 0 & 0 & Q_3(K) & 0 \\ 0 & 0 & 0 & Q_4(K) \end{vmatrix} \tag{6.1}$$

by a similarity transformation, $Q_1(K)$, $Q_2(K)$, . . . are simpler representations. In such a case, $R(K)$ is called *reducible*. If a representation cannot be simplified any further, it is said to be *irreducible*. Γ_1, Γ_2 and Γ_3 in Table I-3 are all irreducible representations. It can be shown generally that the number of irreducible representations is equal to the number of classes. Thus only three irreducible representations exist for the point group $\mathbf{C}_{3v}$. These representations are entirely independent of each other. A point group is classified into *species* according to its irreducible representations. In the point group $\mathbf{C}_{3v}$, the species having the irreducible representations Γ_1, Γ_2 and Γ_3 are called the A_1, A_2 and E species, respectively.†

The sum of the diagonal elements of a matrix is called the *character* of the matrix and is denoted by χ. It is to be noted in Table I-3 that the character of each of the elements belonging to the same class is the same. Thus, using the character, Table I-3 can be simplified to Table I-4. Such

TABLE I-4. THE CHARACTER TABLE OF THE POINT GROUP $\mathbf{C}_{3v}$

$\mathbf{C}_{3v}$	I	$2C_3(z)$	$3\sigma_v$
$A_1(\chi_1)$	1	1	1
$A_2(\chi_2)$	1	1	−1
$E(\chi_3)$	2	−1	0

a table is called the *character table* of the point group $\mathbf{C}_{3v}$. The *character* of a matrix is not changed by a similarity transformation. This can be proved as follows. If a similarity transformation is expressed by $T = S^{-1}RS$, then

$$\chi_T = \sum_i (S^{-1}RS)_{ii} = \sum_{i,j,k} (S^{-1})_{ij} R_{jk} S_{ki} = \sum_{j,k} (SS^{-1})_{kj} R_{jk}$$
$$= \sum_{j,k} I_{kj} R_{jk} = \sum_k R_{kk} = \chi_R$$

Thus any reducible representation can be reduced to its irreducible representations by a similarity transformation which leaves the character unchanged. Therefore the character of the reducible representation, $\chi(K)$, is written

$$\chi(K) = \sum_m a_m \chi_m(K) \tag{6.2}$$

where $\chi_m(K)$ is the character of $Q_m(K)$, and a_m is a positive integer which indicates the number of times $Q_m(K)$ appears in the matrix of Eq. 6.1. Hereafter the character will be used rather than the corresponding representation because a 1:1 correspondence exists between these two, and the former is sufficient for vibrational problems.

It is interesting to note that the following relation holds in Table I-4:

$$\sum_K \chi_i(K)\chi_j(K) = h\delta_{ij} \tag{6.3}$$

† For the labeling of the irreducible representations (species), see Appendix I.

where δ_{ij} is Kronecker's delta (zero for $i \neq j$ and 1 for $i = j$); h is called the *order* of the group and is equal to the total number of the symmetry elements present. If Eq. 6.2 is combined with Eq. 6.3, there results

$$\sum_K \chi(K)\chi_i(K) = \sum_K \sum_m a_m \chi_m(K)\chi_i(K) = \sum_m a_m h \delta_{mi} = h a_m$$

From this, a_m is given by

$$a_m = \frac{1}{h} \sum_K \chi(K)\chi_i(K) \tag{6.4}$$

Here the summation is made over all the symmetry elements. This formula is written more conveniently as

$$\boxed{a_m = \frac{1}{h} \sum n\chi(K)\chi(K)} \tag{6.5}$$

where n is the number of symmetry elements in any one class, and the summation is made over the different classes. As Sec. I-7 will show, this formula is very useful in determining the number of normal vibrations belonging to each species.

I-7. THE NUMBER OF NORMAL VIBRATIONS FOR EACH SPECIES

As shown in Sec. I-5, the $3N - 6$ (or $3N - 5$) normal vibrations of an N-atom molecule can be classified into various species according to their symmetry properties. Using group theory, it is possible to find the number of normal vibrations belonging to each species.† The principle of the method is that all the representations are irreducible if normal coordinates are used as the basis for the representations. For example, the representations for the symmetry operations based on three normal coordinates, Q_1, Q_2 and Q_3, which correspond to the ν_1, ν_2 and ν_3 vibrations in the H_2O molecule of Fig. I-6 are

$$I \begin{bmatrix} Q_1 \\ Q_2 \\ Q_3 \end{bmatrix} = \begin{bmatrix} 1 & 0 & 0 \\ 0 & 1 & 0 \\ 0 & 0 & 1 \end{bmatrix} \begin{bmatrix} Q_1 \\ Q_2 \\ Q_3 \end{bmatrix} \qquad C_2(z) \begin{bmatrix} Q_1 \\ Q_2 \\ Q_3 \end{bmatrix} = \begin{bmatrix} 1 & 0 & 0 \\ 0 & 1 & 0 \\ 0 & 0 & -1 \end{bmatrix} \begin{bmatrix} Q_1 \\ Q_2 \\ Q_3 \end{bmatrix}$$

$$\sigma_v(xz) \begin{bmatrix} Q_1 \\ Q_2 \\ Q_3 \end{bmatrix} = \begin{bmatrix} 1 & 0 & 0 \\ 0 & 1 & 0 \\ 0 & 0 & -1 \end{bmatrix} \begin{bmatrix} Q_1 \\ Q_2 \\ Q_3 \end{bmatrix} \qquad \sigma_v(yz) \begin{bmatrix} Q_1 \\ Q_2 \\ Q_3 \end{bmatrix} = \begin{bmatrix} 1 & 0 & 0 \\ 0 & 1 & 0 \\ 0 & 0 & 1 \end{bmatrix} \begin{bmatrix} Q_1 \\ Q_2 \\ Q_3 \end{bmatrix}$$

Let a representation be written with the $3N$ rectangular coordinates of an N-atom molecule as its basis. If it is decomposed into its irreducible

† The results of the following calculations are tabulated in Ref. 5.

components, the basis for these irreducible representations must be the normal coordinates, and the number of appearances of the same irreducible representation must be equal to the number of normal vibrations belonging to the species represented by this irreducible representation. As stated previously, however, the $3N$ rectangular coordinates involve 6 (or 5) coordinates which correspond to the translational and rotational motions of the molecule as a whole. Therefore the representations which have such coordinates as their basis must be subtracted from the result obtained

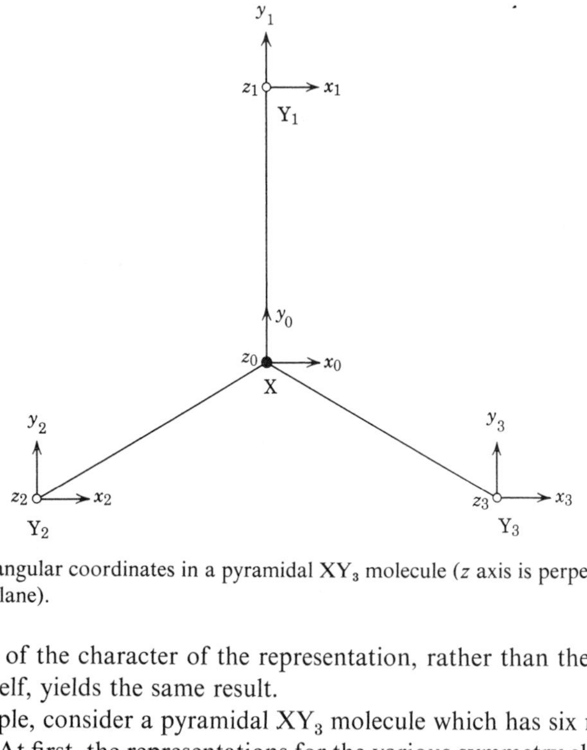

Fig. I-9. Rectangular coordinates in a pyramidal XY_3 molecule (z axis is perpendicular to the paper plane).

above. Use of the character of the representation, rather than the representation itself, yields the same result.

For example, consider a pyramidal XY_3 molecule which has six normal vibrations. At first, the representations for the various symmetry elements must be written with the 12 rectangular coordinates in Fig. I-9 as their basis. Consider pure rotation, C_p^+. If the clockwise rotation of the point (x, y, z) around the z axis by the angle θ brings it to the point denoted by the coordinates (x', y', z'), the relations between these two coordinates are given by

$$\begin{aligned} x' &= x \cos \theta + y \sin \theta \\ y' &= -x \sin \theta + y \cos \theta \\ z' &= z \end{aligned} \tag{7.1}$$

By using matrix notation, this can be written

$$\begin{bmatrix} x' \\ y' \\ z' \end{bmatrix} = C_\theta^+ \begin{bmatrix} x \\ y \\ z \end{bmatrix} = \begin{bmatrix} \cos\theta & \sin\theta & 0 \\ -\sin\theta & \cos\theta & 0 \\ 0 & 0 & 1 \end{bmatrix} \begin{bmatrix} x \\ y \\ z \end{bmatrix} \tag{7.2}$$

Then the character of the matrix is given by

$$\chi(C_\theta^+) = 1 + 2\cos\theta \tag{7.3}$$

The same result is obtained for $\chi(C_\theta^-)$. If this symmetry operation is applied to all the coordinates of the XY_3 molecule, the result is

$$C_\theta \begin{bmatrix} x_0 \\ y_0 \\ z_0 \\ x_1 \\ y_1 \\ z_1 \\ x_2 \\ y_2 \\ z_2 \\ x_3 \\ y_3 \\ z_3 \end{bmatrix} = \left[\begin{array}{c:c:c:c} \mathbf{A} & 0 & 0 & 0 \\ \hdashline 0 & 0 & 0 & \mathbf{A} \\ \hdashline 0 & \mathbf{A} & 0 & 0 \\ \hdashline 0 & 0 & \mathbf{A} & 0 \end{array}\right] \begin{bmatrix} x_0 \\ y_0 \\ z_0 \\ x_1 \\ y_1 \\ z_1 \\ x_2 \\ y_2 \\ z_2 \\ x_3 \\ y_3 \\ z_3 \end{bmatrix} \tag{7.4}$$

where **A** denotes the small square matrix given by Eq. 7.2. Thus the character of this representation is simply given by Eq. 7.3. It should be noted in Eq. 7.4 that only the small matrix **A**, related to the nuclei unchanged by the symmetry operation, appears as a diagonal element. Thus a more general form of the character of the representation for rotation around the axis by θ is

$$\boxed{\chi(R) = N_R\,(1 + 2\cos\theta)} \tag{7.5}$$

where N_R is the number of nuclei unchanged by the rotation. In the present case, $N_R = 1$ and $\theta = 120°$. Therefore

$$\chi(C_3) = 0 \tag{7.6}$$

Identity (I) can be regarded as a special case of Eq. 7.5 in which $N_R = 4$ and $\theta = 0°$. The character of the representation is

$$\chi(I) = 12 \tag{7.7}$$

Pure rotation and identity are called *proper rotation.*

It is evident from Fig. I-9 that a symmetry plane such as σ_1 changes the coordinates from (x_i, y_i, z_i) to $(-x_i, y_i, z_i)$. The corresponding representation is therefore written

$$\sigma_1 \begin{bmatrix} x \\ y \\ z \end{bmatrix} = \begin{bmatrix} -1 & 0 & 0 \\ 0 & 1 & 0 \\ 0 & 0 & 1 \end{bmatrix} \begin{bmatrix} x \\ y \\ z \end{bmatrix} \tag{7.8}$$

The result of such an operation on all the coordinates is

$$\sigma_1 \begin{bmatrix} x_0 \\ y_0 \\ z_0 \\ x_1 \\ y_1 \\ z_1 \\ x_2 \\ y_2 \\ z_2 \\ x_3 \\ y_3 \\ z_3 \end{bmatrix} = \left[\begin{array}{c:c:c:c} \mathbf{B} & 0 & 0 & 0 \\ \hdashline 0 & \mathbf{B} & 0 & 0 \\ \hdashline 0 & 0 & 0 & \mathbf{B} \\ \hdashline 0 & 0 & \mathbf{B} & 0 \end{array}\right] \begin{bmatrix} x_0 \\ y_0 \\ z_0 \\ x_1 \\ y_1 \\ z_1 \\ x_2 \\ y_2 \\ z_2 \\ x_3 \\ y_3 \\ z_3 \end{bmatrix} \tag{7.9}$$

where **B** denotes the small square matrix of Eq. 7.8. Thus the character of this representation is calculated as $2 \times 1 = 2$. It is noted again that the matrix on the diagonal is non-zero only for the nuclei unchanged by the operation. The character for reflection at the plane (σ) is given, in general, by

$$\boxed{\chi(R) = -N_R(1 + 2\cos\theta)} \tag{7.10}$$

with $N_R = 2$ and $\theta = 180°$ in the present case. This gives

$$\chi(\sigma_v) = 2 \tag{7.11}$$

The characters for other operations such as an inversion at the center (i), and a rotation-reflection (S_3, S_4 and S_6) are also obtained from Eq. 7.10 by taking θ as 0°, 60°, 90° and 120°, respectively. Operations such as σ, i and S_p are called *improper rotations*. Thus the character of the representation based on 12 rectangular coordinates is

I	$2C_3$	$3\sigma_v$
12	0	2

(7.12)

In order to determine the number of normal vibrations belonging to each species, the $\chi(R)$ thus obtained must be resolved into the $\chi_i(R)$ of the irreducible representations of each species in Table I-4. First, however, the characters corresponding to the translational and rotational motions of the molecule must be subtracted from the result shown in Eq. 7.12.

The characters for the translational motion of the molecule in the x, y and z directions (denoted by T_x, T_y and T_z) are the same as those obtained in Eqs. 7.5 and 7.10. They are

$$\boxed{\chi_t(R) = \pm(1 + 2\cos\theta)} \qquad (7.13)$$

where the + and − signs are for proper and improper rotations, respectively. The characters for the rotations around the x, y and z axes (denoted by R_x, R_y and R_z) are given by

$$\boxed{\chi_r(R) = +(1 + 2\cos\theta)} \qquad (7.14)$$

for both proper and improper rotations. This is due to the fact that a rotation of the vectors in the plane perpendicular to the x, y and z axes can be regarded as a rotation of the components of angular momentum, M_x, M_y and M_z, about the given axes. If p_x, p_y and p_z are the components of linear momentum in the x, y and z directions, the following relations hold:

$$M_x = yp_z - zp_y$$
$$M_y = zp_x - xp_z$$
$$M_z = xp_y - yp_x$$

Since (x, y, z) and (p_x, p_y, p_z) transform as shown in Eq. 7.2, it follows that

$$C_\theta \begin{bmatrix} M_x \\ M_y \\ M_z \end{bmatrix} = \begin{bmatrix} \cos\theta & \sin\theta & 0 \\ -\sin\theta & \cos\theta & 0 \\ 0 & 0 & 1 \end{bmatrix} \begin{bmatrix} M_x \\ M_y \\ M_z \end{bmatrix}$$

Then a similar relation holds for R_x, R_y and R_z:

$$C_\theta \begin{bmatrix} R_x \\ R_y \\ R_z \end{bmatrix} = \begin{bmatrix} \cos\theta & \sin\theta & 0 \\ -\sin\theta & \cos\theta & 0 \\ 0 & 0 & 1 \end{bmatrix} \begin{bmatrix} R_x \\ R_y \\ R_z \end{bmatrix}$$

Thus the characters for the rotations are given by Eq. 7.14. Therefore the character for the vibration is obtained from

$$\boxed{\chi_v(R) = \chi(R) - \chi_t(R) - \chi_r(R)} \qquad (7.15)$$

It is convenient to tabulate the foregoing calculations as in Table I-5.

TABLE I-5

Symmetry operation	I	$2C_3$	$3\sigma_v$
Kind of rotation	proper		improper
θ	0°	120°	180°
$\cos\theta$	1	$-\frac{1}{2}$	-1
$1 + 2\cos\theta$	3	0	-1
N_R	4	1	2
χ, $\pm N_R(1 + 2\cos\theta)$	12	0	2
χ_t, $\pm(1 + 2\cos\theta)$	3	0	1
χ_r, $+(1 + 2\cos\theta)$	3	0	-1
χ_v, $\chi - \chi_t - \chi_r$	6	0	2

By using the formula in Eq. 6.5 and the character of the irreducible representations in Table I-4, a_m can be calculated as follows:

$$a_m(A_1) = \tfrac{1}{6}[(1)(6)(1) + (2)(0)(1) \quad + (3)(2)(1)] \quad = 2$$
$$a_m(A_2) = \tfrac{1}{6}[(1)(6)(1) + (2)(0)(1) \quad + (3)(2)(-1)] = 0$$
$$a_m(E) = \tfrac{1}{6}[(1)(6)(2) + (2)(0)(-1) + (3)(2)(0)] \quad = 2$$

and

$$\chi_v = 2\chi_{A_1} + 2\chi_E \tag{7.16}$$

In other words, the six normal vibrations of a pyramidal XY_3 molecule are classified into two A_1 and two E species.

This procedure is applicable to any molecule. As another example, a similar calculation is shown in Table I-6 for an octahedral XY_6 molecule. By use of Eq. 6.5 and the character table in Appendix I, the a_m are obtained as

$$\begin{aligned} a_m(A_{1g}) = \tfrac{1}{48}[&(1)(15)(1) + (8)(0)(1) + (6)(1)(1) + (6)(1)(1) \\ &+ (3)(-1)(1) + (1)(-3)(1) + (6)(-1)(1) + (8)(0)(1) \\ &+ (3)(5)(1) + (6)(3)(1)] \\ = 1 & \end{aligned}$$

$$
\begin{aligned}
a_m(A_{1u}) = \tfrac{1}{48}[&(1)(15)(1) + (8)(0)(1) + (6)(1)(1) + (6)(1)(1)\\
&+ (3)(-1)(1) + (1)(-3)(-1) + (6)(-1)(-1) + (8)(0)(-1)\\
&+ (3)(5)(-1) + (6)(3)(-1)]\\
= 0&
\end{aligned}
$$

. . . .

and therefore

$$\chi_v = \chi_{A_{1g}} + \chi_{E_g} + 2\chi_{F_{1u}} + \chi_{F_{2g}} + \chi_{F_{2u}}$$

TABLE I-6

Symmetry operation	I	$8C_3$	$6C_2$	$6C_4$	$3C_4^2 \equiv C_2''$	$S_2 \equiv i$	$6S_4$	$8S_6 \equiv C_3i$	$3\sigma_h$	$6\sigma_d$
Kind of rotation	proper					improper				
θ	0°	120°	180°	90°	180°	0°	90°	120°	180°	180°
$\cos\theta$	1	$-\frac{1}{2}$	−1	0	−1	1	0	$-\frac{1}{2}$	−1	−1
$1 + 2\cos\theta$	3	0	−1	1	−1	3	1	0	−1	−1
N_R	7	1	1	3	3	1	1	1	5	3
χ, $\pm N_R(1 + 2\cos\theta)$	21	0	−1	3	−3	−3	−1	0	5	3
χ_t, $\pm(1 + 2\cos\theta)$	3	0	−1	1	−1	−3	−1	0	1	1
χ_r, $+(1 + 2\cos\theta)$	3	0	−1	1	−1	3	1	0	−1	−1
χ_v, $\chi - \chi_t - \chi_v$	15	0	1	1	−1	−3	−1	0	5	3

I-8. INTERNAL COORDINATES

In Sec. I-3, the potential and the kinetic energies were expressed in terms of rectangular coordinates. If these energies are expressed in terms of *internal coordinates* such as increments of the bond length and bond angle, the corresponding force constants have a clearer physical meaning than those expressed in terms of rectangular coordinates, since these force constants are characteristic of the bond stretching and the angle deformation involved. The number of internal coordinates must be equal to or greater than $3N - 6$ (or $3N - 5$), the degrees of vibrational freedom of an N-atom molecule. If more than $3N - 6$ (or $3N - 5$) coordinates are selected as the internal coordinates, this means that these coordinates are not independent of each other. Figure I-10 illustrates the internal coordinates for various types of molecules.

In linear XYZ (*a*), bent XY_2 (*b*) and pyramidal XY_3 (*c*) molecules, the number of internal coordinates is the same as the number of normal vibrations. In a non-planar X_2Y_2 molecule (*d*) such as H_2O_2, the number of internal coordinates is the same as the number of vibrations if the twisting angle around the central bond ($\Delta\tau$) is considered. In a tetrahedral XY_4 molecule (*e*), however, the number of internal coordinates

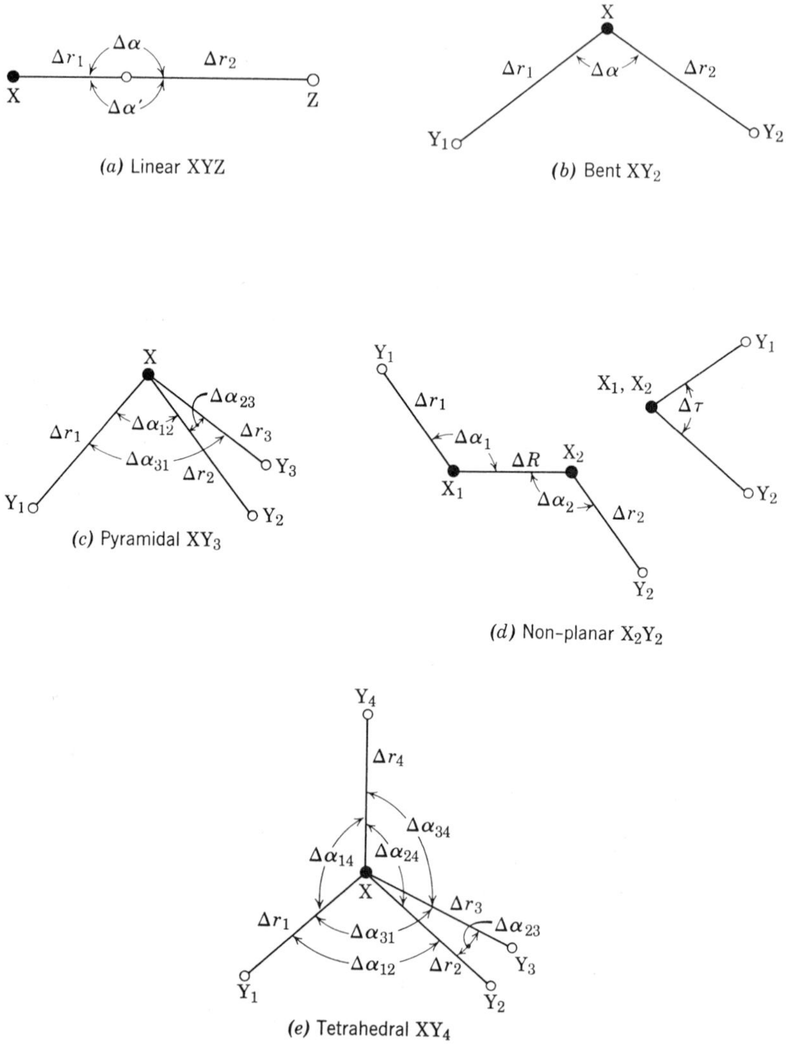

Fig. I-10. Internal coordinates for various molecules.

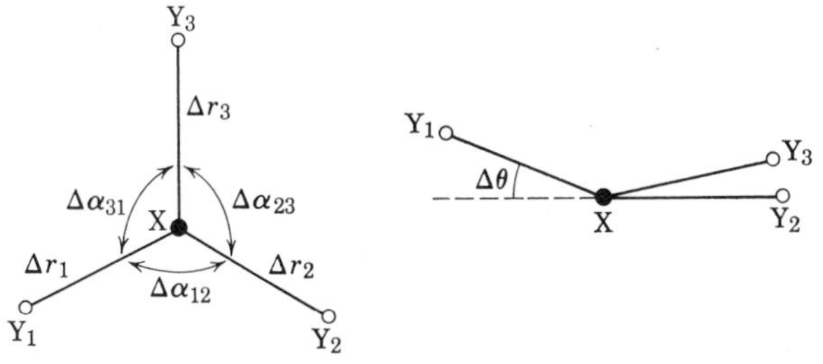

(*f*) Planar XY_3

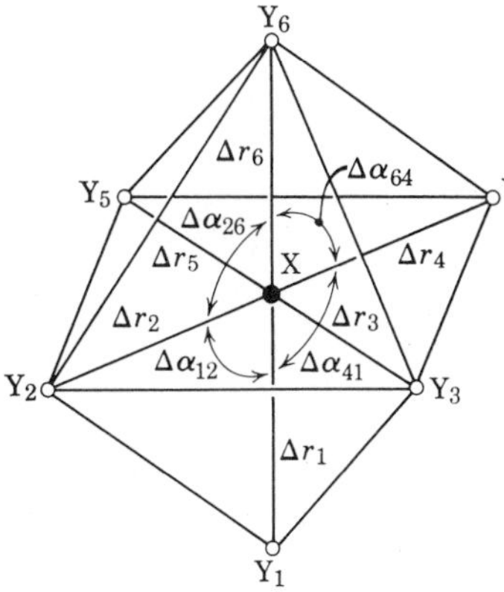

(*g*) Octahedral XY_6
(only four angles are shown)

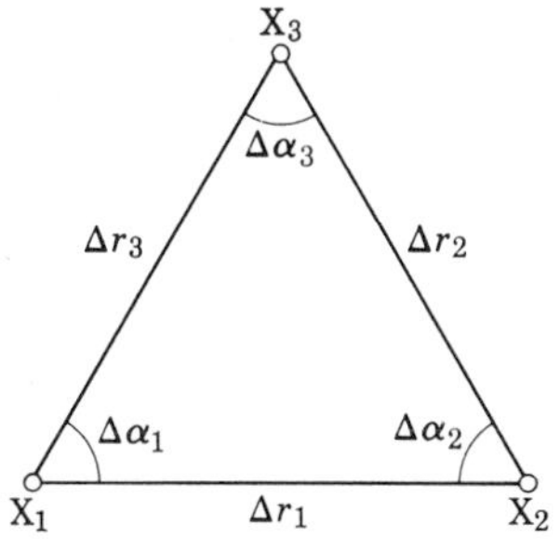

(*h*) Triangular X_3

Fig. I-10 (Continued).

exceeds the number of normal vibrations by one. This is due to the fact that the six angle coordinates around the central atom are not independent of each other. That is, they must satisfy the relation

$$\Delta\alpha_{12} + \Delta\alpha_{23} + \Delta\alpha_{31} + \Delta\alpha_{41} + \Delta\alpha_{42} + \Delta\alpha_{43} = 0 \qquad (8.1)$$

This is called a *redundant condition*. In a planar XY_3 molecule (*f*), the number of internal coordinates is seven when the coordinate, $\Delta\theta$, which represents the deviation from planarity is considered. Since the number of vibrations is six, one redundant condition such as

$$\Delta\alpha_{12} + \Delta\alpha_{23} + \Delta\alpha_{31} = 0 \qquad (8.2)$$

must be involved. Such redundant conditions always exist for the angle coordinates around the central atom. In an octahedral XY_6 molecule (*g*), the number of internal coordinates exceeds the number of normal vibrations by three. This means that, of the twelve angle coordinates around the central atom, three redundant conditions are involved:

$$\begin{aligned} \Delta\alpha_{12} + \Delta\alpha_{26} + \Delta\alpha_{64} + \Delta\alpha_{41} &= 0 \\ \Delta\alpha_{15} + \Delta\alpha_{56} + \Delta\alpha_{63} + \Delta\alpha_{31} &= 0 \\ \Delta\alpha_{23} + \Delta\alpha_{34} + \Delta\alpha_{45} + \Delta\alpha_{52} &= 0 \end{aligned} \tag{8.3}$$

The redundant conditions are more complex in ring compounds. For example, the number of internal coordinates in a triangular X_3 molecule (h) exceeds the number of vibrations by three. One of these redundant conditions (A_1' species) is

$$\Delta\alpha_1 + \Delta\alpha_2 + \Delta\alpha_3 = 0 \tag{8.4}$$

The other two redundant conditions (E' species) involve bond stretching and angle deformation coordinates such as

$$\begin{aligned} (2\Delta r_1 - \Delta r_2 - \Delta r_3) + \frac{r}{\sqrt{3}}(\Delta\alpha_1 + \Delta\alpha_2 - 2\Delta\alpha_3) &= 0 \\ (\Delta r_2 - \Delta r_3) - \frac{r}{\sqrt{3}}(\Delta\alpha_1 - \Delta\alpha_2) &= 0 \end{aligned} \tag{8.5}$$

where r is the equilibrium length of the X—X bond. The redundant conditions mentioned above can be derived by using the method described in Sec. I-11.

The procedure for finding the number of normal vibrations in each species has already been described in Sec. I-7. This procedure is, however, considerably simplified if internal coordinates are used. Again consider a pyramidal XY_3 molecule. Using the internal coordinates shown in Fig. I-10c, the representation for the C_3^+ operation becomes

$$C_3^+ \begin{bmatrix} \Delta r_1 \\ \Delta r_2 \\ \Delta r_3 \\ \Delta\alpha_{12} \\ \Delta\alpha_{23} \\ \Delta\alpha_{31} \end{bmatrix} = \begin{bmatrix} 0 & 0 & 1 & 0 & 0 & 0 \\ 1 & 0 & 0 & 0 & 0 & 0 \\ 0 & 1 & 0 & 0 & 0 & 0 \\ 0 & 0 & 0 & 0 & 0 & 1 \\ 0 & 0 & 0 & 1 & 0 & 0 \\ 0 & 0 & 0 & 0 & 1 & 0 \end{bmatrix} \begin{bmatrix} \Delta r_1 \\ \Delta r_2 \\ \Delta r_3 \\ \Delta\alpha_{12} \\ \Delta\alpha_{23} \\ \Delta\alpha_{31} \end{bmatrix} \tag{8.6}$$

Thus $\chi(C_3^+) = 0$, as does $\chi(C_3^-)$. Similarly, $\chi(I) = 6$ and $\chi(\sigma_v) = 2$. This result is exactly the same as that obtained in Table I-5 using rectangular coordinates. When using internal coordinates, however, the character of the representation is simply given by the number of internal coordinates unchanged by each symmetry operation.

If this procedure is made separately for stretching (Δr) and bending ($\Delta\alpha$) coordinates, it is readily seen that

$$\begin{aligned} \chi^r(R) &= \chi_{A_1} + \chi_E \\ \chi^\alpha(R) &= \chi_{A_1} + \chi_E \end{aligned} \qquad (8.7)$$

Thus it is found that both A_1 and E species have one stretching and one bending vibration, respectively. No consideration of the translational and rotational motions is necessary if the internal coordinates are taken as the basis for the representation.

Another example, one for an octahedral XY_6 molecule, is given in Table I-7. Using Eq. 6.5 and the character table in Appendix I, these

TABLE I-7

	I	$8C_3$	$6C_2$	$6C_4$	$3C_4^2 \equiv C_2''$	$S_2 \equiv i$	$6S_4$	$8S_6 \equiv C_3i$	$3\sigma_h$	$6\sigma_d$
$\chi^r(R)$	6	0	0	2	2	0	0	0	4	2
$\chi^\alpha(R)$	12	0	2	0	0	0	0	0	4	2

characters are resolved into

$$\chi^r(R) = \chi_{A_{1g}} + \chi_{E_g} + \chi_{F_{1u}} \qquad (8.8)$$

$$\chi^\alpha(R) = \chi_{A_{1g}} + \chi_{E_g} + \chi_{F_{1u}} + \chi_{F_{2g}} + \chi_{F_{2u}} \qquad (8.9)$$

A comparison of this result with that obtained in Sec. I-7 immediately suggests that three redundant conditions are included in these bending vibrations (one in A_{1g} and one in E_g). Therefore $\chi^\alpha(R)$ for genuine vibrations becomes

$$\chi^\alpha(R) = \chi_{F_{1u}} + \chi_{F_{2g}} + \chi_{F_{2u}} \qquad (8.10)$$

Thus it is concluded that six stretching and nine bending vibrations are distributed as indicated in Eqs. 8.8 and 8.10, respectively. Although the method given above is simpler than that of Sec. I-7, caution must be exercised with respect to the bending vibrations whenever redundancy is involved. In such a case, a comparison of the results obtained from both methods is useful in finding the species of redundancy.

I-9. SELECTION RULES FOR INFRARED AND RAMAN SPECTRA

According to quantum mechanics,[1–5] the selection rule for the infrared spectrum is determined by the integral:

$$[\mu]_{v'v''} = \int \psi_{v'}(Q_a)\mu\psi_{v''}(Q_a)\, dQ_a \qquad (9.1)$$

Here μ is the dipole moment in the electronic ground state, ψ is the vibrational eigenfunction given by Eq. 2.7, and v' and v'' are the vibrational quantum numbers before and after the transition, respectively. The activity of the normal vibration whose normal coordinate is Q_a is being determined. By resolving the dipole moment into the three components in the x, y and z directions, there results

$$\begin{aligned}
[\mu_x]_{v'v''} &= \int \psi_{v'}(Q_a)\mu_x\psi_{v''}(Q_a)\,dQ_a \\
[\mu_y]_{v'v''} &= \int \psi_{v'}(Q_a)\mu_y\psi_{v''}(Q_a)\,dQ_a \qquad (9.2)\\
[\mu_z]_{v'v''} &= \int \psi_{v'}(Q_a)\mu_z\psi_{v''}(Q_a)\,dQ_a
\end{aligned}$$

If one of these integrals is not zero, the normal vibration associated with Q_a is infrared active. If all the integrals are zero, the vibration is infrared inactive.

Similarly, the selection rule for the Raman spectrum is determined by the integral:

$$[\alpha]_{v'v''} = \int \psi_{v'}(Q_a)\alpha\psi_{v''}(Q_a)\,dQ_a \qquad (9.3)$$

Here α is the electronic polarizability of the molecule and consists of six components, α_{xx}, α_{yy}, α_{zz}, α_{xy}, α_{yz} and α_{xz}. Thus Eq. 9.3 may be resolved into six components:

$$\begin{aligned}
[\alpha_{xx}]_{v'v''} &= \int \psi_{v'}(Q_a)\alpha_{xx}\psi_{v''}(Q_a)\,dQ_a \\
[\alpha_{yy}]_{v'v''} &= \int \psi_{v'}(Q_a)\alpha_{yy}\psi_{v''}(Q_a)\,dQ_a \qquad (9.4)\\
&\cdots\cdots\cdots\cdots \\
&\cdots\cdots\cdots\cdots
\end{aligned}$$

If one of these integrals is not zero, the normal vibration associated with Q_a is Raman active. If all the integrals are zero, the vibration is Raman inactive.

It is possible to decide whether the integrals of Eqs. 9.2 and 9.4 are zero or non-zero from a consideration of symmetry. As stated in Sec. I-1, the vibrations of interest are the fundamentals in which transitions occur from $v' = 0$ to $v'' = 1$. It is evident from the form of the vibrational eigenfunction (Eq. 2.8) that $\psi_0(Q_a)$ is invariant under any symmetry operation, whereas the symmetry of $\psi_1(Q_a)$ is the same as that of Q_a.

Thus the integral does not vanish when the symmetry of μ_x, for example, is the same as that of Q_a. If the symmetry properties of μ_x and Q_a differ in even one symmetry element of the group, the integral becomes zero. In other words, for the integral to be non-zero Q_a must belong to the same species as μ_x. More generally, the normal vibration associated with Q_a becomes infrared active when at least one of the components of the dipole moment belongs to the same species as Q_a. Similar conclusions are obtained for the Raman spectrum.

Since the species of the normal vibration can be determined by the methods described in Secs. I-7 and I-8, it is necessary only to determine the species of the components of the dipole moment and polarizability of the molecule. This can be done as follows. The components of the dipole moment, μ_x, μ_y and μ_z, transform as do those of translational motion, T_x, T_y and T_z, respectively. These have been discussed in Sec. I-7. Thus the character of the dipole moment is given by Eq. 7.13, which is

$$\boxed{\chi_\mu(R) = \pm(1 + 2\cos\theta)} \tag{9.5}$$

where + and − have the same meaning as before. In a pyramidal XY_3 molecule, Eq. 9.5 gives

	I	$2C_3$	$3\sigma_v$
$\chi_\mu(R)$	3	0	1

Using Eq. 6.5, this is resolved into $A_1 + E$. It is obvious that μ_z belongs to A_1. Then μ_x and μ_y must belong to E. In fact, the pair, μ_x and μ_y, transforms as follows.

$$I\begin{bmatrix}\mu_x\\ \mu_y\end{bmatrix} = \begin{bmatrix}1 & 0\\ 0 & 1\end{bmatrix}\begin{bmatrix}\mu_x\\ \mu_y\end{bmatrix} \qquad C_3^+\begin{bmatrix}\mu_x\\ \mu_y\end{bmatrix} = \begin{bmatrix}-\frac{1}{2} & \frac{\sqrt{3}}{2}\\ -\frac{\sqrt{3}}{2} & -\frac{1}{2}\end{bmatrix}\begin{bmatrix}\mu_x\\ \mu_y\end{bmatrix}$$

$$\chi(I) = 2 \qquad\qquad \chi(C_3^+) = -1$$

$$\sigma_1\begin{bmatrix}\mu_x\\ \mu_y\end{bmatrix} = \begin{bmatrix}-1 & 0\\ 0 & 1\end{bmatrix}\begin{bmatrix}\mu_x\\ \mu_y\end{bmatrix}$$

$$\chi(\sigma_1) = 0$$

Thus it is found that μ_z belongs to A_1 and (μ_x, μ_y) belong to E.

The character of the representation of the polarizability is given by

$$\boxed{\chi_\alpha(R) = 2\cos\theta(1 + 2\cos\theta)} \tag{9.6}$$

for both proper and improper rotations. This can be derived as follows. The polarizability in the x, y and z directions is related to that in X, Y and Z coordinates by

$$\begin{bmatrix} \alpha_{XX} & \alpha_{XY} & \alpha_{XZ} \\ \alpha_{YX} & \alpha_{YY} & \alpha_{YZ} \\ \alpha_{ZX} & \alpha_{ZY} & \alpha_{ZZ} \end{bmatrix} = \begin{bmatrix} C_{Xx} & C_{Xy} & C_{Xz} \\ C_{Yx} & C_{Yy} & C_{Yz} \\ C_{Zx} & C_{Zy} & C_{Zz} \end{bmatrix} \begin{bmatrix} \alpha_{xx} & \alpha_{xy} & \alpha_{xz} \\ \alpha_{yx} & \alpha_{yy} & \alpha_{yz} \\ \alpha_{zx} & \alpha_{zy} & \alpha_{zz} \end{bmatrix} \begin{bmatrix} C_{Xx} & C_{Yx} & C_{Zx} \\ C_{Xy} & C_{Yy} & C_{Zy} \\ C_{Xz} & C_{Yz} & C_{Zz} \end{bmatrix}$$

where C_{Xx}, etc., denote the direction cosines between the two axes subscripted. If a rotation through θ around the Z axis superimposes the X, Y and Z axes on the x, y and z axes, the preceding relation becomes

$$C_\theta \begin{bmatrix} \alpha_{xx} & \alpha_{xy} & \alpha_{xz} \\ \alpha_{yx} & \alpha_{yy} & \alpha_{yz} \\ \alpha_{zx} & \alpha_{zy} & \alpha_{zz} \end{bmatrix} = \begin{bmatrix} \cos\theta & \sin\theta & 0 \\ -\sin\theta & \cos\theta & 0 \\ 0 & 0 & 1 \end{bmatrix} \begin{bmatrix} \alpha_{xx} & \alpha_{xy} & \alpha_{xz} \\ \alpha_{yx} & \alpha_{yy} & \alpha_{yz} \\ \alpha_{zx} & \alpha_{zy} & \alpha_{zz} \end{bmatrix} \begin{bmatrix} \cos\theta & -\sin\theta & 0 \\ \sin\theta & \cos\theta & 0 \\ 0 & 0 & 1 \end{bmatrix}$$

This can be written

$$C_\theta \begin{bmatrix} \alpha_{xx} \\ \alpha_{yy} \\ \alpha_{zz} \\ \alpha_{xy} \\ \alpha_{xz} \\ \alpha_{yz} \end{bmatrix} = \begin{bmatrix} \cos^2\theta & \sin^2\theta & 0 & 2\sin\theta\cos\theta & 0 & 0 \\ \sin^2\theta & \cos^2\theta & 0 & -2\sin\theta\cos\theta & 0 & 0 \\ 0 & 0 & 1 & 0 & 0 & 0 \\ -\sin\theta\cos\theta & \sin\theta\cos\theta & 0 & 2\cos^2\theta - 1 & 0 & 0 \\ 0 & 0 & 0 & 0 & \cos\theta & \sin\theta \\ 0 & 0 & 0 & 0 & -\sin\theta & \cos\theta \end{bmatrix} \begin{bmatrix} \alpha_{xx} \\ \alpha_{yy} \\ \alpha_{zz} \\ \alpha_{xy} \\ \alpha_{xz} \\ \alpha_{yz} \end{bmatrix}$$

Thus the character of this representation is given by Eq. 9.6. The same results are obtained for improper rotations. In a pyramidal XY_3 molecule, Eq. 9.6 gives

	I	$2C_3$	$3\sigma_v$
$\chi_\alpha(R)$	6	0	2

Using Eq. 6.5, this is resolved into $2A_1 + 2E$. Again, it is immediately seen that the component α_{zz} belongs to A_1, and the pair α_{zx} and α_{zy} belongs to E since

$$\begin{bmatrix} zx \\ zy \end{bmatrix} = z\begin{bmatrix} x \\ y \end{bmatrix} \approx A_1 \times E = E$$

If a vector of unit length is considered, the relation

$$x^2 + y^2 + z^2 = 1$$

holds. Since α_{zz} belongs to A_1, $\alpha_{xx} + \alpha_{yy}$ must belong to A_1. Then the pair $\alpha_{xx} - \alpha_{yy}$ and α_{xy} must belong to E. As a result, the character table of the point group $\mathbf{C}_{3v}$ is completed as in Table I-8. Thus it is concluded

TABLE I-8. CHARACTER TABLE OF THE POINT GROUP $\mathbf{C}_{3v}$

$\mathbf{C}_{3v}$	I	$2C_3$	$3\sigma_v$		
A_1	+1	+1	+1	μ_z	$\alpha_{xx} + \alpha_{yy}, \alpha_{zz}$
A_2	+1	+1	−1		
E	+2	−1	0	(μ_x, μ_y)	$(\alpha_{xz}, \alpha_{yz}), (\alpha_{xx} - \alpha_{yy}, \alpha_{xy})$

A doubly degenerate pair is represented by two terms in parentheses.

that, in the point group $\mathbf{C}_{3v}$, both the A_1 and the E vibrations are infrared as well as Raman active, while the A_2 vibrations are inactive.

Complete character tables like Table I-8 have already been worked out for all the point groups. Therefore no elaborate treatment such as that described in this section is necessary in practice. Appendix I gives complete character tables for the point groups which appear frequently in this book. From these tables, the selection rules for the infrared and Raman spectra are obtained immediately; *the vibration is infrared or Raman active if it belongs to the same species as one of the components of the dipole moment or polarizability, respectively.* For example, the character table of the point group $\mathbf{O}_h$ tells immediately that only the F_{1u} vibrations are infrared active and only the A_{1g}, E_g and F_{2g} vibrations are Raman active, for the components of the dipole moment or the polarizability belong to these species in this point group. It is to be noted in these character tables that (1) a totally symmetric vibration is Raman active in any point group and (2) the infrared and Raman active vibrations always belong to *u* and *g* types, respectively, in the point groups having a center of symmetry.

Suppose that a molecule has several probable structures each of which belongs to a different point group. Then the number of infrared and Raman active fundamentals should be different for each structure. Therefore the most probable model can be selected by comparing the observed number of infrared and Raman active fundamentals with that predicted theoretically for each model. This method is widely used for the elucidation of molecular structure of inorganic, organic and coordination compounds. Studies of infrared dichroism and depolarization of Raman lines, described in Sec. I-15, are also useful for this purpose. In Part II, the number of infrared and Raman active fundamentals are compared for XY_3 (planar, $\mathbf{D}_{3h}$, and pyramidal, $\mathbf{C}_{3v}$), XY_4 (square-planar, $\mathbf{D}_{4h}$, and tetrahedral, $\mathbf{T}_d$), XY_5 (trigonal bipyramidal, $\mathbf{D}_{3h}$, and tetragonal pyramidal, $\mathbf{C}_{4v}$) and other molecules. Recently, the structures of various metal carbonyl compounds (Sec. III-6) have been determined by this simple technique.

It should be noted, however, that this method does not give a clear-cut answer if the predicted number of infrared and Raman active fundamentals is similar for various probable structures. Furthermore, a practical difficulty arises in determining the number of fundamentals from the observed spectrum, since the intensities of overtone and combination bands are sometimes comparable to those of fundamentals when they appear as satellite bands of the fundamental. This is particularly true when overtone and combination bands are enhanced anomalously by *Fermi resonance* (accidental degeneracy).[5] For example, the frequency of the first overtone of the ν_2 vibration of CO_2 (667 cm^{-1}) is very close to that of the ν_1 vibration (1337 cm^{-1}). Since these two vibrations belong to the same symmetry species (Σ_g^+), they interact with each other and give rise to two strong Raman lines at 1388 and 1286 cm^{-1}. Fermi resonances similar to that observed for CO_2 may occur for a number of other molecules. It is to be noted also that the number of observed bands depends on the resolving power of the instrument used (Sec. III-6). Finally it should be remembered that the molecular symmetry in the isolated state is not necessarily the same as that in the crystalline state (Sec. II-4). Therefore this method must be applied with caution to spectra obtained for compounds in the crystalline state.

I-10. PRINCIPLE OF THE NORMAL COORDINATE ANALYSIS†

As described in Sec. I-3, the frequency of the normal vibration is determined by the kinetic and potential energies of the system. The kinetic energy is determined by the masses of the individual atoms and their geometrical arrangement in the molecule. On the other hand, the potential energy arises from interaction between the individual atoms and is described in terms of the force constants. Since the potential energy provides valuable information about the nature of interatomic forces, it is highly desirable to obtain the force constants from the observed frequencies. This is usually done by calculating the frequencies, assuming a suitable set of the force constants. If the agreement between the calculated and observed frequencies is satisfactory, this particular set of the force constants is adopted as a representation of the potential energy of the system.

To calculate the vibrational frequencies, it is necessary first to express both the potential and kinetic energies in terms of some common coordinates (Sec. I-3). Internal coordinates (Sec. I-8) are more suitable for this purpose than rectangular coordinates, since (1) the force constants expressed in terms of internal coordinates have a clearer physical meaning than those expressed in terms of rectangular coordinates, and (2) a set of internal coordinates does not involve translational and rotational motion of the molecule as a whole.

Using the internal coordinates, R_i, the potential energy is written

$$2V = \tilde{\mathbf{R}}\mathbf{F}\mathbf{R} \tag{10.1}$$

For a bent Y_1XY_2 molecule such as that in Fig. I-10*b*, **R** is a column matrix of the form

$$\mathbf{R} = \begin{bmatrix} \Delta r_1 \\ \Delta r_2 \\ \Delta\alpha \end{bmatrix}$$

$\tilde{\mathbf{R}}$ is its transpose:

$$\tilde{\mathbf{R}} = [\Delta r_1 \quad \Delta r_2 \quad \Delta\alpha]$$

and **F** is a matrix whose components are the force constants:

† For details, see Refs. 12, 13 and 14.

$$\mathbf{F} = \begin{bmatrix} f_{11} & f_{12} & r_1 f_{13} \\ f_{21} & f_{22} & r_2 f_{23} \\ r_1 f_{31} & r_2 f_{32} & r_1 r_2 f_{33} \end{bmatrix} \equiv \begin{bmatrix} F_{11} & F_{12} & F_{13} \\ F_{21} & F_{22} & F_{23} \\ F_{31} & F_{32} & F_{33} \end{bmatrix} \qquad (10.2)\dagger$$

Here r_1 and r_2 are the equilibrium lengths of the X—Y_1 and X—Y_2 bonds, respectively.

The kinetic energy is not easily expressed in terms of the same internal coordinates. Wilson[15] has shown, however, that the kinetic energy can be written

$$2T = \tilde{\dot{\mathbf{R}}}\mathbf{G}^{-1}\dot{\mathbf{R}} \qquad (10.3)$$

where $\mathbf{G}^{-1}$ is the reciprocal of the **G** matrix, which will be defined later.

If Eqs. 10.1 and 10.3 are combined with Newton's equation,

$$\frac{d}{dt}\left(\frac{\partial T}{\partial \dot{R}_k}\right) + \frac{\partial V}{\partial R_k} = 0 \qquad (3.6)$$

the following secular equation, which is similar to Eq. 3.19, is obtained.

$$\begin{vmatrix} F_{11} - (G^{-1})_{11}\lambda & F_{12} - (G^{-1})_{12}\lambda & \cdots \\ F_{21} - (G^{-1})_{21}\lambda & F_{22} - (G^{-1})_{22}\lambda & \cdots \\ \vdots & \vdots & \end{vmatrix} \equiv |\mathbf{F} - \mathbf{G}^{-1}\lambda| = 0 \qquad (10.4)$$

By multiplying by a $|\mathbf{G}|$ matrix of the form

$$\begin{vmatrix} G_{11} & G_{12} & \cdots \\ G_{21} & G_{22} & \cdots \\ \vdots & \vdots & \end{vmatrix} \equiv |\mathbf{G}| \qquad (10.5)$$

from the left of Eq. 10.4, the following equation is obtained.

$$\begin{vmatrix} \sum G_{1t}F_{t1} - \lambda & \sum G_{1t}F_{t2} & \cdots \\ \sum G_{2t}F_{t1} & \sum G_{2t}F_{t2} - \lambda & \cdots \\ \vdots & \vdots & \end{vmatrix} \equiv |\mathbf{GF} - \mathbf{E}\lambda| = 0 \qquad (10.6)$$

† f_{11} and f_{22} are the stretching force constants of the X—Y_1 and X—Y_2 bonds, respectively. f_{33} is the bending force constant of the Y_1XY_2 angle. The other symbols represent interaction force constants between stretching and stretching or between stretching and bending vibrations. f_{13} (or f_{31}), f_{23} (or f_{32}) and f_{33} are multiplied by r_1, r_2 and r_1r_2, respectively, to make the dimensions of all the force constants the same.

Here **E** is the unit matrix, and λ is related to the wave number, $\tilde{\nu}$, by the relation $\lambda = 4\pi^2c^2\tilde{\nu}^2$.† The order of the equation is equal to the number of internal coordinates used.

The **F** matrix can be written by assuming a suitable set of force constants. If the **G** matrix is constructed by the following method, the vibrational frequencies are obtained by solving Eq. 10.6. The **G** matrix is defined as

$$\mathbf{G} = \mathbf{B}\mathbf{M}^{-1}\tilde{\mathbf{B}} \tag{10.7}$$

Here $\mathbf{M}^{-1}$ is a diagonal matrix whose components are μ_i, where μ_i is the reciprocal of the mass of the ith atom. For a bent XY_2 molecule,

$$\mathbf{M}^{-1} = \begin{bmatrix} \mu_1 & 0 & 0 \\ 0 & \mu_1 & 0 \\ 0 & 0 & \mu_3 \end{bmatrix}$$

where μ_3 and μ_1 are the reciprocals of the masses of the X and Y atoms, respectively. The **B** matrix is defined as

$$\mathbf{R} = \mathbf{B}\mathbf{X} \tag{10.8}$$

where **R** and **X** are column matrices whose components are the internal and rectangular coordinates, respectively. For a bent XY_2 molecule, Eq. 10.8 is written

$$\begin{bmatrix} \Delta r_1 \\ \Delta r_2 \\ \Delta\alpha \end{bmatrix} = \left[\begin{array}{ccc|ccc|ccc} -s & -c & 0 & 0 & 0 & 0 & s & c & 0 \\ 0 & 0 & 0 & s & -c & 0 & -s & c & 0 \\ -c/r & s/r & 0 & c/r & s/r & 0 & 0 & -2s/r & 0 \end{array}\right] \begin{bmatrix} \Delta x_1 \\ \Delta y_1 \\ \Delta z_1 \\ \Delta x_2 \\ \Delta y_2 \\ \Delta z_2 \\ \Delta x_3 \\ \Delta y_3 \\ \Delta z_3 \end{bmatrix} \tag{10.9}$$

where $s = \sin \alpha/2$, $c = \cos \alpha/2$ and r is the equilibrium distance between X and Y. (See Fig. I-11.)

† λ should not be confused with λ_w (wavelength).

If unit vectors such as those in Fig. I-11 are considered, Eq. 10.9 can be written in a more compact form using vector notation:

$$\begin{bmatrix} \Delta r_1 \\ \Delta r_2 \\ \Delta\alpha \end{bmatrix} = \begin{bmatrix} \mathbf{e}_{31} & 0 & -\mathbf{e}_{31} \\ 0 & \mathbf{e}_{32} & -\mathbf{e}_{32} \\ \mathbf{p}_{31}/r & \mathbf{p}_{32}/r & -(\mathbf{p}_{31}+\mathbf{p}_{32})/r \end{bmatrix} \begin{bmatrix} \boldsymbol{\rho}_1 \\ \boldsymbol{\rho}_2 \\ \boldsymbol{\rho}_3 \end{bmatrix} \tag{10.10}$$

Here $\boldsymbol{\rho}_1$, $\boldsymbol{\rho}_2$ and $\boldsymbol{\rho}_3$ are the displacement vectors of the atoms, 1, 2 and 3, respectively. This can be written simply as

$$\mathbf{R} = \mathbf{S}\cdot\boldsymbol{\rho} \tag{10.11}$$

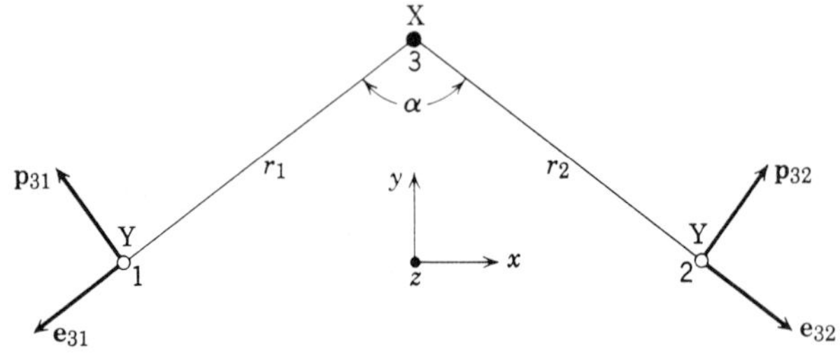

Fig. I-11. Unit vectors in a bent XY_2 molecule.

where the dot represents the scalar product of the two vectors. The advantage of the **S** matrix is that it is possible to write its vector components (**S** vectors) according to the following simple formulas.

(1) Bond stretching.

$$\underline{2 \qquad\qquad 1} \rightarrow \mathbf{e}_{21} \qquad \Delta r_{21} = \mathbf{e}_{21}\cdot\boldsymbol{\rho}_1 - \mathbf{e}_{21}\cdot\boldsymbol{\rho}_2 \tag{10.12}$$

(2) Angle bending (Fig. I-11).

$$\Delta\alpha_{132} = \mathbf{p}_{31}\cdot\boldsymbol{\rho}_1/r + \mathbf{p}_{32}\cdot\boldsymbol{\rho}_2/r - (\mathbf{p}_{31}+\mathbf{p}_{32})\cdot\boldsymbol{\rho}_3/r \tag{10.13}$$

Formulas for obtaining the **S** vectors of other internal coordinates such as those of out-of-plane ($\Delta\theta$) and torsional ($\Delta\tau$) vibrations are also available.[12,13]

By using the **S** matrix, Eq. 10.7 is written

$$\mathbf{G} = \mathbf{S}\mathbf{M}^{-1}\tilde{\mathbf{S}} \tag{10.14}$$

For a bent XY_2 molecule, this becomes

$$\mathbf{G} = \begin{bmatrix} \mathbf{e}_{31} & 0 & -\mathbf{e}_{31} \\ 0 & \mathbf{e}_{32} & -\mathbf{e}_{32} \\ \mathbf{p}_{31}/r & \mathbf{p}_{32}/r & -(\mathbf{p}_{31}+\mathbf{p}_{32})/r \end{bmatrix} \begin{bmatrix} \mu_1 & 0 & 0 \\ 0 & \mu_1 & 0 \\ 0 & 0 & \mu_3 \end{bmatrix} \times$$

$$\begin{bmatrix} \mathbf{e}_{31} & 0 & \mathbf{p}_{31}/r \\ 0 & \mathbf{e}_{32} & \mathbf{p}_{32}/r \\ -\mathbf{e}_{31} & -\mathbf{e}_{32} & -(\mathbf{p}_{31}+\mathbf{p}_{32})/r \end{bmatrix}$$

$$= \begin{bmatrix} (\mu_3+\mu_1)\mathbf{e}_{31}{}^2 & \mu_3\mathbf{e}_{31}\cdot\mathbf{e}_{32} & \frac{\mu_1}{r}\mathbf{e}_{31}\cdot\mathbf{p}_{31} + \frac{\mu_3}{r}\mathbf{e}_{31}\cdot(\mathbf{p}_{31}+\mathbf{p}_{32}) \\ & (\mu_3+\mu_1)\mathbf{e}_{32}{}^2 & \frac{\mu_1}{r}\mathbf{e}_{32}\cdot\mathbf{p}_{32} + \frac{\mu_3}{r}\mathbf{e}_{32}\cdot(\mathbf{p}_{31}+\mathbf{p}_{32}) \\ & & \frac{\mu_1}{r^2}\mathbf{p}_{31}{}^2 + \frac{\mu_1}{r^2}\mathbf{p}_{32}{}^2 + \frac{\mu_3}{r}(\mathbf{p}_{31}+\mathbf{p}_{32})^2 \end{bmatrix}$$

Considering

$$\mathbf{e}_{31} = \mathbf{e}_{32} = \mathbf{p}_{31} = \mathbf{p}_{32} = 1, \quad \mathbf{e}_{31}\cdot\mathbf{p}_{31} = \mathbf{e}_{32}\cdot\mathbf{p}_{32} = 0,$$

$$\mathbf{e}_{31}\cdot\mathbf{e}_{32} = \cos\alpha, \quad \mathbf{e}_{31}\cdot\mathbf{p}_{32} = \mathbf{e}_{32}\cdot\mathbf{p}_{31} = -\sin\alpha, \text{ and}$$

$$(\mathbf{p}_{31}+\mathbf{p}_{32})^2 = 2(1-\cos\alpha)$$

the **G** matrix is calculated as

$$\mathbf{G} = \begin{bmatrix} \mu_3+\mu_1 & \mu_3\cos\alpha & -\frac{\mu_3}{r}\sin\alpha \\ & \mu_3+\mu_1 & -\frac{\mu_3}{r}\sin\alpha \\ & & \frac{2\mu_1}{r^2} + \frac{2\mu_3}{r^2}(1-\cos\alpha) \end{bmatrix} \tag{10.15}$$

If the **G** matrix elements obtained are written for each combination of internal coordinates, there results

$$\begin{aligned} G(\Delta r_1, \Delta r_1) &= \mu_3 + \mu_1 \\ G(\Delta r_2, \Delta r_2) &= \mu_3 + \mu_1 \\ G(\Delta r_1, \Delta r_2) &= \mu_3\cos\alpha \\ G(\Delta\alpha, \Delta\alpha) &= \frac{2\mu_1}{r^2} + \frac{2\mu_3}{r^2}(1-\cos\alpha) \\ G(\Delta r_1, \Delta\alpha) &= -\frac{\mu_3}{r}\sin\alpha \\ G(\Delta r_2, \Delta\alpha) &= -\frac{\mu_3}{r}\sin\alpha \end{aligned} \tag{10.16}$$

If such calculations are made for several types of molecules, it is immediately seen that the **G** matrix elements themselves have many regularities. Decius[16] developed general formulas for writing **G** matrix elements.† Some of them are

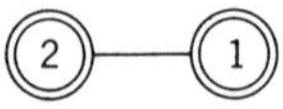

$$G_{rr}^{2} = \mu_1 + \mu_2$$

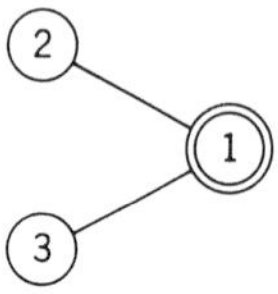

$$G_{rr}^{1} = \mu_1 \cos \phi$$

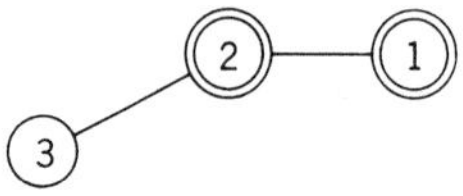

$$G_{r\phi}^{2} = -\rho_{23}\mu_2 \sin \phi$$

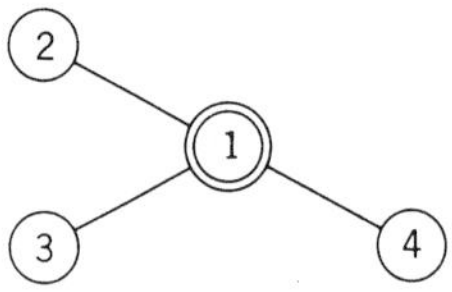

$$G_{r\phi}^{1}\begin{pmatrix}1\\1\end{pmatrix} = -(\rho_{13} \sin \phi_{213} \cos \psi_{234} + \rho_{14} \sin \phi_{214} \cos \psi_{243})\mu_1$$

$$G_{\phi\phi}^{3} = \rho_{12}^{2}\mu_1 + \rho_{23}^{2}\mu_3 + (\rho_{12}^{2} + \rho_{23}^{2} - 2\rho_{12}\rho_{23} \cos \phi)\mu_2$$

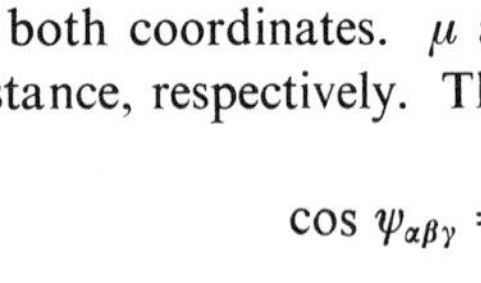

$$G_{\phi\phi}^{2}\begin{pmatrix}1\\1\end{pmatrix} = (\rho_{12}^{2} \cos \psi_{314})\mu_1 + [(\rho_{12} - \rho_{23} \cos \phi_{123} - \rho_{24} \cos \phi_{124})\rho_{12} \cos \psi_{314} + (\sin \phi_{123} \sin \phi_{124} \sin^2 \psi_{314} + \cos \phi_{324} \cos \psi_{314})\rho_{23}\rho_{24}]\mu_2$$

Here the atoms surrounded by a double circle indicate the atoms common to both coordinates. μ and ρ denote the reciprocals of mass and bond distance, respectively. The solid angle, $\psi_{\alpha\beta\gamma}$, in Fig. I-12 is defined as

$$\cos \psi_{\alpha\beta\gamma} = \frac{\cos \phi_{\alpha\delta\gamma} - \cos \phi_{\alpha\delta\beta} \cos \phi_{\beta\delta\gamma}}{\sin \phi_{\alpha\delta\beta} \sin \phi_{\beta\delta\gamma}} \tag{10.17}$$

The correspondence between the Decius formulas and the results obtained in Eq. 10.16 is evident.

† See also Refs. 17 and 18.

With the Decius formulas, the **G** matrix elements of a pyramidal XY_3 molecule have been calculated and are shown in Table I-9.

TABLE I-9

	Δr_1	Δr_2	Δr_3	$\Delta\alpha_{23}$	$\Delta\alpha_{31}$	$\Delta\alpha_{12}$
Δr_1	A	B	B	C	D	D
Δr_2	—	A	B	D	C	D
Δr_3	—	—	A	D	D	C
$\Delta\alpha_{23}$	—	—	—	E	F	F
$\Delta\alpha_{31}$	—	—	—	—	E	F
$\Delta\alpha_{12}$	—	—	—	—	—	E

$$A = G_{rr}{}^{2} = \mu_X + \mu_Y$$

$$B = G_{rr'}{}^{1} = \mu_X \cos\alpha$$

$$C = G_{r\phi}{}^{1}\binom{1}{1} = -\frac{2}{r}\,\frac{\cos\alpha\,(1-\cos\alpha)\mu_X}{\sin\alpha}$$

$$D = G_{r\phi}{}^{2} = -\frac{\mu_X}{r}\sin\alpha$$

$$E = G_{\phi\phi}{}^{3} = \frac{2}{r^2}\,[\mu_Y + \mu_X(1-\cos\alpha)]$$

$$F = G_{\phi\phi}{}^{2}\binom{1}{1} = \frac{\mu_Y}{r^2}\,\frac{\cos\alpha}{1+\cos\alpha} + \frac{\mu_X}{r^2}\,\frac{(1+3\cos\alpha)(1-\cos\alpha)}{1+\cos\alpha}$$

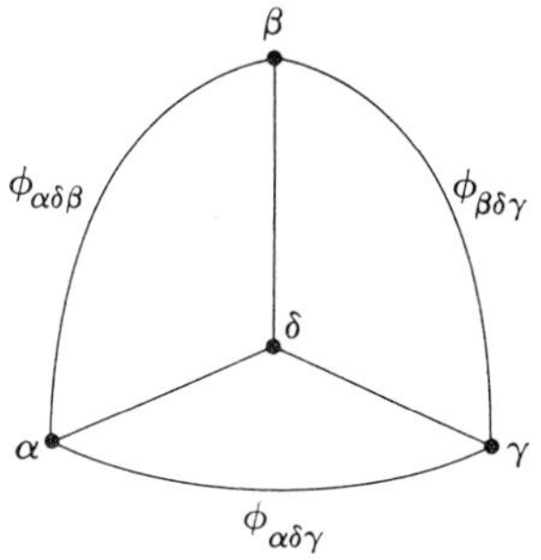

Fig. I-12.

I-11. UTILIZATION OF SYMMETRY PROPERTIES

Considering the equivalence of the two X—Y bonds of a bent XY_2 molecule, the **F** and **G** matrices obtained in Eqs. 10.2 and 10.15 are written

$$\mathbf{F} = \begin{bmatrix} f_{11} & f_{12} & rf_{13} \\ f_{12} & f_{11} & rf_{13} \\ rf_{13} & rf_{13} & r^2 f_{33} \end{bmatrix} \tag{11.1}$$

$$\mathbf{G} = \begin{bmatrix} \mu_3 + \mu_1 & \mu_3\cos\alpha & -\dfrac{\mu_3}{r}\sin\alpha \\ \mu_3\cos\alpha & \mu_3 + \mu_1 & -\dfrac{\mu_3}{r}\sin\alpha \\ -\dfrac{\mu_3}{r}\sin\alpha & -\dfrac{\mu_3}{r}\sin\alpha & \dfrac{2\mu_1}{r^2} + \dfrac{2\mu_3}{r^2}(1-\cos\alpha) \end{bmatrix} \tag{11.2}$$

Both of these matrices are of the form

$$\begin{bmatrix} A & C & D \\ C & A & D \\ D & D & B \end{bmatrix} \tag{11.3}$$

The appearance of the same elements is evidently due to the equivalence of the two internal coordinates, Δr_1 and Δr_2. Such symmetrically equivalent sets of internal coordinates are seen in many other molecules, such as those in Fig. I-10. In these cases, it is possible to reduce the order of the **F** and **G** matrices (and hence the order of the secular equation resulting from them) by a coordinate transformation.

Let the internal coordinates **R** be transformed by

$$\mathbf{R}' = \mathbf{U}\mathbf{R} \tag{11.4}$$

More explicitly,

$$\begin{bmatrix} R_1' \\ R_2' \\ \cdot \\ \cdot \\ \cdot \\ R_j' \end{bmatrix} = \begin{bmatrix} u_{11} & u_{12} & \cdots & u_{1k} \\ u_{21} & u_{22} & \cdots & u_{2k} \\ \cdot & \cdot & \cdots & \cdot \\ \\ u_{j1} & u_{j2} & \cdots & u_{jk} \end{bmatrix} \begin{bmatrix} R_1 \\ R_2 \\ \cdot \\ \cdot \\ \cdot \\ R_k \end{bmatrix} \tag{11.5}$$

Here **U** is an orthogonal matrix ($\tilde{\mathbf{U}}\mathbf{U} = \mathbf{E}$) whose elements must satisfy the relations

$$\sum_k (u_{jk})^2 = 1 \quad \text{(normalization)} \tag{11.6}$$

$$\sum_k u_{jk}u_{lk} = 0 \quad \text{(orthogonality)} \tag{11.7}$$

Furthermore, the symmetry of the molecule must be taken into consideration in constructing the **U** matrix. The new sets of coordinates, $R_1', \ldots, R_j'$, thus obtained are linear combinations of internal coordinates and are called (internal) *symmetry coordinates*. An appropriate choice of these u elements can usually be made through intuition and experience. It follows from Eqs. 11.6 and 11.7 that the relations

$$u_{ak} = \pm(1/q)^{1/2} \tag{11.8}$$

$$u_{ak}^2 + u_{bk}^2 = 2/q \tag{11.9}$$

$$u_{ak}^2 + u_{bk}^2 + u_{ck}^2 = 3/q \tag{11.10}$$

must hold for degeneracies 1, 2 and 3, respectively. Here q is the total number of symmetrically equivalent internal coordinates, and (u_{ak}, u_{bk})

and (u_{ak}, u_{bk}, u_{ck}) represent the elements of the kth internal coordinates for doubly and triply degenerate combinations, respectively.

In a bent XY_2 molecule, Δr_1 and Δr_2 are equivalent. Then, from Eqs. 11.6, 11.7 and 11.8, the symmetry coordinates are

$$R_1' = (1/\sqrt{2})\,\Delta r_1 + (1/\sqrt{2})\,\Delta r_2$$
$$R_3' = (1/\sqrt{2})\,\Delta r_1 - (1/\sqrt{2})\,\Delta r_2 \qquad (11.11)$$

Consider the symmetry property of the R_3' coordinate. If the identity operation is performed, each internal coordinate is transformed into itself. Thus

$$(I)R_3' = (1/\sqrt{2})\,\Delta r_1 - (1/\sqrt{2})\,\Delta r_2 = (+1)R_3'$$

If the operation $C_2(z)$ is applied, Δr_1 is transformed into Δr_2, and Δr_2 into Δr_1. Thus

$$(C_2(z))R_3' = (1/\sqrt{2})\,\Delta r_2 - (1/\sqrt{2})\,\Delta r_1 = (-1)R_3'$$

The operations $\sigma(xz)$ and $\sigma(yz)$ give the same results as $C_2(z)$ and I, respectively. Thus the characters for the operations I, $C_2(z)$, $\sigma(xz)$ and $\sigma(yz)$ are $+1$, -1, -1, $+1$, respectively. In other words, R_3' belongs to the B_2 species of the point group $\mathbf{C}_{2v}$. Similarly, it can be shown that R_1' belongs to the A_1 species. It is evident that R_1' and R_3' represent the coordinates corresponding to the *symmetric and antisymmetric stretching vibrations*, respectively. Evidently, the bending coordinate, $\Delta\alpha$, belongs to the A_1 species. Therefore the complete $\mathbf{U}$ matrix of the bent XY_2 molecule is written

$$\begin{bmatrix} R_1'(A_1) \\ R_2'(A_1) \\ R_3'(B_2) \end{bmatrix} = \begin{bmatrix} 1/\sqrt{2} & 1/\sqrt{2} & 0 \\ 0 & 0 & 1 \\ 1/\sqrt{2} & -1/\sqrt{2} & 0 \end{bmatrix} \begin{bmatrix} \Delta r_1 \\ \Delta r_2 \\ \Delta\alpha \end{bmatrix} \qquad (11.12)$$

If the $\mathbf{F}$ and $\mathbf{G}$ matrices of the type (11.3) are transformed by the relations

$$\mathbf{F}' = \mathbf{U}\mathbf{F}\tilde{\mathbf{U}}$$
$$\mathbf{G}' = \mathbf{U}\mathbf{G}\tilde{\mathbf{U}} \qquad (11.13)$$

where $\mathbf{U}$ is given by Eq. 11.12, they become formally

$$\mathbf{F}', \mathbf{G}' = \left[\begin{array}{cc|c} A + C & \sqrt{2}\,D & 0 \\ \sqrt{2}\,D & B & 0 \\ \hline 0 & 0 & A - C \end{array}\right] \qquad (11.14)$$

Or, more explicitly,

$$\mathbf{F}' = \left[\begin{array}{cc|c} f_{11} + f_{12} & r\sqrt{2}f_{13} & 0 \\ r\sqrt{2}f_{13} & r^2 f_{33} & 0 \\ \hline 0 & 0 & f_{11} - f_{12} \end{array}\right] \tag{11.15}$$

$$\mathbf{G}' = \left[\begin{array}{cc|c} \mu_3(1 + \cos\alpha) + \mu_1 & -\frac{2}{r}\mu_3 \sin\alpha & 0 \\ -\frac{2}{r}\mu_3 \sin\alpha & \frac{2\mu_1}{r^2} + \frac{2\mu_3}{r^2}(1 - \cos\alpha) & 0 \\ \hline 0 & 0 & \mu_3(1 - \cos\alpha) + \mu_1 \end{array}\right] \tag{11.16}$$

It can be shown, in general, that the transformed secular equation, $|\mathbf{G}'\mathbf{F}' - \mathbf{E}\lambda| = 0$, obtained by the orthogonal transformation above, has the same roots as the original one. Since $|\mathbf{G}'\mathbf{F}' - \mathbf{E}\lambda| = 0$ can be resolved into one quadratic (A_1) and one first order (B_2) secular equation, in a bent XY_2 molecule, it is necessary only to solve these low order secular equations. The advantage of solving the former equation is therefore that it can be resolved into several equations of lower order.† In general, the burden of computation rapidly increases as the order of the secular equation becomes large. Therefore a coordinate transformation such as that shown above greatly reduces the labor involved in calculation.

In a pyramidal XY_3 molecule (Fig. I-10c), Δr_1, Δr_2 and Δr_3 are the equivalent set. So are $\Delta\alpha_{23}$, $\Delta\alpha_{31}$ and $\Delta\alpha_{12}$. It is already known from Eq. 8.7 that one A_1 and one E vibration is involved both in the stretching and in the bending vibrations. Considering the relations given by Eqs. 11.6, 11.7, 11.8 and 11.9, the symmetry coordinates for the three stretching vibrations are selected as follows:

$$\begin{aligned} R_1'(A_1) &= (1/\sqrt{3})\,\Delta r_1 + (1/\sqrt{3})\,\Delta r_2 + (1/\sqrt{3})\,\Delta r_3 \\ R_{2a}'(E) &= (2/\sqrt{6})\,\Delta r_1 - (1/\sqrt{6})\,\Delta r_2 - (1/\sqrt{6})\,\Delta r_3 \\ R_{2b}'(E) &= \qquad\qquad\quad (1/\sqrt{2})\,\Delta r_2 - (1/\sqrt{2})\,\Delta r_3 \end{aligned} \tag{11.17}$$

† As shown in Eqs. 10.1 and 10.3, the potential and kinetic energies in terms of internal coordinates involve cross products. This makes the order of the secular equation high. On the other hand, the equation could be resolved completely if normal coordinates were used (Sec. I-3). Although symmetry coordinates are not so satisfactory as normal coordinates, the order of the secular equation, $|\mathbf{G}'\mathbf{F}' - \mathbf{E}\lambda| = 0$, in terms of symmetry coordinates becomes lower than that of $|\mathbf{GF} - \mathbf{E}\lambda| = 0$ in terms of internal coordinates.

It is evident that R_1' transforms according to the character of the A_1 species of the point group $\mathbf{C}_{3v}$. That the pair R_{2a}' and R_{2b}' belongs to the E species can be proved as follows. For example, for the C_3^+ operation,

$$(C_3^+)R_{2a}' = (2/\sqrt{6})\,\Delta r_3 - (1/\sqrt{6})\,\Delta r_1 - (1/\sqrt{6})\,\Delta r_2 = AR_{2a}' + BR_{2b}'$$

$$(C_3^+)R_{2b}' = (1/\sqrt{2})\,\Delta r_1 - (1/\sqrt{2})\,\Delta r_2 = A'R_{2a}' + B'R_{2b}'$$

where A, B, A' and B' are constants. Substituting for R_{2a}' and R_{2b}' in the right side of these equations from Eqs. 11.17, and equating coefficients, it is found that

$$A = -1/2, \quad B = \sqrt{3}/2, \quad A' = -\sqrt{3}/2, \quad B' = -1/2$$

That is, the transformation caused by the operation C_3^+ is written

$$C_3^+\begin{bmatrix} R_{2a}' \\ R_{2b}' \end{bmatrix} = \begin{bmatrix} -1/2 & \sqrt{3}/2 \\ -\sqrt{3}/2 & -1/2 \end{bmatrix}\begin{bmatrix} R_{2a}' \\ R_{2b}' \end{bmatrix}$$

Thus the character of the transformation matrix for this operation is -1. In a similar manner, it can be shown that the characters for the operations I and σ_v are 2 and 0, respectively.

The symmetry coordinates for the three angle coordinates are similar to those in Eqs. 11.17. Therefore the complete $\mathbf{U}$ matrix is written

$$\begin{bmatrix} R_1'(A_1) \\ R_2'(A_1) \\ R_{3a}'(E) \\ R_{4a}'(E) \\ R_{3b}'(E) \\ R_{4b}'(E) \end{bmatrix} = \begin{bmatrix} 1/\sqrt{3} & 1/\sqrt{3} & 1/\sqrt{3} & 0 & 0 & 0 \\ 0 & 0 & 0 & 1/\sqrt{3} & 1/\sqrt{3} & 1/\sqrt{3} \\ 2/\sqrt{6} & -1/\sqrt{6} & -1/\sqrt{6} & 0 & 0 & 0 \\ 0 & 0 & 0 & 2/\sqrt{6} & -1/\sqrt{6} & -1/\sqrt{6} \\ 0 & 1/\sqrt{2} & -1/\sqrt{2} & 0 & 0 & 0 \\ 0 & 0 & 0 & 0 & 1/\sqrt{2} & -1/\sqrt{2} \end{bmatrix}\begin{bmatrix} \Delta r_1 \\ \Delta r_2 \\ \Delta r_3 \\ \Delta\alpha_{23} \\ \Delta\alpha_{31} \\ \Delta\alpha_{12} \end{bmatrix} \tag{11.18}$$

The $\mathbf{G}$ matrix of a pyramidal XY_3 molecule has already been calculated (see Table I-9). By using Eq. 11.13, the new $\mathbf{G}'$ matrix becomes

$$\mathbf{G}' = \left[\begin{array}{cc|cc|cc} A+2B & C+2D & & & & \\ C+2D & E+2F & \multicolumn{2}{c|}{0} & \multicolumn{2}{c}{0} \\ \hline & & A-B & C-D & & \\ \multicolumn{2}{c|}{0} & C-D & E-F & \multicolumn{2}{c}{0} \\ \hline & & & & A-B & C-D \\ \multicolumn{2}{c|}{0} & \multicolumn{2}{c|}{0} & C-D & E-F \end{array}\right] \tag{11.19}$$

Here A, B, etc., denote the elements in Table I-9. The **F** matrix transforms similarly. Therefore it is necessary only to solve two quadratic equations for the A_1 and E species.

For the tetrahedral XY_4 molecule shown in Fig. I-10*e*, group theory (Secs. I-7, I-8) predicts one A_1 and one F_2 stretching, and one E and one F_2 bending vibration. The **U** matrix for the four stretching coordinates becomes

$$\begin{bmatrix} R_1'(A_1) \\ R_{2a}'(F_2) \\ R_{2b}'(F_2) \\ R_{2c}'(F_2) \end{bmatrix} = \begin{bmatrix} 1/2 & 1/2 & 1/2 & 1/2 \\ 1/\sqrt{6} & 1/\sqrt{6} & -2/\sqrt{6} & 0 \\ 1/\sqrt{12} & 1/\sqrt{12} & 1/\sqrt{12} & -3/\sqrt{12} \\ -1/\sqrt{2} & 1/\sqrt{2} & 0 & 0 \end{bmatrix} \begin{bmatrix} \Delta r_1 \\ \Delta r_2 \\ \Delta r_3 \\ \Delta r_4 \end{bmatrix} \tag{11.20}$$

whereas the **U** matrix for the six bending coordinates becomes

$$\begin{bmatrix} R_1'(A_1) \\ R_{2a}'(E) \\ R_{2b}'(E) \\ R_{3a}'(F_2) \\ R_{3b}'(F_2) \\ R_{3c}'(F_2) \end{bmatrix} =$$

$$\begin{bmatrix} 1/\sqrt{6} & 1/\sqrt{6} & 1/\sqrt{6} & 1/\sqrt{6} & 1/\sqrt{6} & 1/\sqrt{6} \\ 2/\sqrt{12} & -1/\sqrt{12} & -1/\sqrt{12} & -1/\sqrt{12} & -1/\sqrt{12} & 2/\sqrt{12} \\ 0 & 1/2 & -1/2 & 1/2 & -1/2 & 0 \\ 2/\sqrt{12} & -1/\sqrt{12} & -1/\sqrt{12} & 1/\sqrt{12} & 1/\sqrt{12} & -2/\sqrt{12} \\ 1/\sqrt{6} & 1/\sqrt{6} & 1/\sqrt{6} & -1/\sqrt{6} & -1/\sqrt{6} & -1/\sqrt{6} \\ 0 & 1/2 & -1/2 & -1/2 & 1/2 & 0 \end{bmatrix} \begin{bmatrix} \Delta\alpha_{12} \\ \Delta\alpha_{23} \\ \Delta\alpha_{31} \\ \Delta\alpha_{14} \\ \Delta\alpha_{24} \\ \Delta\alpha_{34} \end{bmatrix} \tag{11.21}$$

The symmetry coordinate $R_1'(A_1)$ in Eq. 11.21 represents a *redundant coordinate* (see Eq. 8.1). In such a case, a coordinate transformation reduces the order of the matrix by one since all the **G** matrix elements related to this coordinate become zero. Conversely, this result provides a general method of finding redundant coordinates. Suppose the elements of the **G** matrix are calculated in terms of internal coordinates such as those in Table I-9. If a suitable combination of internal coordinates is made so that $\sum_j G_{ij} = 0$ (where j refers to all the equivalent internal coordinates), such a combination is a redundant coordinate.† By using the **U** matrices in Eqs. 11.20 and 11.21, the problem of solving a tenth order secular equation for a tetrahedral XY_4 molecule is reduced to that of solving two first order (A_1 and E) and one quadratic (F_2) equation.

I-12. POTENTIAL FIELDS AND FORCE CONSTANTS

Using Eqs. 10.1 and 11.1, the potential energy of a bent XY_2 molecule is written

$$2V = f_{11}(\Delta r_1)^2 + f_{11}(\Delta r_2)^2 + f_{33}r^2(\Delta\alpha)^2 + 2f_{12}(\Delta r_1)(\Delta r_2) + 2f_{13}r(\Delta r_1)(\Delta\alpha) + 2f_{13}r(\Delta r_2)(\Delta\alpha) \quad (12.1)$$

This type of potential field is called a *generalized valence force* (GVF) field.‡ It consists of stretching and bending force constants as well as the interaction force constants between them. When using such a potential field, four force constants are needed to describe the potential energy of a bent XY_2 molecule. Since only three vibrations are observed in practice, it is impossible to determine all four force constants simultaneously. One method used to circumvent this difficulty is to calculate the vibrational frequencies of isotopic molecules (e.g., D_2O and HDO for H_2O), assuming the same set of force constants. This method is satisfactory, however, only for simple molecules. As molecules become more complex, the number of interaction force constants in the generalized valence force field becomes too large to allow any reliable evaluation.

In another approach, Shimanouchi[19] introduced the *Urey-Bradley force* (UBF) *field*[20] which consists of stretching and bending force constants, as well as repulsive force constants between non-bonded atoms. The general form of the potential field is given by

$$V = \sum_i [\tfrac{1}{2}K_i(\Delta r_i)^2 + K_i'r_i(\Delta r_i)] + \sum_i [\tfrac{1}{2}H_i r_{i\alpha}^2(\Delta\alpha_i)^2 + H_i' r_{i\alpha}^2(\Delta\alpha_i)] + \sum_i [\tfrac{1}{2}F_i(\Delta q_i)^2 + F_i'q_i(\Delta q_i)] \quad (12.2)$$

Here Δr_i, $\Delta\alpha_i$ and Δq_i are the changes in the bond lengths, bond angles, and distances between non-bonded atoms, respectively. The symbols K_i, K_i', H_i, H_i', F_i and F_i' represent the stretching, bending and repulsive force constants, respectively. Furthermore, r_i, $r_{i\alpha}$ and q_i are the values

† More general methods for finding redundant coordinates are given in Refs. 13 and 18*a*.

‡ A potential field consists of stretching and bending force constants only is called a simple valence force field.

of the distances at the equilibrium positions and are inserted to make the force constants dimensionally similar.

Using the relation

$$q_{ij}^2 = r_i^2 + r_j^2 - 2r_ir_j \cos \alpha_{ij} \tag{12.3}$$

and considering that the first derivatives can be equated to zero in the equilibrium case, the final form of the potential field becomes

$$\begin{aligned} V = \tfrac{1}{2}\sum_i [K_i + \sum_{j(\neq i)} (t_{ij}^2F_{ij}' + s_{ij}^2F_{ij})](\Delta r_i)^2 \\ + \tfrac{1}{2}\sum_{i<j} [H_{ij} - s_{ij}s_{ji}F_{ij}' + t_{ij}t_{ji}F_{ij}](r_{ij}\,\Delta\alpha_{ij})^2 \\ + \sum_{i<j} [-t_{ij}t_{ji}F_{ij}' + s_{ij}s_{ji}F_{ij}](\Delta r_i)(\Delta r_j) \\ + \sum_{i\neq j} [t_{ij}s_{ji}F_{ij}' + t_{ji}s_{ij}F_{ij}](r_j/r_i)^{1/2}(\Delta r_i)(r_{ij}\,\Delta\alpha_{ij}) \end{aligned} \tag{12.4}$$

Here

$$\begin{aligned} s_{ij} &= (r_i - r_j \cos \alpha_{ij})/q_{ij} \\ s_{ji} &= (r_j - r_i \cos \alpha_{ij})/q_{ij} \\ t_{ij} &= (r_j \sin \alpha_{ij})/q_{ij} \\ t_{ji} &= (r_i \sin \alpha_{ij})/q_{ij} \end{aligned} \tag{12.5}$$

In a bent XY_2 molecule, Eq. 12.4 becomes

$$\begin{aligned} V = \tfrac{1}{2}(K + t^2F' + s^2F)[(\Delta r_1)^2 + (\Delta r_2)^2] \\ + \tfrac{1}{2}(H - s^2F' + t^2F)(r\,\Delta\alpha)^2 \\ + (-t^2F' + s^2F)(\Delta r_1)(\Delta r_2) \\ + ts(F' + F)(\Delta r_1)(r\,\Delta\alpha) \\ + ts(F' + F)(\Delta r_2)(r\,\Delta\alpha) \end{aligned} \tag{12.6}$$

where

$$\begin{aligned} s &= r(1 - \cos \alpha)/q \\ t &= (r \sin \alpha)/q \end{aligned}$$

Comparing Eqs. 12.6 and 12.1, the following relations are obtained between the force constants of the generalized valence force field and those of the Urey-Bradley force field.

$$\begin{aligned} f_{11} &= K + t^2F' + s^2F \\ r^2f_{33} &= (H - s^2F' + t^2F)r^2 \\ f_{12} &= -t^2F' + s^2F \\ rf_{13} &= ts(F' + F)r \end{aligned} \tag{12.7}$$

Although the Urey-Bradley field has four force constants, F' is usually taken as $-\frac{1}{10}F$, with the assumption that the repulsive energy between non-bonded atoms is proportional to $1/r^9$. Thus only three force constants, K, H and F, are needed to construct the **F** matrix.

The number of the force constants in the Urey-Bradley field is, in general, much smaller than that in the generalized valence force field. In addition, the former field has the advantages that (1) the force constants have a clearer physical meaning than those of the generalized valence force field, and (2) they are transferable from molecule to molecule. For example, the force constants obtained for $SiCl_4$ and $SiBr_4$ can be used for $SiCl_3Br$, $SiCl_2Br_2$ and $SiClBr_3$. Mizushima, Shimanouchi and their co-workers[13] and Overend and Scherer[20a] have given many examples which demonstrate transferability of the force constants in the Urey-Bradley force field. This property of the Urey-Bradley force constants is highly useful in calculations for complex molecules. It should be mentioned, however, that ignorance of the interactions between non-neighboring stretching vibrations and between bending vibrations in the Urey-Bradley field sometimes causes difficulties in adjusting the force constants to fit the observed frequencies. In such a case, it is possible to improve the results by introducing more force constants.[20a,21]

The normal coordinate analysis developed in Secs. I-10–12 has already been applied to a number of molecules of various structures. In Parts II and III, references are cited for each type. Appendix II lists the **G** and **F** matrix elements for typical molecules, and Appendix III gives a detailed procedure for a normal coordinate analysis of a complex system such as a metal acetylacetonate.

I-13. SOLUTION OF THE SECULAR EQUATION

Once the **G** and **F** matrices are obtained, the next step is to solve the matrix secular equation:

$$|\mathbf{GF} - \mathbf{E}\lambda| = 0 \tag{10.6}$$

In diatomic molecules, $\mathbf{G} = G_{11} = 1/\mu$ and $\mathbf{F} = F_{11} = K$. Then $\lambda = G_{11}F_{11}$ and $\tilde{\nu} = \sqrt{\lambda}/2\pi c = \sqrt{K/\mu}/2\pi c$ (Eq. 2.6). If the units of mass and force constant are atomic weight and 10^5 dynes/cm (or md/A), respectively,† λ is related to $\tilde{\nu}$ (cm^{-1}) by

$$\tilde{\nu} = 1303.16\sqrt{\lambda}$$

or

$$\lambda = 0.588851 \left(\frac{\tilde{\nu}}{1000}\right)^2 \tag{13.1}$$

† Although the bond distance is involved in both the **G** and the **F** matrices, it is cancelled during multiplication of the **G** and **F** matrix elements. Therefore any unit can be used for the bond distance.

As an example, for the HF molecule $\mu = 0.9573$ and $K = 9.65$ in these units. Then, from Eqs. 2.6 and 13.1, $\tilde{\nu}$ is 4139 cm^{-1}; this is in good agreement with the observed frequency corrected for anharmonicity (see Table II-1). For convenience, a conversion table for $\tilde{\nu}$ (cm^{-1}) and λ (calculated in the units mentioned above) is given in Appendix IV.

The **F** and **G** matrix elements of a bent XY_2 molecule are given in Eqs. 11.15 and 11.16, respectively. The secular equation for the A_1 species is quadratic:

$$|\mathbf{GF} - \mathbf{E}\lambda| = \begin{vmatrix} G_{11}F_{11} + G_{12}F_{21} - \lambda & G_{11}F_{12} + G_{12}F_{22} \\ G_{21}F_{11} + G_{22}F_{21} & G_{21}F_{12} + G_{22}F_{22} - \lambda \end{vmatrix} = 0 \quad (13.2)$$

If this is expanded into an algebraic equation, there results

$$\lambda^2 - (G_{11}F_{11} + G_{22}F_{22} + 2G_{12}F_{12})\lambda + (G_{11}G_{22} - G_{12}{}^2)(F_{11}F_{22} - F_{12}{}^2) = 0 \quad (13.3)$$

For the H_2O molecule,

$$\mu_1 = \mu_H = 1/1.008 = 0.99206$$
$$\mu_3 = \mu_O = 1/16.000 = 0.06250$$
$$r = 0.96(\text{A}), \quad \alpha = 105^\circ$$
$$\sin\alpha = \sin 105^\circ = 0.96593$$
$$\cos\alpha = \cos 105^\circ = -0.25882$$

Then the **G** matrix elements of Eq. 11.16 are

$$G_{11} = \mu_1 + \mu_3(1 + \cos\alpha) = 1.03838$$
$$G_{12} = -\frac{\sqrt{2}}{r}\mu_3 \sin\alpha = -0.08893$$
$$G_{22} = \frac{1}{r^2}[2\mu_1 + 2\mu_3(1 - \cos\alpha)] = 2.32364$$

If the force constants in terms of the generalized valence force field are selected as

$$f_{11} = 8.428, \quad f_{12} = -0.105$$
$$f_{13} = 0.252, \quad f_{33} = 0.768$$

the **F** matrix elements of Eq. 11.15 are

$$F_{11} = f_{11} + f_{12} = 8.32300$$
$$F_{12} = \sqrt{2}\, r f_{13} = 0.35638$$
$$F_{22} = r^2 f_{33} = 0.70779$$

Using these values, Eq. 13.3 becomes

$$\lambda^2 - 10.22370\lambda + 13.86174 = 0$$

Solution of this equation gives

$$\lambda_1 = 8.6146 \qquad \lambda_2 = 1.6091$$

If these values are converted to $\tilde{\nu}$ through Eq. 13.1,

$$\tilde{\nu}_1 = 3824 \text{ cm}^{-1} \qquad \tilde{\nu}_2 = 1653 \text{ cm}^{-1}$$

With the same set of force constants, the frequency of the B_2 vibration is calculated as

$$\begin{aligned}\lambda_3 &= G_{33}F_{33} = [\mu_1 + \mu_3(1 - \cos\alpha)](f_{11} - f_{12})\\ &= 9.1366\\ \tilde{\nu}_3 &= 3939 \text{ cm}^{-1}\end{aligned}$$

These frequencies are in good agreement with the observed frequencies corrected for anharmonicity ($\omega_1 = 3825$ cm^{-1}, $\omega_2 = 1654$ cm^{-1} and $\omega_3 = 3936$ cm^{-1}).

If the secular equation is third order, it gives rise to a cubic equation:

$$\begin{aligned}&\lambda^3 - (G_{11}F_{11} + G_{22}F_{22} + G_{33}F_{33} + 2G_{12}F_{12} + 2G_{13}F_{13} + 2G_{23}F_{23})\lambda^2\\
&+ \left\{\begin{vmatrix} G_{11} & G_{12} \\ G_{21} & G_{22} \end{vmatrix}\begin{vmatrix} F_{11} & F_{12} \\ F_{21} & F_{22} \end{vmatrix} + \begin{vmatrix} G_{12} & G_{13} \\ G_{22} & G_{23} \end{vmatrix}\begin{vmatrix} F_{12} & F_{13} \\ F_{22} & F_{23} \end{vmatrix}\right.\\
&+ \begin{vmatrix} G_{11} & G_{13} \\ G_{21} & G_{23} \end{vmatrix}\begin{vmatrix} F_{11} & F_{13} \\ F_{21} & F_{23} \end{vmatrix} + \begin{vmatrix} G_{11} & G_{12} \\ G_{31} & G_{32} \end{vmatrix}\begin{vmatrix} F_{11} & F_{12} \\ F_{31} & F_{32} \end{vmatrix}\\
&+ \begin{vmatrix} G_{12} & G_{13} \\ G_{32} & G_{33} \end{vmatrix}\begin{vmatrix} F_{12} & F_{13} \\ F_{32} & F_{33} \end{vmatrix} + \begin{vmatrix} G_{11} & G_{13} \\ G_{31} & G_{33} \end{vmatrix}\begin{vmatrix} F_{11} & F_{13} \\ F_{31} & F_{33} \end{vmatrix}\\
&+ \begin{vmatrix} G_{21} & G_{22} \\ G_{31} & G_{32} \end{vmatrix}\begin{vmatrix} F_{21} & F_{22} \\ F_{31} & F_{32} \end{vmatrix} + \begin{vmatrix} G_{22} & G_{23} \\ G_{32} & G_{33} \end{vmatrix}\begin{vmatrix} F_{22} & F_{23} \\ F_{32} & F_{33} \end{vmatrix}\\
&+ \left.\begin{vmatrix} G_{21} & G_{23} \\ G_{31} & G_{33} \end{vmatrix}\begin{vmatrix} F_{21} & F_{23} \\ F_{31} & F_{33} \end{vmatrix}\right\}\lambda - \begin{vmatrix} G_{11} & G_{12} & G_{13} \\ G_{21} & G_{22} & G_{23} \\ G_{31} & G_{32} & G_{33} \end{vmatrix}\begin{vmatrix} F_{11} & F_{12} & F_{13} \\ F_{21} & F_{22} & F_{23} \\ F_{31} & F_{32} & F_{33} \end{vmatrix} = 0\end{aligned} \tag{13.4}$$

Thus it is possible to solve the secular equation by expanding it into an algebraic equation. If the order of the secular equation is higher than three, direct expansion such as shown above becomes too cumbersome. There are several methods of calculating the coefficients of an algebraic equation using indirect expansion.[10a,10b,12] In Appendix III, the Frame method is used to solve eighth order secular equations. The use of the electronic computer greatly reduces the burden of calculation.

I-14. THE SUM RULE AND THE PRODUCT RULE

Let $\lambda_1, \lambda_2, \ldots, \lambda_n$ be the roots of the secular equation, $|\mathbf{GF} - \mathbf{E}\lambda| = 0$. Then it is suspected from Eqs. 13.3 and 13.4 that the relation

$$\lambda_1 \lambda_2 \cdots \lambda_n = |\mathbf{G}|\,|\mathbf{F}| \tag{14.1}$$

holds for this molecule. Suppose that a second molecule has exactly the same $|\mathbf{F}|$ as that in Eq. 14.1. Then a similar relation

$$\lambda_1' \lambda_2' \cdots \lambda_n' = |\mathbf{G}'|\,|\mathbf{F}|$$

holds for the second molecule. It follows that

$$\frac{\lambda_1 \lambda_2 \cdots \lambda_n}{\lambda_1' \lambda_2' \cdots \lambda_n'} = \frac{|\mathbf{G}|}{|\mathbf{G}'|} \tag{14.2}$$

Since

$$\tilde{\nu} = \frac{1}{2\pi c}\sqrt{\lambda}$$

Eq. 14.2 can be written

$$\frac{\tilde{\nu}_1 \tilde{\nu}_2 \cdots \tilde{\nu}_n}{\tilde{\nu}_1' \tilde{\nu}_2' \cdots \tilde{\nu}_n'} = \sqrt{\frac{|\mathbf{G}|}{|\mathbf{G}'|}} \tag{14.3}$$

This is called the *product rule*, and its validity has been confirmed by using pairs of molecules such as H_2O and D_2O, CH_4 and CD_4.

It is also seen from Eqs. 13.3 and 13.4 that

$$\lambda_1 + \lambda_2 + \cdots + \lambda_n = \sum_n \lambda = \sum_{i,j} G_{ij} F_{ij} \tag{14.4}$$

Let σ_k denote $\sum_{ij} G_{ij} F_{ij}$ for k different molecules, all of which have the same $\mathbf{F}$ matrix. If a suitable combination of molecules is taken so that

$$\begin{aligned}\sigma_1 + \sigma_2 + \cdots + \sigma_k &= (\textstyle\sum G_{ij}F_{ij})_1 + (\sum G_{ij}F_{ij})_2 + \cdots + (\sum G_{ij}F_{ij})_k \\ &= [(\textstyle\sum G_{ij})_1 + (\sum G_{ij})_2 + \cdots + (\sum G_{ij})_k](\sum F_{ij}) \\ &= 0\end{aligned}$$

then it follows that

$$(\textstyle\sum\lambda)_1 + (\sum\lambda)_2 + \cdots + (\sum\lambda)_k = 0 \tag{14.5}$$

This is called the *sum rule*, and it has been verified for such combinations as H_2O, D_2O and HDO where

$$2\sigma(\text{HDO}) - \sigma(\text{H}_2\text{O}) - \sigma(\text{D}_2\text{O}) = 0$$

Such relations between the frequencies of isotopic molecules are highly useful in making band assignments.

I-15. INFRARED DICHROISM AND THE POLARIZATION OF RAMAN LINES

As stated in Secs. I-7 and I-8, it is possible, by using group theory, to classify the normal vibrations into various species. Experimentally, measurements of infrared dichroism and the polarization of Raman lines are also useful in determining the species of the observed bands.

The character table of the point group $\mathbf{C}_{3v}$ in Table I-8 indicates that the A_1 vibrations become infrared active by absorbing radiation whose electric vector vibrates in the z direction (μ_z), whereas the E vibrations become infrared active by absorbing radiation whose electric vectors vibrate in the x and y directions (μ_x and μ_y). In other words, it is possible to distinguish the vibrations belonging to the A_1 and the E species by using polarized radiation to measure the infrared spectrum.

Infrared dichroism can be observed by measuring the spectra of a single crystal (or any anisotropic material), by means of polarized radiation, whose electric vectors vibrate parallel and perpendicular to the crystal axis (or any anisotropic axis). If the orientation of the molecules with respect to the crystal axis is known, it is possible to estimate the *dichroic ratio* (the ratio of the intensities in directions parallel and perpendicular to the crystal axis) by considering the angle between the crystal axis and the direction of the polarized radiation. Evidently, dichroism is at a maximum when a single crystal consisting of planar molecules which are oriented parallel to each other is irradiated by polarized light whose electric vector is first parallel and then perpendicular to the molecular plane. In this case, only the in-plane vibrations are excited by the light polarized parallel to the molecular plane, whereas only the out-of-plane vibrations are excited by the light polarized perpendicular to it. It should be noted, however, that the molecules in a crystal lattice are usually not oriented parallel to each other. Therefore the observed dichroism is of a smaller magnitude than the maximum just mentioned.

For compounds whose crystal structures are known, measurements of infrared dichroism can be used for assigning normal vibrations to each species. Conversely, the orientation of the molecules can be determined from the dichroism measurements. It should be noted, however, that the symmetry of the molecule (in the crystalline state) is often different from that in the gaseous state. Furthermore, the value of the dichroic ratio is affected by several other factors, such as disorder in the crystal structure and the purity of the polarized light.

Raman lines are usually polarized, and the degree of polarization depends on the symmetry of the normal vibration. Suppose that the incident light (natural light) is traveling in the $-y$ direction, and the scattered light is observed in the x direction. If the scattered light is resolved into y ($\|$) and z ($\perp$) components by using an analyzer, the ratio of the intensities in these two directions, ρ_n,

$$\rho_n = \frac{I_{\|}(y)}{I_{\perp}(z)} \tag{15.1}$$

is called the *degree of depolarization.*

It can be shown theoretically[11,12] that ρ_n of the normal vibration associated with normal coordinate Q_a is expressed by

$$\rho_n = \frac{I_{\|}}{I_{\perp}} = \frac{6\beta^2}{45\alpha^2 + 7\beta^2} \tag{15.2}$$

where

$$\alpha = \frac{1}{3}\left[\left(\frac{\partial\alpha_{xx}}{\partial Q_a}\right)_0 + \left(\frac{\partial\alpha_{yy}}{\partial Q_a}\right)_0 + \left(\frac{\partial\alpha_{zz}}{\partial Q_a}\right)_0\right]$$

$$\beta^2 = \frac{1}{2}\left[\left(\frac{\partial\alpha_{xx}}{\partial Q_a} - \frac{\partial\alpha_{yy}}{\partial Q_a}\right)_0^2 + \left(\frac{\partial\alpha_{yy}}{\partial Q_a} - \frac{\partial\alpha_{zz}}{\partial Q_a}\right)_0^2 + \left(\frac{\partial\alpha_{zz}}{\partial Q_a} - \frac{\partial\alpha_{xx}}{\partial Q_a}\right)_0^2 + 6\left\{\left(\frac{\partial\alpha_{xy}}{\partial Q_a}\right)_0^2 + \left(\frac{\partial\alpha_{yz}}{\partial Q_a}\right)_0^2 + \left(\frac{\partial\alpha_{zx}}{\partial Q_a}\right)_0^2\right\}\right]$$

α becomes zero for all non-totally symmetric vibrations. This rule holds for molecules with and without degenerate vibrations.[5] Therefore $\rho_n = 6/7 = 0.857$ for non-totally symmetric vibrations. Such Raman lines are said to be *depolarized.* On the other hand, α is not zero for totally symmetric vibrations. Then ρ_n is in the range $0 < \rho_n < 6/7$, and the Raman lines are said to be *polarized.*

I-16. GROUP FREQUENCIES AND BAND ASSIGNMENTS

From the observation of the infrared spectra of a number of compounds having a common group of atoms, it is found that, regardless of the rest of the molecule, this common group absorbs over a narrow range of frequencies, called the *group frequency.* For example, the group frequencies of the methyl group are 3000–2860, 1470–1400, 1380–1200 and 1200–800 cm^{-1}. Group frequencies have been found for a number of organic and inorganic groups, and they have been summarized as *group frequency charts,*[26,29,33,34] which are highly useful in identifying the atomic groups from infrared spectra. Group frequency charts for inorganic and coordination compounds are shown in Appendix V as well as in Figs. II-21 and II-22 of Part II.

The concept of a group frequency rests on the assumption that the vibrations of the particular group are relatively independent of those of the rest of the molecule. As stated in Sec. I-5, however, all the nuclei of the molecule perform their harmonic oscillations in a normal vibration. Thus an *isolated vibration*, which the group frequency would have to be, cannot be expected in polyatomic molecules. If a group includes relatively light atoms such as hydrogen (OH, NH, NH_2, CH, CH_2, CH_3, etc.) or relatively heavy atoms such as the halogens (CCl, CBr, CI, etc.), when compared to other atoms in the molecule, the idea of an isolated vibration may be justified since the amplitude (or velocity) of the harmonic oscillation of these atoms is relatively larger or smaller when compared with those of the other atoms in the same molecule. Vibrations of groups having multiple bonds (C≡C, C≡N, C=C, C=N, C=O, etc.) may also be relatively independent of the rest of the molecule if the groups do not belong to a conjugated system.

If atoms of similar mass are connected by bonds of similar strength (force constant), the amplitude of oscillation is similar for each atom of the whole system. Therefore it is not possible to isolate the group frequencies in a system like

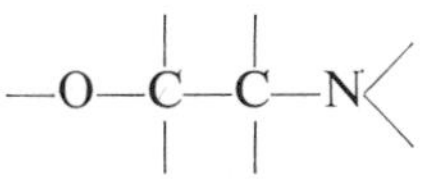

A similar situation may occur in a system where resonance effects average out the single and multiple bonds by conjugation. Examples of this effect are seen in the metal chelate compounds of β-diketones, α-diimines and oxalic acid (discussed in Part III). Where the group frequency approximation is permissible, the mode of vibration corresponding to this frequency can be inferred empirically from the band assignments obtained theoretically for simple molecules. If *coupling* between various group vibrations is serious, it is necessary to make a theoretical analysis for each individual compound, using a method like the following one.

In order to determine the modes of normal vibrations, it is necessary to calculate the **L** matrix, defined by

$$\mathbf{R} = \mathbf{LQ} \tag{16.1}$$

where **R** and **Q** are column matrices whose components are internal (or symmetry) coordinates and normal coordinates, respectively, and **L** is a matrix whose columns consist of eigenvectors for each of the eigenvalues.†

† If Eq. 10.6 is solved (using proper force constants), the roots (eigenvalues of the matrix), $\lambda_1, \lambda_2, \ldots, \lambda_N$, are obtained. For each λ_N, there is an eigenvector $\mathbf{l}_N$ which satisfies the relation

$$\mathbf{GFl}_N = \lambda_N \mathbf{l}_N$$

where $\mathbf{l}_N$ is a column matrix which has i elements such as $L_{1N}, L_{2N}, \ldots, L_{iN}$. $\mathbf{l}_N$ can be calculated when the secular equation is solved by using the Frame method for example (Appendix III). Assembly by columns of the elements obtained for each λ gives the **L** matrix.

Like Eq. 3.10, Eq. 16.1 indicates the relation between the internal and the normal coordinates. This may be written explicitly as

$$\begin{aligned} R_1 &= L_{11}Q_1 + L_{12}Q_2 + \cdots + L_{1N}Q_N \\ R_2 &= L_{21}Q_1 + L_{22}Q_2 + \cdots + L_{2N}Q_N \\ &\cdots\cdots\cdots\cdots\cdots\cdots \\ R_i &= L_{i1}Q_1 + L_{i2}Q_2 + \cdots + L_{iN}Q_N \end{aligned} \tag{16.2}$$

In a normal vibration in which the normal coordinate Q_N changes with frequency ν_N, all the internal coordinates, R_1, R_2, . . . , R_i, change with the same frequency. The amplitude of oscillation is, however, different for each internal coordinate. The relative ratio of the amplitudes of the internal coordinates in a normal vibration associated with Q_N is given by

$$L_{1N}:L_{2N}: \cdots :L_{iN} \tag{16.3}$$

If one of these elements is relatively large compared with others, the normal vibration is said to be predominantly due to the vibration caused by the change of this internal coordinate.

It should be noted, however, that the dimension of L for a stretching coordinate is different from that for a bending coordinate. Morino and Kuchitsu[22] have shown that the *potential energy distribution* in each internal coordinate gives a better measure of the band assignments than the simple ratio of L elements. The potential energy of the whole molecule for a given normal vibration associated with Q_N is expressed as

$$V = \tfrac{1}{2}Q_N^2 \sum_{ij} F_{ij}L_{iN}L_{jN} \tag{16.4}$$

where $F_{ij}L_{iN}L_{jN}$ indicates the distribution of the potential energy in each internal coordinate. Since, in general, the value of $F_{ij}L_{iN}L_{jN}$ is large when $i = j$, only the $F_{ii}L_{iN}^2$ terms are significant. Thus the ratios of the $F_{ii}L_{iN}^2$ terms provide a reasonable measure of the relative contribution of each internal coordinate R_i to the normal coordinate Q_N. If any $F_{ii}L_{iN}^2$ term is exceedingly large in the series, this vibration can be assigned to the internal coordinate R_i. If $F_{ii}L_{iN}^2$ and $F_{jj}L_{jN}^2$ are of the same magnitude and relatively large compared with others, the normal vibration associated with Q_N is assigned to a coupled vibration between R_i and R_j.

References

1. L. Pauling and E. B. Wilson, *Introduction to Quantum Mechanics*, McGraw-Hill, 1937.
2. H. Eyring, J. Walter and G. E. Kimball, *Quantum Chemistry*, Wiley, 1944.
3. W. Kauzmann, *Quantum Chemistry*, Academic Press, 1957.
4. G. Herzberg, *Molecular Spectra and Molecular Structure, I: Spectra of Diatomic Molecules*, Van Nostrand, 1950.

5. G. Herzberg, *Molecular Spectra and Molecular Structure, II: Infrared and Raman Spectra of Polyatomic Molecules*, Van Nostrand, 1945.
6. A. B. F. Duncan, "Theory of Infrared and Raman Spectra," in W. West, *Chemical Applications of Spectroscopy*, Interscience, 1956.
7. S. Bhagavantam, *Theory of Groups and its Application to Physical Problems*, Andhra University, Waltair, 1951.
8. V. Heine, *Group Theory in Quantum Mechanics*, Pergamon, London, 1960.
9. A. C. Aitken, *Determinants and Matrices*, Interscience, 1951.
10. R. A. Frazer, W. J. Duncan and A. R. Collar, *Elementary Matrices*, Cambridge, 1960.
10*a*. P. S. Dwyer, *Linear Computations*, Wiley, 1951.
10*b*. V. N. Faddeeva, *Computational Methods of Linear Algebra*, translated by C. D. Benster, Dover, 1959.
11. S. Mizushima, "Raman Effect," *Handbuch der Physik*, Vol. XXVI, Springer, Berlin, 1957.
12. E. B. Wilson, J. C. Decius and P. C. Cross, *Molecular Vibrations*, McGraw-Hill, 1955.
13. S. Mizushima and T. Shimanouchi, *Infrared Absorption and the Raman Effect*, Kyoritsu, Tokyo, 1958.
14. A. G. Meister and F. F. Cleveland, "Molecular Spectra II," *Publs. Ill. Inst. Technol.*, 1948.
15. E. B. Wilson, *J. Chem. Phys.*, **7,** 1047 (1939); **9,** 76 (1941).
16. J. C. Decius, *J. Chem. Phys.*, **16,** 1025 (1948).
17. S. M. Ferigle and A. G. Meister, *J. Chem. Phys.*, **19,** 982 (1951).
18. T. Shimanouchi, *J. Chem. Phys.*, **25,** 660 (1956).
18*a*. Z. Cihla and J. Plíva, *Collection Czechoslov. Chem. Communs.*, **26,** 1903 (1961).
19. T. Shimanouchi, *J. Chem. Phys.*, **17,** 245, 734, 848 (1949).
20. H. C. Urey and C. A. Bradley, *Phys. Rev.*, **38,** 1969 (1931).
20*a*. J. Overend and J. R. Scherer, *J. Chem. Phys.*, **32,** 1289, 1296, 1720 (1960); **33,** 446 (1960); **34,** 547 (1961).
21. I. Nakagawa, *J. Chem. Soc. Japan*, **77,** 1030 (1956).
22. Y. Morino and K. Kuchitsu, *J. Chem. Phys.*, **20,** 1809 (1952).

General References

23. G. R. Harrison, R. C. Lord and J. R. Loofbourow, *Practical Spectroscopy*, Prentice-Hall, 1948.
24. S. Bhagavantam, *Scattering of Light and the Raman Effect*, Andhra University, Waltair, 1940.
25. J. H. Hibben, *The Raman Effect and Its Chemical Applications*, Reinhold, 1939.
26. L. J. Bellamy, *Infrared Spectra of Complex Molecules*, Wiley, 1957.
27. S. Mizushima, *Structure of Molecules and Internal Rotation*, Academic Press, 1954.
28. W. Brügel, *Einfuhrung in die Ultrarotspektroskopie*, Verlag, Weinheim, 1954.
29. R. N. Jones and C. Sandorfy, "The Application of Infrared and Raman Spectrometry to the Elucidation of Molecular Structure," in W. West, *Chemical Applications of Spectroscopy*, Interscience, 1956.
30. J. Lecomte, " Spectroscopie dans l'infrarouge," Handbuch der Physik, Vol. XXVI, Springer, Berlin, 1957.
30*a*. P. Barchewitz, *Spectroscopie Infrarouge I. Vibrations Moléculaires*, Gauthier-Villars, Paris, 1961.

31. F. A. Cotton, "The Infrared Spectra of Transition Metal Complexes," in J. Lewis and R. G. Wilkins, *Modern Coordination Chemistry*, Interscience, 1960.
32. K. E. Lawson, *Infrared Absorption of Inorganic Substances*, Reinhold, 1961.
33. F. A. Miller and C. H. Wilkins, "Infrared Spectra and Characteristic Frequencies of Inorganic Ions," *Anal. Chem.*, **24,** 1253 (1952).
34. F. A. Miller, G. L. Carlson, F. F. Bentley and W. H. Jones, "Infrared Spectra of Inorganic Ions in the CsBr Region," *Spectrochim. Acta*, **16,** 135 (1960).
35. L. Pauling, *The Nature of the Chemical Bond*, Cornell, 1960.
36. A. F. Wells, *Structural Inorganic Chemistry*, Oxford, 1950.
37. A. D. Cross, *An Introduction to Practical Infrared Spectroscopy*, Butterworths, 1960.
38. G. M. Barrow, *Introduction to Molecular Spectroscopy*, McGraw-Hill, 1962.
39. R. P. Bauman, *Absorption Spectroscopy*, Wiley, 1962.

Inorganic Compounds

Part II

II-1. DIATOMIC MOLECULES

As shown in Sec. I-2, diatomic molecules have only one vibration along the chemical bond; its frequency is given by

$$\tilde{\nu} = \frac{1}{2\pi c}\sqrt{\frac{K}{\mu}}$$

where K is the force constant, μ the reduced mass and c the velocity of light. In homopolar X—X molecules ($\mathbf{D}_{\infty h}$), the vibration is not infrared active but is Raman active, whereas, in heteropolar X—Y molecules ($\mathbf{C}_{\infty v}$), it is both infrared and Raman active. Table II-1 lists the observed fundamental frequencies together with ω_e values corrected for anharmonicity (see Sec. I-2). Except for the ions, the values were obtained in the gas phase.

A large amount of information about these diatomic molecules is available, but only the fundamental frequencies of chemically interesting compounds are reviewed briefly here. *Hydrogen halides* polymerize in the condensed phases. *Hydrogen fluoride* polymerizes even in the gaseous phase. Hydrogen halides also form molecular compounds with organic solvents. Table II-2 indicates the effects on the frequency of polymerization and association with the solvent. In mixed crystals of HCl and HBr at low temperatures, Hiebert and Hornig[5] have found that the H—Br stretching frequency in the mixed crystals is higher than in pure HBr crystals whereas the H—Cl stretching frequency in the mixed crystals is lower than in pure HCl crystals. *Alkali halides* dimerize in the gaseous state, and a normal coordinate analysis has been carried out by Berkowitz[7] using this electrostatic model:

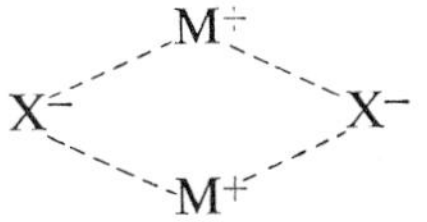

Nitric oxide (NO) exists as a dimer in the condensed phases at low temperatures.[8] Fateley et al.[9] have shown that the NO stretching frequencies are 1883 (monomer), 1862 and 1768 (*cis* dimer) and 1740 (*trans* dimer) cm^{-1}. According to Millen and Watson,[10] *the nitrosonium ion* ($[NO]^+$) in nitric acid absorbs at 2220 cm^{-1}. *Halogens* form molecular compounds

TABLE II-1. VIBRATIONAL FREQUENCIES OF DIATOMIC MOLECULES (cm^{-1})

Molecule	Observed Frequency	ω_e	Molecule	Observed Frequency	ω_e
H_2	4161.13	4395.24	$N^{14}O^{16}$	1876.11	1904.03
HD	3632.06	3817.09	$N^{15}O^{16}$	1843.04	—
				1842.76	—
D_2	2993.55	3118.46	$[NO]^+$	2220	—
HF^{19}	3961.64	4138.52	$C^{12}O^{16}$	2143.16	2170.21
DF	—	2998.25	$C^{13}O^{16}$	2096.07	2141.41
TF	2443.8	2508.54	$C^{12}N^{14}$	—	2068.71
HCl^{35}	2886.01	2989.74	F_2	892.1	—
HCl^{37}	2883.89	—	$Cl_2{}^{35}$	557	564.9
DCl^{35}	2091.05	2144.77	Br_2	316.8	323.2
DCl^{37}	2088.05	2141.82	I_2	213.3†	214.57
TCl^{35}	1739.10	1775.86	FCl^{35}	773.88	—
TCl^{37}	1735.51	1772.11	FCl^{37}	766.61	793.2
HBr^{79}	2558.76	2649.67	FBr	665†	671
HBr^{81}	2558.40	2648.60	FI	604†	610
TBr	1519.26	1550.06	$Cl^{35}Br$	439.5	—
HI	2229.60	2309.53	$Cl^{35}I$	381.5	384.18
HO	—	3735.21	BrI	266.8†	268.4
DO	—	2720.9	K[CN]	2080	—
$N_2{}^{14}$	2331	2359.61	Na[OH]	3637.4	—
$O_2{}^{16}$	1555	1580.36	Na[OD]	2681.1	—

For alkali halide vapor, see Ref. 1.
T = tritium (H^3).

† From band spectra.

TABLE II-2. VIBRATIONAL FREQUENCIES OF HYDROGEN HALIDES IN VARIOUS PHASES (cm^{-1})

State	HF	HCl	HBr	HI
Gas (monomer)	3962	2886	2558	2230
Gas (polymer)	3500–3400, 3380–3330 [2]	—	—	—
Liquid	3375[3]	—	—	—
Solid	3420, 3060 [4]	2746, 2704 [5]	2438, 2404 [5]	2120[5]
Organic solvent (mesitylene)	—	2712[6] 2393 (ether)	2416[6]	2132[6]

with organic solvents. For example, the band of ICl in the gaseous state at 381.5 cm^{-1} shifts to 275 cm^{-1} in pyridine solution.[11] For other diatomic molecules such as hydrides, oxides, sulfides and halides, see Ref. 4 of Part I.

The *cyanide ion* ($[CN]^-$) is easily characterized by a relatively sharp and weak band at 2250–2050 cm^{-1}. To illustrate this, the infrared spectrum of KCN is shown in Fig. II-1. Table II-3 lists the CN stretching frequencies

TABLE II-3. THE C≡N STRETCHING FREQUENCIES IN SIMPLE CYANIDES (CM^{-1})

Compound	Infrared	Raman	Reference
NaCN	2080	2085	12
KCN	2080	2081	12
$Ba(CN)_2$	2080	—	12
AgCN[a]	2178	—	12
CuCN[a]	2172	—	13
AuCN[a]	2239	—	14

[a] In these compounds, the metal—CN bond is essentially covalent.

of simple cyanides. It is interesting to note that *phosphorus tricyanide* ($P(CN)_3$) exhibits a CN stretching band at 2204 cm^{-1},[15] whereas *boron tricyanide* ($B(CN)_3$) has no absorption in this region because of a marked decrease in the CN bond order.[15a] For cyano complexes, see Sec. III-5. Langseth and Møller[16] have done a normal coordinate analysis for the linear *cyanogen* molecule, N≡C—C≡N.

The *hydroxyl ion* ($[OH]^-$) is characterized by a sharp band at 3700–3500 cm^{-1}. In general, the hydroxyl OH stretching band is sharper and at a higher frequency than the OH stretching bands of water. Figures II-2*a* and II-2*b* compare the infrared spectra of LiOH, $LiOH{\cdot}H_2O$ and H_2O.[17] Table II-4 gives the OH stretching frequencies in various metal hydroxides.

TABLE II-4. THE O—H STRETCHING FREQUENCIES IN METAL HYDROXIDES (CM^{-1})

Compound	Infrared	Raman[25]	References
LiOH	3678	3664	17, 18, 18*a*
$LiOH{\cdot}H_2O$	3574	3563	17, 19
NaOH	3637	3633	20
KOH	3600	—	21, 22
$Ca(OH)_2$	3644	3618	23, 24
$Mg(OH)_2$	3698	—	25, 26

For other metal hydroxides, see Refs. 27–31.

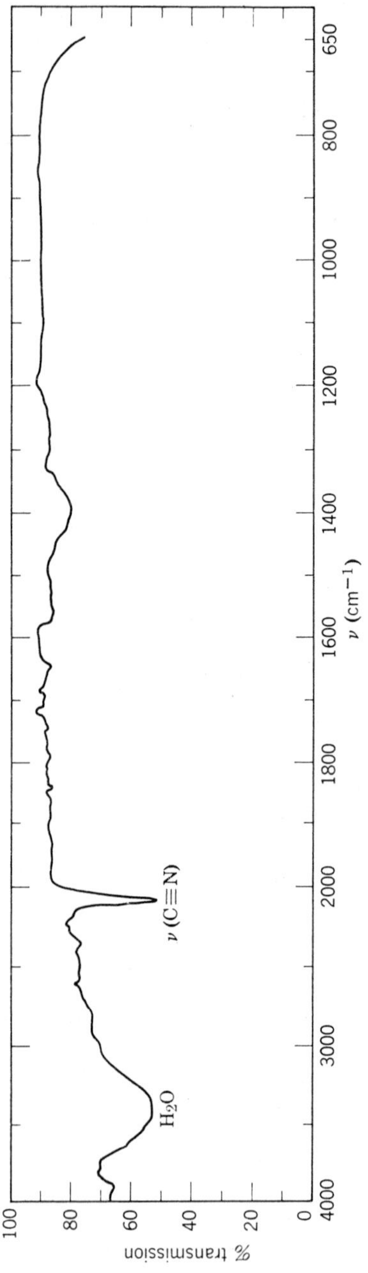

Fig. II-1. The infrared spectrum of KCN.

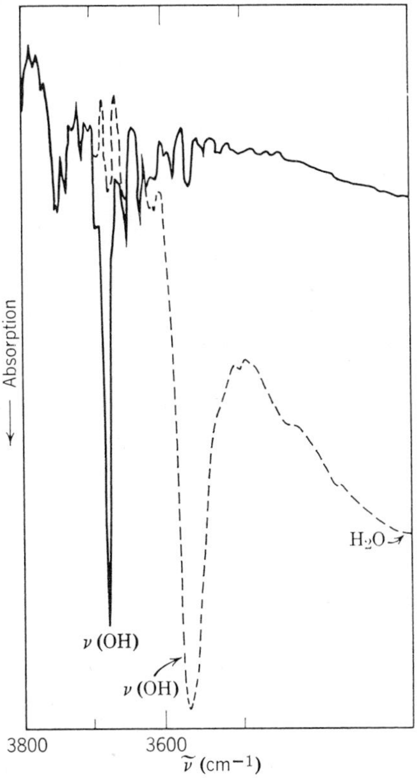

Fig. II-2*a*. Infrared spectra of LiOH (solid line) and $LiOH \cdot H_2O$ (broken line).[17]

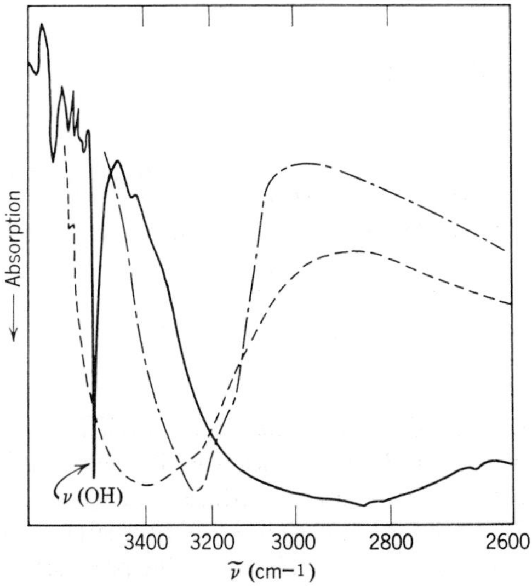

Fig. II-2*b*. Infrared spectra of $LiOH \cdot H_2O$ (295°K) (solid line); H_2O liquid (295°K) (broken line); H_2O solid (180°K) (dot-dash line).[17]

The relation between the OH stretching frequency and the electronegativity of the metal in a series of compounds of the type $(C_6H_5)_3M$—OH has been discussed by West and Baney.[32]

Some metal hydroxides exhibit M—O—H bending bands at 1200–600 cm^{-1}, corresponding to the C—O—H bending bands at 1350–600 cm^{-1} in organic alcohols.[33,33a] The presence of such absorption bands has been reported in various metal hydroxides[34–37] and in weak acids such as H_3BO_3[38] and H_5IO_6.[39] The frequency of this vibration may depend on the strength of the M—O bond as well as on that of hydrogen bonds. Hartert and Glemser[40] have found a relation between the O—H distance and the O—H stretching and M—O—H bending frequencies. Williams and Page[41] have shown that $Na_2SnO_3 \cdot 3H_2O$ should be written $Na_2[Sn(OH)_6]$, since this compound exhibits an M—O—H bending band at 898 cm^{-1} instead of the H—O—H bending band near 1630 cm^{-1}.

II-2. LINEAR TRIATOMIC MOLECULES

(1) X_3 and YXY Molecules ($D_{\infty h}$)

The three normal modes of vibration of linear X_3 and YXY molecules have already been shown in Fig. I-6. ν_1 is not infrared active but is Raman active, whereas ν_2 and ν_3 are infrared active but not Raman active (mutual exclusion rule). Table II-5 lists the fundamental frequencies for compounds of these types. Long and co-workers[55] have done a normal coordinate analysis for *carbon suboxide* (C_3O_2) assuming a linear model, whereas Rix[56] proposed the bent model.

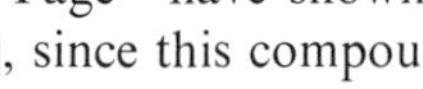

$$O=C=C=C=O$$

$D_{\infty h}$

$$C=C=C \overset{\displaystyle O}{\underset{\displaystyle O}{}}$$

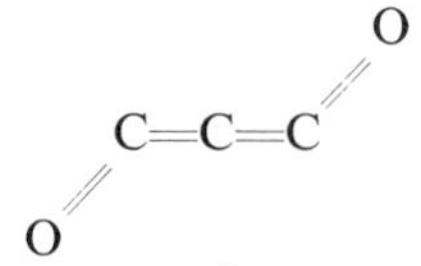

C_{2h}

As illustrated in the formula below, *beryllium dihalides* (BeX_2, X = F or Cl) are dimeric in the gaseous state[57] although they are polymeric in the

$$X-Be\overset{\displaystyle X}{\underset{\displaystyle X}{}}Be-X$$

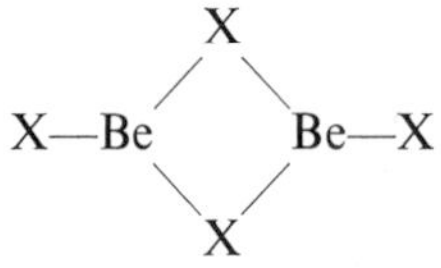

crystalline state.[58] In addition to the bands listed in Table II-5 for the *hydrogen bifluoride ion* ([HF_2]$^-$), Jones and Penneman[50] have observed bands at 1105, 1015 and 780 cm^{-1} on addition of excess HF to a saturated solution of KHF_2. It has been suggested that these bands may be attributed to a polymeric species such as [H_2F_3]$^-$. The presence of the *nitronium ion* ($[NO_2]^+$) in mixtures of concentrated HNO_3 and H_2SO_4 has been demonstrated by Ingold and co-workers.[59]

$$HNO_3 + 2H_2SO_4 \rightleftharpoons [NO_2]^+ + 2[HSO_4]^- + [H_3O]^+$$

Recently, Marcus and Fresco[52] made an extensive infrared study of mixtures of strong acids.

TABLE II-5. VIBRATIONAL FREQUENCIES OF LINEAR X_3 AND YXY MOLECULES

Molecule	State	ν_1	ν_2	ν_3	References
$C^{12}O_2$	gas	(1343)[a]	667	2349	42
	solid (−190°C)	—	660, 653	2344	43, 43*a*
	aq. sol'n	—	—	2342	44
$C^{13}O_2$	gas	—	(649)	2284	45
	solid (−190°C)	—	637	2280	43, 43*a*
$C^{14}O_2$	gas	—	632	2226	45
CS_2	gas	658	397	1533	46
	liquid	657	397	1510	46
CSe_2	gas	(368)	(308)	1303	46
	liquid	368	300	1267	46
$HgCl_2$	gas	(360)	(70)	413	47
$HgBr_2$	gas	(225)	(41)	293	47
HgI_2	gas	(156)	(33)	—	47
$K[N_3]$	solid	1344	645	2041	48, 48*a*
$NH_4[N_3]$	solid (phase I)	1345	652	2030	49
$K[HF_2]$	solid	—	1233	1473	50
	aq. sol'n	—	1206	1536	50
$K[DF_2]$	solid	—	885	1045	50
	aq. sol'n	—	873	1102	50
$[(CH_3)_4N][HCl_2]$	solid	—	1180	1565	51
$[NO_2]^+$	conc. HNO_3	1400	(667)	2360	52
$Na_2[CN_2]$	solid	1234	598	2120	53
$[UO_2]^{2+}$	aq. sol'n	860	210	930	54

[a] Average of two frequencies split by the Fermi resonance. (See Sec. I-9.)

The configuration of the *uranyl ion* ($[UO_2]^{2+}$) in simple salts has been a subject of considerable interest in past years. If it is linear, only ν_2 and ν_3 are infrared active but neither is Raman active. If it is bent, all vibrations are both infrared and Raman active. Thus it is theoretically possible to distinguish these two structures by the activity of the three fundamentals in both spectra. Although the linear structure is favored by many investigators,[54,60] the ν_2 and ν_3 vibrations have been observed in the Raman spectrum. In order to explain this anomaly, Sutton[61] postulated that ν_2 and ν_3 appear in the Raman spectrum both because of polarization of the two U=O bonds and because of the asymmetrical field produced by a complexing anion. Penneman and Jones[62] have studied the infrared spectra of a series of compounds having the structures $XO_2(ClO_4)_2$ and $[XO_2(CH_3COO)_3]^-$ where X is Np, U, Pu or Am; they have found that the X=O stretching force constant decreases in going from Np to Am. Their finding contradicts the results of an x-ray study on

$$Na[XO_2(CH_3COO)_3]$$

crystals which suggests that the X=O distance decreases in the order U > NP > Pu > Am. In other words, the shortest X=O bond, which occurs in the Am compound, has the smallest X=O stretching force constant in this series. They explained this apparent contradiction by postulating that the bond, though shortened by contraction of the electron shells of the metal, is weakened by interaction with the extra valence shell electrons. On the basis of the x-ray and infrared data of a number of compounds containing $[UO_2]^{2+}$, Jones[63] derived a general formula relating the U=O distance and the U=O stretching force constant. For the infrared spectra and structures of simple $[UO_2]^{2+}$ salts, see Refs. 64–68. Recently McGlynn et al.[68a] found that, in a series of complexes of the type $K_xUO_2L_y(NO_3)_2$, both the ν_3 and ν_1 frequencies of the UO_2 group decrease as L is changed along the *spectrochemical series*,

$[CN]^- >$ en† $> NH_3 > [NCS]^- > [ONO]^- >$ py† $> H_2O > F^- > [NO_3]^-$

which Tsuchida[68b] obtained from the ultraviolet spectral study of cobaltic complexes.

(2) XYZ Molecules ($C_{\infty v}$)

In linear XYZ molecules, the three normal modes of vibration shown in Fig. II-3 are both infrared and Raman active. Table II-6 gives the fundamental frequencies for compounds of this type. For the *hydrogen cyanide* tetramer, Webb and colleagues[83] proposed structure I, whereas Wadsten and Andersson[84] preferred the dimeric structure II on the basis of the results of x-ray and infrared studies. Recently, however, Penfold

$$\begin{array}{cc} H_2N-C-C\equiv N & N\equiv C-C=N-H \\ \parallel & \mid \\ H_2N-C-C\equiv N & H \\ \text{I} & \text{II} \end{array}$$

† en = ethylenediamine; py = pyridine.

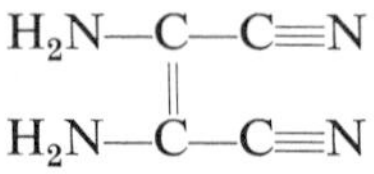

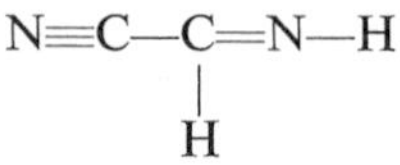

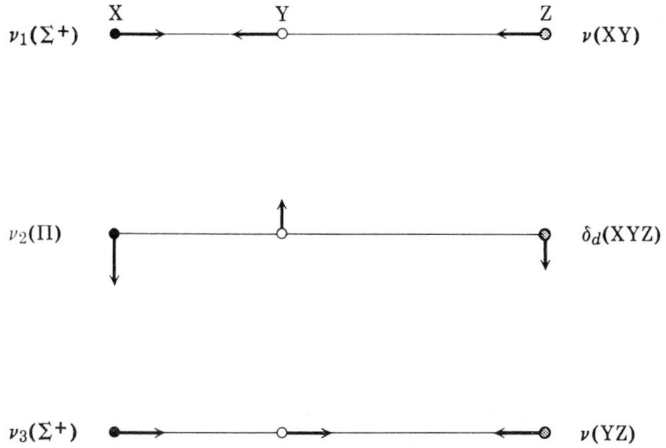

Fig. II-3. Normal modes of vibration of linear XYZ molecules.

and Lipscomb[84a] have shown from x-ray analysis that structure I is correct for this compound. The infrared spectra of the charge-transfer complexes between *iodine cyanide* (ICN) and halogens have been studied by Person et al.[85]

Figure II-4 shows the effect of isotopic substitution on the infrared spectra of KNCS crystals as obtained by Jones.[81] As Table II-6 indicates,

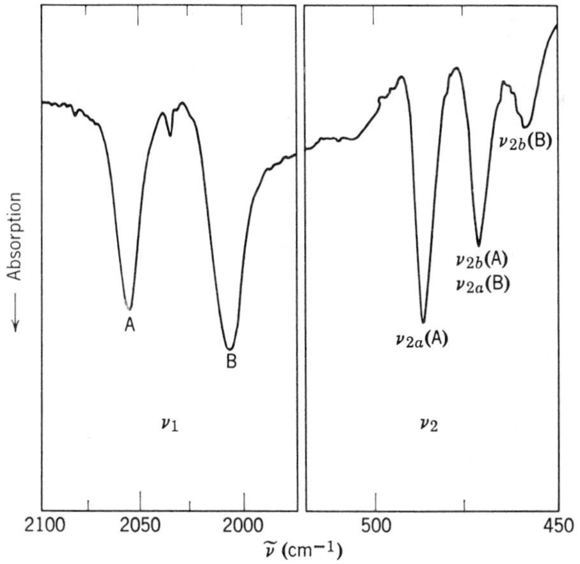

Fig. II-4. Infrared spectra of mixture of $KN^{14}C^{12}S^{32}$ (A) and $KN^{14}C^{13}S^{32}$ (B) in the solid state.[81]

TABLE II-6. VIBRATIONAL FREQUENCIES OF LINEAR XYZ MOLECULES (cm^{-1})

Molecule [XYZ]	State	ν_1	ν_2	ν_3	References
$HC^{12}N$	gas	3311	712	2097	69
$HC^{13}N$	gas	3295	706	—	70
$DC^{12}N$	gas	2630	569	1925	69
$DC^{13}N$	gas	2585	—	1916	70
TCN	gas	2460	513	1724	71
FCN	gas	1077	449	2290	72, 72*a*
ClCN	gas	714	380	2219	73
	liquid	730	394	2206	74
	solid (−180°C)	734	398	2212	73
BrCN	gas	574	342.5	2200	73
	liquid	568	357	2191	75
	solid (−180°C)	572.5	363.5	2194	73
ICN	liquid	470	321	2158	76
	solid (−180°C)	452	329	2176	73
$N^{14}N^{14}O$	gas	1286	589	2224	77
	solid (80°K)	1293	591	2238	78
$N^{14}N^{15}O$	gas	1281	576	2178	77
	solid (80°K)	1196	—	—	78
$N^{15}N^{14}O$	gas	1271	586	2203	77
	solid (80°K)	1280	—	2220	78
$N^{15}N^{15}O$	gas	1266	572	2156	77
SCO	gas	859	524	2064	79
SCSe	gas	506	(355)	1435	46
	liquid	502	(350)	(1408)	46
SCTe	CS_2 sol'n	423	(337)	1347	46
$K[N^{14}C^{12}S^{32}]$	solid (mull)	2041	—	747	80
	solid (KBr disk)	2053	486, 471	748	80
	aq. sol'n	2066	470	743	81
$K[N^{14}C^{13}S^{32}]$	solid	2006	470, 458	743	81
$K[N^{14}C^{12}S^{34}]$	solid	2052	487, 470	739	81
$K[N^{14}C^{13}S^{34}]$	solid	2005	470, 458	733	81
K[NCSe]	solid	2070	424, 416	558	81*a*
$K[NC^{12}O]$	solid	2165	637, 628	1207	82, 82*a*
$K[NC^{13}O]$	solid	2112	620, 612	1195	82, 82*a*

the doubly degenerate ν_2 vibration splits into two bands in the NCS and NCO salts because the crystal field removes the degeneracy. The structure of *thiocyanogen trichloride* cannot be Cl_3—SCN, but it is either

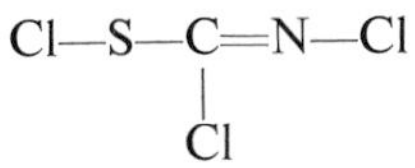

or

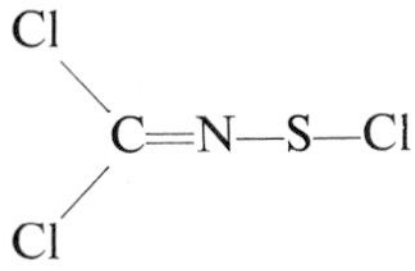

since a strong band is observed at 1600 cm^{-1} instead of a C≡N stretching band near 2100 cm^{-1}.[86,86a] Nelson and Pullin[87] have obtained the infrared spectra of *thiocyanogen* and *thiocyanogen halides.* Reference 87*a* lists infrared spectra of inorganic thiocyanates. For calculation of the force constants in linear triatomic molecules, see Refs. 88–88*b*.

II-3. BENT TRIATOMIC MOLECULES

Bent triatomic molecules have the three normal modes of vibration shown in Fig. I-6. The vibrations are both infrared and Raman active whether the molecule is symmetrical (XY_2 and X_3, $\mathbf{C}_{2v}$) or asymmetrical (XYZ and XXY, $\mathbf{C}_s$). Tables II-7 and II-8 list the fundamental frequencies for a number of bent triatomic molecules. Table II-7 indicates that, in most compounds, the antisymmetric stretching frequency (ν_3) is higher than the symmetric one (ν_1). However, this is not true for O_3, F_2O, $[NO_2]^-$ and H_2O (ice). Vibrational frequencies of *water* in various organic solvents have been studied by Greinacher et al.[117] For example, dioxane solutions of water exhibit three bands at 3518, 1638 and 3584 cm^{-1}. Apparently, hydrogen bonding between water and dioxane is responsible for the shifts of the stretching modes to lower frequencies and for the shift of the bending mode to a higher frequency. The spectrum of water in saturated solutions of alkali and alkaline earth halides has been studied by Waldron.[93] Lippincott and co-workers[118] have found that the O—H stretching band in ice (ca. 3200 cm^{-1}) is shifted to 3600 cm^{-1} under high pressure (9000 atm). The vibrational spectra of *lattice water* and *coordinated water* will be discussed in Sec. III-3.

Solutions of *hydrogen sulfide* (H_2S) in organic solvents have been studied by Josien and Saumagne.[119] Their results show, for example, that the band at 2627 cm^{-1} in the gaseous state is shifted to 2482 cm^{-1} in pyridine solution. Anbar and colleagues[120] have recently compared the frequencies of $AgNO_2^{16}$ and $AgNO_2^{18}$ in Nujol mulls. An example of the infrared spectrum of a metal nitrite is shown in Fig. II-5. For the frequencies of other nitrites, see Ref. 121. The *selenium dioxide* (SeO_2) polymer in the crystalline state has been studied by Giguère and Falk.[110]

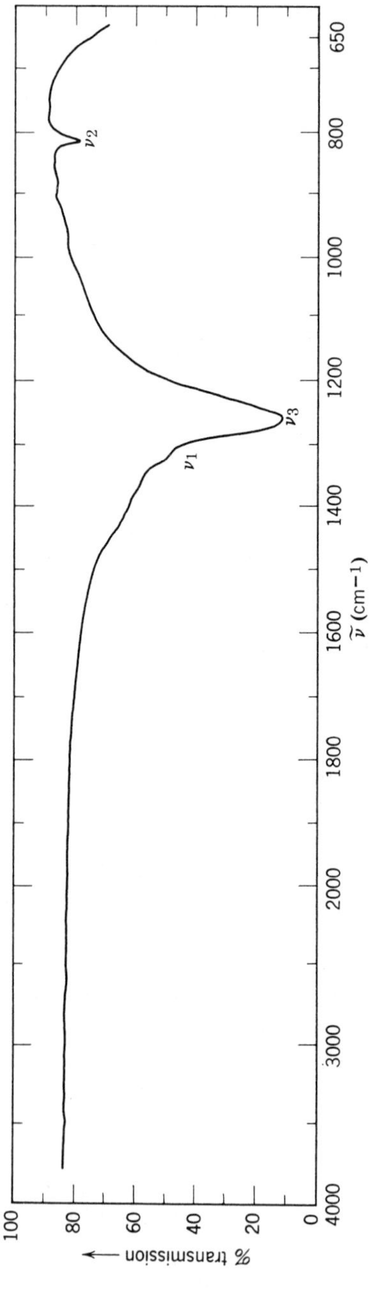

Fig. II-5. The infrared spectrum of $NaNO_2$.

Table II-7. Vibrational Frequencies of Bent XY_2 and X_3 Molecules (cm^{-1})

Molecule	State	ν_1	ν_2	ν_3	Reference
H_2O^{16}	gas	3657	1595	3756	89
	liquid	3219	1627	3445	90
	solid (−78°C)	3400	1620	3220	91
H_2O^{18}	gas	(3647)	(1586)	(3744)	92
HDO^{16}	gas	2727	1402	3707	89
	liquid	2520	1455	3405	93
	solid (−190°C)	2416	1490	3275	91
D_2O^{16}	gas	2671	1178	2788	89
	solid (−190°C)	(2520)	1210	2432	91
D_2O^{18}	gas	2657	1169	2764	94
THO	gas	—	1324	3720	95
TDO	gas	—	—	2735	95
T_2O	gas	—	996	2370	95
H_2S	gas	2615	1183	(2627)	96
	solid (66°K)	2532 2523	1186 1171	2544	97
HDS	gas	—	1090	—	98
	solid (66°K)	—	1026	2535	97
D_2S	gas	1892	934	2000	98
	solid (66°K)	1843 1835	857	1854	97
H_2Se	gas	2260	1074	2350	99
HDSe	gas	1691	905	2352	99
D_2Se	gas	1630	745	1696	99
O_3	gas	1110	705	1043	100
F_2O	gas	929	461	826	101
Cl_2O	gas	688	320	969	102
ClO_2	gas	943	445	1111	103
$Na[ClO_2]$	aq. sol'n	790	400	(840)	104
$N^{14}O_2$	gas	1318	750	1618	105
	solid	—	750	1624	9
$N^{15}O_2$	gas	1306	740	1580	105
$Na[N^{14}O_2]$	solid (mull)	1328	828.2	1261	106
$Na[N^{15}O_2]$	solid (mull)	1303	824	—	106
${SO_2}^{16}$	gas	1151	518	1362	107
	solid (−180°C)	1147	521	1330 1308	108
	aq. sol'n	1157	—	1332	44
$SO^{16}O^{18}$	gas	1122	507	1341	109
${SO_2}^{18}$	gas	—	—	1316	109
SeO_2	gas	900–910	(400)	967	110
SCl_2	liquid	514	208	535	111

TABLE II-8. VIBRATIONAL FREQUENCIES OF BENT XYZ MOLECULES IN THE GASEOUS STATE (CM^{-1})

Molecule (XYZ)	ν_1 $\nu(XY)$	ν_2 $\delta(XYZ)$	ν_3 $\nu(YZ)$	Reference
HOCl	3626	1242	739	112
DOCl	2674	911	739	112
ONF	1844	521	766	113
$ON^{14}Cl^{35}$	1800	332	605	114
$ON^{15}Cl^{35}$	1769	331	590	114
$ON^{14}Cl^{37}$	—	325	—	115
ONBr	1801	(265)	542	116

II-4. PYRAMIDAL FOUR-ATOM MOLECULES

(1) XY_3 Molecules (C_{3v})

The four normal modes of vibration of a pyramidal XY_3 molecule are shown in Fig. II-6. These four vibrations are both infrared and Raman active. Table II-9 lists the fundamental frequencies of molecules of the

TABLE II-9. VIBRATIONAL FREQUENCIES OF PYRAMIDAL XY_3 MOLECULES (CM^{-1})

Molecule	State	ν_1	ν_2	ν_3	ν_4	References
NH_3	gas	3336, 3338*	932, 968*	3414	1628	122, 123
	solid (−190°C)	3223	1060	3378	1646	124
ND_3	gas	2420	746, 749*	2556	1191	125
	solid (−190°C)	2318	815	2500	1196	124
$N^{15}H_3$	gas	3335	926, 961*	—	1625	126
NT_3	gas	2016	647	2163	1000	127
PH_3	gas	2327	990, 992*	2421	1121	128
PD_3	gas	1694	730	(1698)	806	128
PT_3	gas	1398	623	1401	668	127
AsH_3	gas	2122	906	2185	1005	128
AsD_3	gas	1534	660	—	714	128
AsT_3	gas	1256	553	1258	590	127
SbH_3	gas	1891	782	1894	831	129
SbD_3	gas	1359	561	1362	593	129
$[OH_3]ClO_4$	solid	3285	1175	3100	1577	130

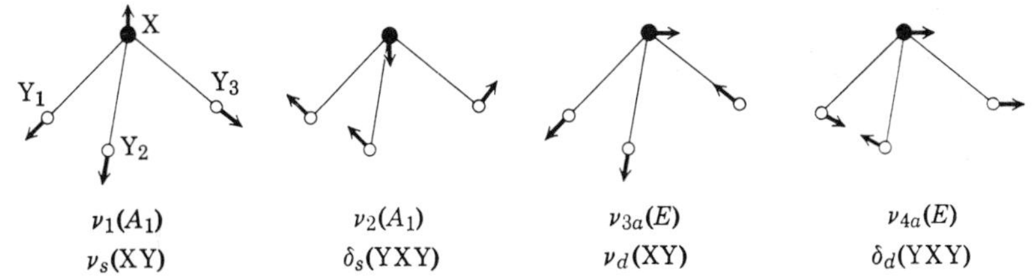

Fig. II-6. Normal modes of vibration of pyramidal XY_3 molecules.

XH_3 type. Several bands marked by an asterisk (*) in Table II-9 are split in two because of *inversion doubling*. This arises in pyramidal XY_3 molecules, where the two configurations shown in the sketch are equally

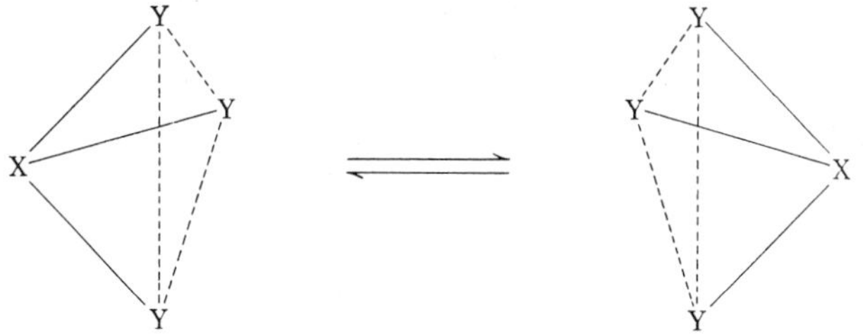

probable. If the potential barrier between these two configurations is small, the molecule may resonate between the two structures. As a result, each vibrational level splits into two (positive and negative). Transitions between levels of different sign are allowed in the infrared spectrum, whereas those between levels of the same sign are allowed in the Raman spectrum. The

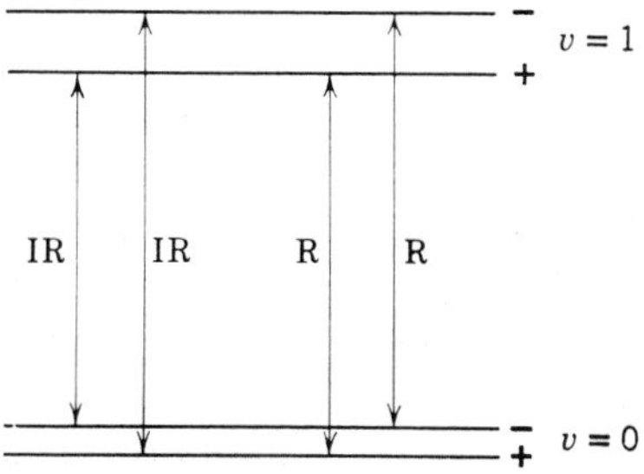

transition between the two levels at $v = 0$ is also observed in the microwave region ($\tilde{\nu} = 0.79\ \text{cm}^{-1}$). If the potential barrier is sufficiently high and if the three Y groups are not identical, optical isomers may be anticipated. Weston[131] has shown through calculation of the potential barrier that phosphorus compounds may have optical isomers at low temperatures, and compounds of arsenic and antimony may be optically active even at room temperature.

Water in acid hydrates such as $HClO_4 \cdot H_2O$ exists as the *hydronium ion* ($[OH_3]^+$). The infrared spectrum of the hydronium ion has been studied by several investigators.[132–135] For infrared and Raman studies of related compounds, see the following references: liquid ammonia (136, 137),

TABLE II-10. VIBRATIONAL FREQUENCIES OF PYRAMIDAL XY_3 MOLECULES (CM^{-1})

Molecule	ν_1	ν_2	ν_3	ν_4	References
NF_3	1032	647	905	493	145, 146
PF_3	892	487	860	344	145, 147
AsF_3	707	341	644	274	148
PCl_3	507	260	494	189	149, 150
$AsCl_3$	412	194	307	155	149
$SbCl_3$	377	164	356	128	149, 310*a*
$[GeCl_3]^-$	320	162	253	139	151
$[SnCl_3]^-$	297	128	256	103	152*a*
PBr_3	392	161	392	116	149
$AsBr_3$	(284)	128	275	98	151*a*
$SbBr_3$	254	101	245	81	152
$[SnBr_3]^-$	211	83	181	65	152*a*
PI_3	303	111	325	79	153
AsI_3	216	94	221	70	153

$NH_3 \cdot H_2O$ crystal (138), partially deuterated ammonia (139, 140) and partially deuterated phosphine (141). For a normal coordinate analysis of XH_3 compounds, see Refs. 142–144.

Table II-10 lists the fundamental frequencies of halogen compounds of the XY_3 type. It is interesting that the hydrogen compounds in Table II-9 have symmetric stretching and bending frequencies (ν_1 and ν_2) which are lower than the antisymmetric stretching and bending frequencies (ν_3 and ν_4), respectively, while the opposite prevails in the halogen compounds in Table II-10. The vibrational spectra of *chloroammonia* (NH_xCl_{3-x}) and *nitrogen trichloride* (NCl_3) have been studied by Moore.[154] Schatz[155] has done a normal coordinate analysis for NF_3.

Table II-11 lists the fundamental frequencies of various ions of the XY_3 type. ν_1 and ν_3 are near each other for all these ions. Thus the stretching vibrations are usually observed as one strong, broad band. The infrared spectra of a number of metal *chlorates* ($[ClO_3]^-$) have been obtained by Rocchiccioli[157] and Duveau.[158] Recently Dasent and Waddington[161] studied the infrared spectra of metal *iodates* ($[IO_3]^-$) and related compounds. It was suggested that extra bands observed at 480–420 cm^{-1} may be due to the metal-oxygen vibration. Figure II-7 shows the infrared spectra of $KClO_3$ and KIO_3 in the solid state. Rocchiccioli[165] has measured

TABLE II-11. VIBRATIONAL FREQUENCIES OF PYRAMIDAL XY_3 IONS (CM)$^{-1}$

Ion	State	ν_1	ν_2	ν_3	ν_4	References
$[ClO_3]^-$	solid (R)	930	620	975	486	156, 157
	solid (IR)	910	617	960	493	156, 158, 158*a*
	sol'n (R)	930	610	982	479	159
$[BrO_3]^-$	sol'n (R)	806	421	836	356	159, 160
$[IO_3]^-$	sol'n (R)	779	390	826	330	161, 162
$[SO_3]^{2-}$	sol'n (R)	967	620	933	469	163, 164
	solid (IR)	1010	633	961	496	163, 165
$[SeO_3]^{2-}$	sol'n (R)	807	432	737	374	166, 167
$[TeO_3]^{2-}$	sol'n (R)	758	364	703	326	166

the infrared spectra of a number of metal *sulfites* ($[SO_3]^{2-}$). The infrared spectra of Na_2SO_3 and K_2SeO_3 in the solid state are compared in Fig. II-8. According to Depaigne-Delay et al.,[168] the stannate ion ($[SnO_3]^{2-}$) is planar in the Pb(II) and Ba(II) salts, and slightly pyramidal in the Cu(II) salt. Interpretations of the vibrational spectra of metal *titanates* ($[TiO_3]^{2-}$) are based on the distorted octahedral TiO_6 unit ($\mathbf{D}_{4h}$ symmetry) in the crystalline state.[169]

TABLE II-12. RELATIONSHIP BETWEEN $\mathbf{C}_{3v}$ AND $\mathbf{C}_s$

$C_{3v}(XY_3)$	$\nu_1(A_1)$ $\nu_s(XY)$	$\nu_2(A_1)$ $\delta_s(YXY)$	$\nu_3(E)$ $\nu_d(XY)$		$\nu_4(E)$ $\delta_d(YXY)$	
	↓	↓	↙	↘	↙	↘
$C_s(ZXY_2)$	$\nu_1(A')$ $\nu_s(XZ)$	$\nu_3(A')$ $\delta_s(YXZ)$	$\nu_2(A')$ $\nu_s(XY)$	$\nu_5(A'')$ $\nu_{as}(XY)$	$\nu_4(A')$ $\delta_s(YXY)$	$\nu_6(A'')$ $\delta_{as}(YXZ)$

(2) ZXY_2 Molecules (C_s)

Substitution of a Z atom for one Y atom in the XY_3 molecule lowers the symmetry from $\mathbf{C}_{3v}$ to $\mathbf{C}_s$. As a result, the degenerate vibrations split into two bands. Thus six vibrations are observed, all of which are infrared and Raman active. The relation between $\mathbf{C}_{3v}$ and $\mathbf{C}_s$ is shown in Table II-12. Table II-13 lists the fundamental frequencies of pyramidal ZXY_2 molecules. The last compound in this table is *selenious acid*, the

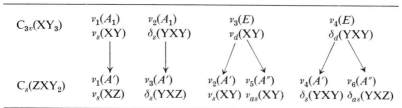

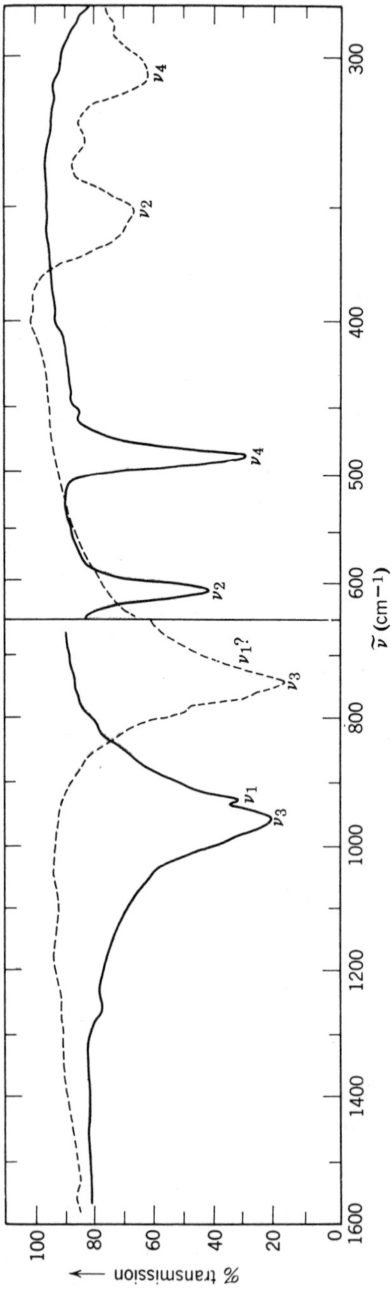

Fig. II-7. Infrared spectra of $KClO_3$ (solid line) and KIO_3 (broken line).

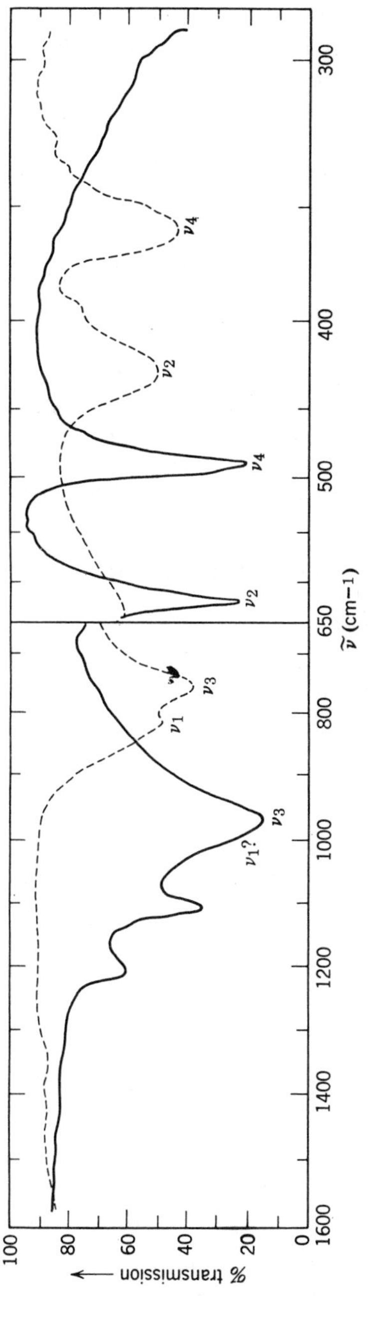

Fig. II-8. Infrared spectra of Na_2SO_3 (solid line) and K_2SeO_3 (broken line).

band assignments for which were made on the assumption that each OH group is a single atom (O*) having the same mass as the OH group. Recently, Simon and Paetzold[178] made an extensive study of the vibrational spectra of selenium compounds. Cotton and Horrocks[179] have carried out a normal coordinate analysis of *thionyl halides* (X_2SO, X = F, Cl or Br).

TABLE II-13. VIBRATIONAL FREQUENCIES OF PYRAMIDAL ZXY_2 MOLECULES (CM^{-1})

Molecule (ZXY_2)	$\nu_1(A')$	$\nu_2(A')$	$\nu_3(A')$	$\nu_4(A')$	$\nu_5(A'')$	$\nu_6(A'')$	References
OSF_2	1308	801	526	326	721	393	403*a*, 170
$OSCl_2$	1229	490	194	344	443	284	403*a*, 171–173
$OSBr_2$	1121	405	120	267	379	223	174
$OSeF_2$	1012	664	373	278	605	308	175
$OSeCl_2$	995	388	161	279	347	255	175
$[OSeO*_2]^{2-}$	831	702	430	336	690	364	176, 177

II-5. PLANAR FOUR-ATOM MOLECULES

(1) XY_3 Molecules (D_{3h})

The four normal modes of vibration of planar XY_3 molecules are shown in Fig. II-9. ν_2, ν_3 and ν_4 are infrared active, and ν_1, ν_3 and ν_4 are Raman active. Table II-14 lists the observed fundamental frequencies of molecules

TABLE II-14. VIBRATIONAL FREQUENCIES OF PLANAR XY_3 MOLECULES (CM^{-1})

Molecule	ν_1	ν_2	ν_3	ν_4	References
$B^{10}F_3$	888	718	1505	482	180, 181
$B^{11}F_3$	888	691	1454	480	180, 182
$B^{10}Cl_3$	471	480	995	244	183, 183*a*
$B^{11}Cl_3$	471	460	956	243	183, 183*a*
$B^{10}Br_3$	278	395	856	150	184
$B^{11}Br_3$	278	375	820	150	184
$B^{10}I_3$	190	352	737	100	184
$B^{11}I_3$	190	336	704	100	184
SO_3	1069	652	1330	532	185, 185*a*
$La[BO_3]$	939	718, 790	1275	595, 614	186
$In[BO_3]$	—	740, 765	1260	672	186
$H_3[BO_3]$	1060	668–648	1490–1428	545	38

of this type. As an example, the infrared spectrum of Sc[BO_3] is shown in Fig. II-10. Lindeman and Wilson[187] and Goubeau et al.[188] have studied the infrared spectra of *boron mixed halides* such as BF_2Cl and $BFCl_2$. Heslop and Linnett[189] have done a normal coordinate analysis of *boron trihalides*. Gerding and Nijveld[190] have found from Raman spectra that *liquid sulfur trioxide* (SO_3) exists as a cyclic trimer. Recently,

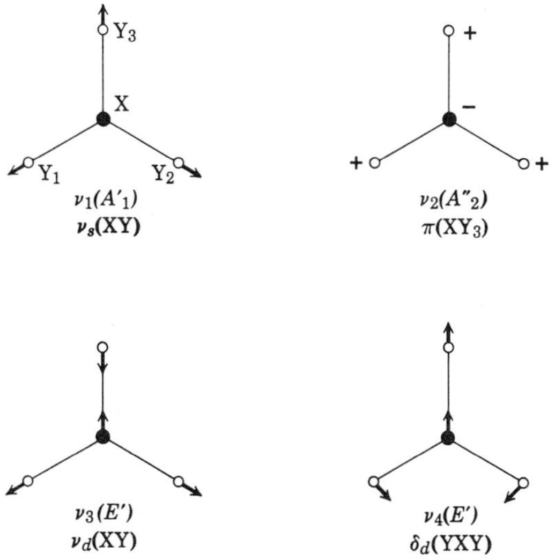

Fig. II-9. Normal modes of vibration of planar XY_3 molecules.

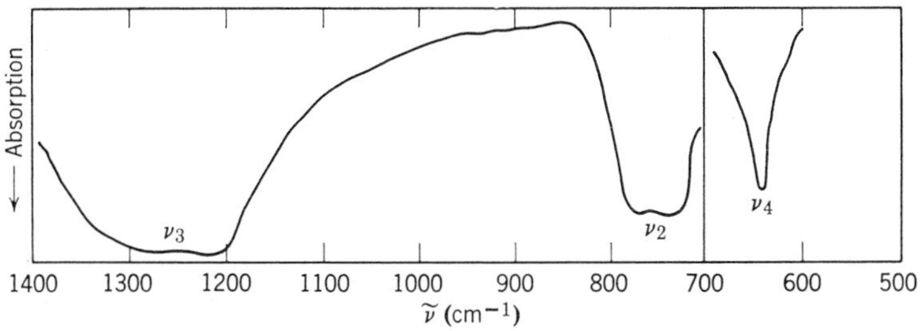

Fig. II-10. The infrared spectrum of $ScBO_3$ (18% B^{10}, 82% B^{11}) in Nujol.[186]

Gillespie and Robinson[190a] made detailed band assignments for this compound. Duval and Lecomte[191] have measured the infrared spectra of a number of *metal orthoborates and metaborates*. Although *orthoboric acid* (H_3BO_3) does not belong to this group, the observed frequencies are listed in Table II-14, with the OH group regarded as a single atom. For more detailed assignments for boric acid, see Refs. 38 and 192–194. The infrared spectra of *metaboric acid* ($[HBO_2]_3$, cyclic trimer) and its deuterated compound have been studied by Parsons.[194a]

Table II-15 lists the observed infrared and Raman frequencies of some carbonates and nitrates. It is interesting to note that calcite and aragonite exhibit different spectra although their chemical compositions are the same.

TABLE II-15. VIBRATIONAL FREQUENCIES OF CARBONATES AND NITRATES (cm^{-1})

Compound		ν_1	ν_2	ν_3	ν_4	References
$CaCO_3$ (calcite)	IR	—	879	1429–1492	706	195
	R	1087	—	1432	714	195
$CaCO_3$ (aragonite)	IR	1080	866	1492, 1504	706, 711	195
	R	1084	852	1460	704	195
$MgCO_3$ (magnesite)	R	1096	—	1460	735	196
$CaMg[CO_3]_2$(dolomite)	R	1099	—	1444	724	196
$SrCO_3$(strontianite)	R	1076	850	1449, 1438, 1406	703	197
$KNO_3{}^{16}$	IR	1049	828	1768, 974 *a	716	198
$KNO_3{}^{18}$	IR	1028	817	1755, 969 *a	705	198
$NaNO_3$	IR	—	831	1405	692	195
	R	1068	—	1385	726	195, 199
NH_4NO_3	IR	1050	830	1350	715	200, 201
$TlNO_3$	IR	1044	822	1410–1280	697, 713	200
$Pb[NO_3]_2$	IR	1018	807, 831	1400–1310	723	200

[a] According to Anbar et al.,[198] ν_3(1390 cm^{-1}) splits into two bands in decalin mull. It seems more reasonable, however, to assign the strong and broad band observed at ca. 1400 cm^{-1} to the ν_3 mode.

Evidently, this is due to the difference in crystal structure. In order to make a detailed study of the spectra of crystals, it is necessary to consider the spectra from the point of view of *site grop* or *factor group* analysis. According to Halford,[202] the spectrum of a molecule in the crystalline state is governed by a new selection rule derived from *site symmetry*—the local symmetry of the crystalline environment around the center of gravity of the molecule in the unit cell. The site symmetry can be determined immediately if the space group of the crystal, the point group of the molecule and the number of molecules in the unit cell are known. In general, the site symmetry is lower than the molecular symmetry in the free state. Thus the selection rule for the gaseous state is relaxed in the crystalline state. Therefore bands forbidden in the gaseous state may appear weakly, and the degenerate vibrations may split in the crystalline state.

By using site group analysis, it is easily found that the site symmetry of the carbonate ion in a calcite crystal is $\mathbf{D}_3$ whereas it is $\mathbf{C}_s$ in aragonite. Then the selection rules differ as shown in Table II-16. There is no change in the selection rule in going from the free carbonate ion to calcite. In aragonite, however, ν_1 becomes infrared active, and ν_3 and ν_4 each split into two bands. As Table II-15 indicates, the observed spectra are in good

TABLE II-16. CORRELATION TABLE FOR $\mathbf{D}_{3h}$, $\mathbf{D}_3$, $\mathbf{C}_{2v}$ and $\mathbf{C}_s$

Point Group	ν_1	ν_2	ν_3	ν_4
$\mathbf{D}_{3h}$	A_1'(R)	A_2''(I)	E'(I, R)	E'(I, R)
$\mathbf{D}_3$	A_1(R)	A_2(I)	E(I, R)	E(I, R)
$\mathbf{C}_{2v}$	A_1(I, R)	B_1(I, R)	A_1(I, R) + B_2(I, R)	A_1(I, R) + B_2(I, R)
$\mathbf{C}_s$	A'(I, R)	A''(I, R)	A'(I, R) + A'(I, R)	A'(I, R) + A'(I, R)

agreement with the predictions. This is also seen in the comparison of the Raman spectra of magnesite and dolomite (calcite type) and strontianite (aragonite type).

It is to be noted that, besides the internal vibrations of the molecule, the spectra obtained in the crystalline state exhibit *lattice vibrations*—the vibrations due to the translational and torsional motions of the molecule as a whole. Although their frequencies are usually below 300 cm^{-1}, they appear in the higher frequency region as combination bands with the internal vibrations and thus complicate the spectrum (see Fig. II-17). Another approach to the analysis of crystal spectra has been developed by Bhagavantam and Venkatarayudu. For details of their method of *factor group* analysis, see Refs. 195 and 203.

Duval and co-workers,[204] Louisfert[205] and Buijs and Schutte[205a] have measured the infrared spectra of a number of metal carbonates and nitrates. For complex carbonates, see Sec. III-3(*a*). In Fig. II-11 the infrared spectra of KNO_3 and $Ba(NO_3)_2$ are shown for comparison. Although the site group analysis does not predict splitting of the ν_2 band, Decius[206] has found that the ν_2 vibration of KNO_3 splits slightly because of coupling between neighboring ions. In the $NaNO_3$ crystal, this coupling is small because the distance between two neighboring ions is much greater than that in the KNO_3 crystal. Ferraro[207] has measured the infrared spectra of a number of metal nitrates and has found that the

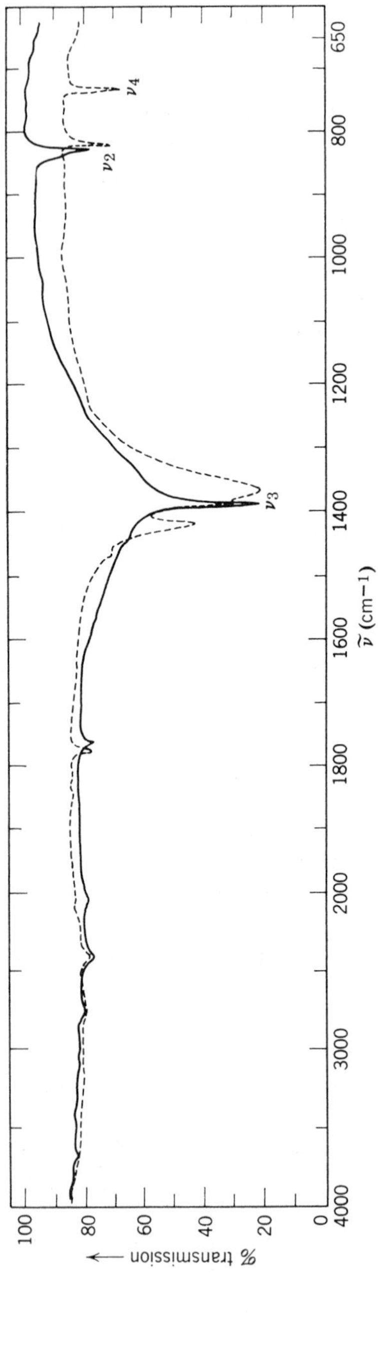

Fig. II-11. Infrared spectra of KNO_3 (solid line) and $Ba(NO_3)_2$ (broken line).

$\mathbf{D}_{3h}$ symmetry of the free ion is progressively lowered to $\mathbf{C}_{2v}$ in going from a monovalent to a tetravalent metal. Similar observations were made by Addison and Gatehouse[208] for transition metal nitrates.

(2) $ZXY_2(C_{2v})$ and $ZXYW(C_s)$ Molecules

If one of the Y atoms of a planar XY_3 molecule is replaced by a Z atom, the symmetry is lowered to $\mathbf{C}_{2v}$. If two of the Y atoms are replaced by

TABLE II-17. VIBRATIONAL FREQUENCIES OF ZXY_2 AND ZXYW MOLECULES (cm^{-1})

Y—X(—Y)—Y (D_{3h})	$\nu_1(A_1')$ $\nu_s(XY)$	$\nu_2(A_2'')$ $\pi(XY_3)$	$\nu_3(E')$ $\nu_d(XY)$		$\nu_4(E')$ $\delta_d(YXY)$		
Z—X(—Y)—Y (C_{2v})	$\nu_1(A_1)$ $\nu(XZ)$	$\nu_6(B_1)$ $\pi(ZXY_2)$	$\nu_2(A_1)$ $\nu_s(XY)$	$\nu_4(B_2)$ $\nu_{as}(XY)$	$\nu_3(A_1)$ $\delta_s(ZXY)$	$\nu_5(B_2)$ $\delta_{as}(ZXY)$	
Z—X(—Y)—W (C_s)	$\nu_1(A')$ $\nu(XZ)$	$\nu_6(A'')$ $\pi(ZXYW)$	$\nu_2(A')$ $\nu(XY)$	$\nu_4(A')$ $\nu(XW)$	$\nu_3(A')$ $\delta(ZXY)$	$\nu_5(A')$ $\delta(ZXW)$	References
(HO)—NO_2	886	765	1320	1710	—	583	209, 210
(DO)—NO_2	888	764	1313	1685	—	543	209, 210
F—NO_2	822	742	1312	1793	460	570	211
Cl—NO_2	794	651	1293	1685	411	367	212, 213
O=CF_2	1928	774	965	1249	584	626	214–216
O=CCl_2	1827	580	569	849	285	440	214–217
O=CBr_2	1828	512	425	757	181	350	214
O=CClF	1868	667	776	1095	501	415	214–218
O=CBrCl	1828	547	517	806	240	372	214
O=CBrF	1874	620	721	1068	398	335	214, 219
O=CHF	1837	—	2981	1065	1343	663	220
O=CDF	1797	857	2262	1073	968	658	220
F—ClF_2	528	364	752	703	326	434	221
F—BrF_2	(528)	(289)	674	613	(300)	(384)	221

The band assignments for some of these compounds differ among investigators.

two different atoms, W and Z, the symmetry is lowered further to $\mathbf{C}_s$. As a result, the selection rules are changed as shown in Table II-16. For both cases, all six vibrations become active in the infrared and Raman spectra. Table II-17 lists the observed fundamental frequencies of molecules of these two types. Band assignments shown for HNO_3 and DNO_3 assume the OH group to be a single atom having the same mass as the

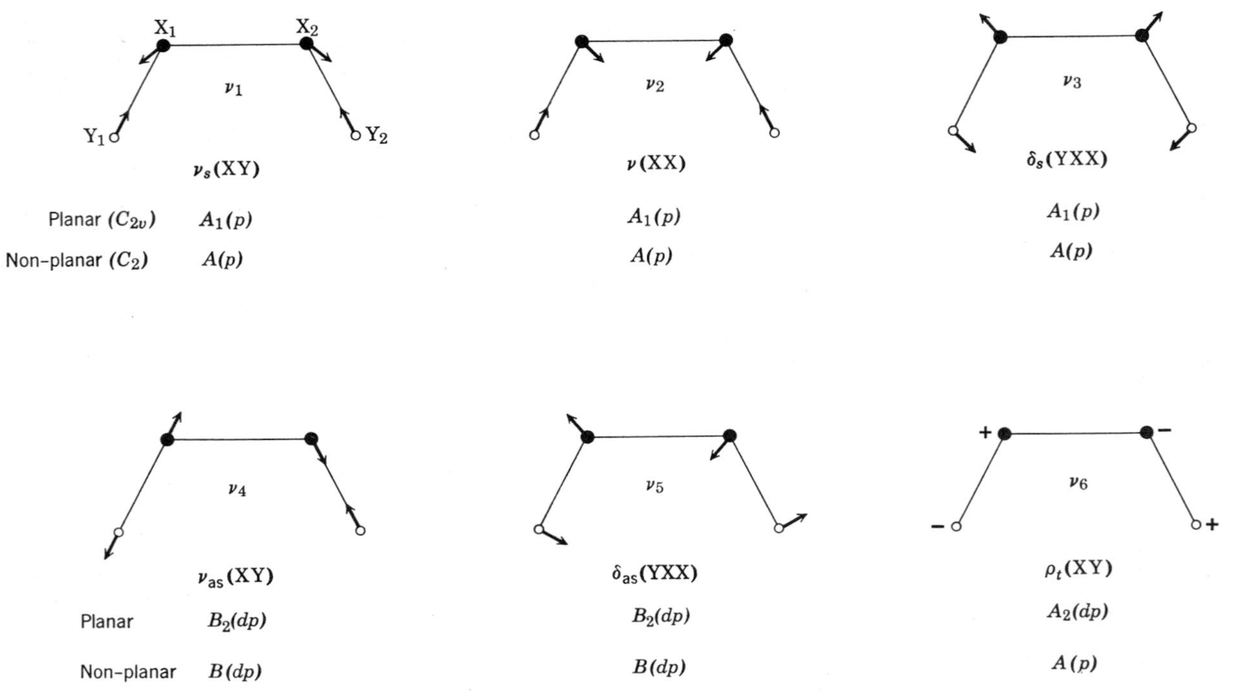

Fig. II-12. Normal modes of vibration of non-linear X_2Y_2 molecules (p: polarized; dp: depolarized).[235]

OH group. The O—H stretching, N—O—H bending and O—H twisting vibrations are observed at 3560, 1335 and 465 cm^{-1}, respectively, in the infrared spectrum of HNO_3 vapor.[209] It is interesting to note that ClF_3 and BrF_3 are planar T-shaped molecules having $\mathbf{C}_{2v}$ symmetry. For normal coordinate analyses of the planar XY_3 molecules, see Refs. 223–223*b*. For those of planar ZXY_2 molecules, see Refs. 214, 222 and 222*a*.

II-6. OTHER FOUR-ATOM MOLECULES

(1) X_2Y_2 Molecules

Although several different models have been suggested for molecules like H_2O_2, the non-planar ($\mathbf{C}_2$) (twisting angle about the X_1—X_2 axis of about 90°) and planar *cis* ($\mathbf{C}_{2v}$) models are most probable. Figure II-12 shows the six normal modes of vibration and the band assignments for these two models. It is not easy to distinguish between the two models

TABLE II-18. VIBRATIONAL FREQUENCIES OF X_2Y_2 MOLECULES (CM^{-1})

Molecule	State	ν_1	ν_2	ν_3	ν_4	ν_5	ν_6	References
H_2O_2	gas (IR)	—	(890)	—	3610	1260	465, 575	224–226
	liq. (IR)	—	878	—	3360	1350	635	224–227
	liq. (R)	3364	880	1402	—	—	—	228–229
	solid (IR)	—	878	1430	3320	1380	472, 660, 792	224, 227, 229, 229*a*
D_2O_2	gas (IR)	—	—	(1007)	2661	923, 947	—	224, 227
	liq. (IR)	—	878	—	2482	1004	538	22, 227
	liq. (R)	2472	880	1013	—	—	—	228
	solid (IR)	—	880	—	2470	1000	480	224
H_2S_2	gas (IR)	—	—	—	2557	897	—	230, 231
	liq. (IR)	(2509)	509	—	—	882	—	230
	liq. (R)	2509	509	883	—	—	—	232, 233
	solid (IR)	(2495)	501	(868)	2480	890	—	230
F_2S_2	liq. (IR)	745	526	—	807	—	—	234
Cl_2S_2	liq. (IR)	438	448	203	538	242	—	238, 236
	liq. (R)	437	451	207	541	241	104	235, 237
Br_2S_2	liq. (IR)	—	354	176	531	196	—	238
	liq. (R)	302	355	172	529	200	66	239
Cl_2Se_2	liq. (R)	288	367	130	418	146	87	239
Br_2Se_2	liq. (R)	204	265	94	292	106	50	239

from the vibrational spectra since the only difference between the two occurs in the ν_6 vibration. This is infrared inactive and Raman depolarized in the planar model but infrared active and Raman polarized in the non-planar model. It is generally recognized, however, that the non-planar model is more probable than the planar *cis* model. Table II-18 lists the fundamental frequencies of some molecules belonging to this group.

$NH_3 \cdot H_2O_2$ exists as *ammonium hydroperoxide* ($[NH_4]^+[OOH]^-$) in the

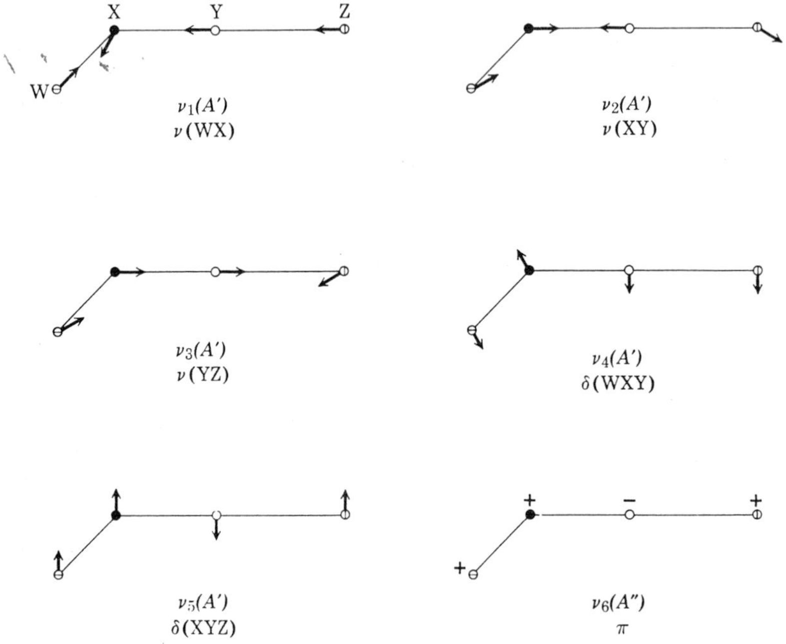

Fig. II-13. Normal modes of vibration of non-linear WXYZ molecules.

crystalline state.[240,241] Fehér and co-workers[242,232] have studied the Raman spectra of *hydrogen polysulfides* (H_2S_x, $x = 2$–8). In alkaline and alkaline earth peroxides such as *sodium peroxide* (Na_2O_2), the absence of the O—O stretching vibration near 880 cm^{-1} in the infrared spectra may demonstrate the presence of the O—O ion, since the O—O stretching vibration of the ion should be infrared inactive.[243] Ketelaar and colleague[238,235] have obtained the frequencies of S_2Cl_2 and S_2Br_2 from *simultaneous transitions*† observed in the infrared spectra of mixtures of each of these compounds with CS_2. As Table II-18 shows, these values are in good agreement

† These are similar to the combination bands in one molecule, but here vibrations of two different molecules are combined in the mixture because of transient molecular collisions.

with those of the Raman spectra. Normal coordinate analyses have been done for H_2O_2[225] and X_2S_2, where X is a halogen.[235]

(2) Other Planar Molecules (C_s)

Planar four-atom molecules of the XY_3, XYZY and WXYZ types have six modes of vibration such as shown in Fig. II-13. All these vibrations are both infrared and Raman active. Table II-19 lists the fundamental

TABLE II-19. VIBRATIONAL FREQUENCIES OF PLANAR FOUR-ATOM MOLECULES (CM^{-1})

104197

Molecule	State	ν_1	ν_2	ν_3	ν_4	ν_5	ν_6	References
HN_3	gas	3336	2140	1274	1150	522	672	244
	solid (80°K)	3090	2162	1299	1180	—	—	244
DN_3	gas	2480	2141	1183	955	498	638	244
	solid (80°K)	2308	2155	1230	977	—	—	244
HNCO	gas	3531	2274	1327	797	572	(670)	245, 246
	solid	3133	2246	1326	—	—	—	
HNCS	gas	3536	1963	995	817	469	600	247, 248
cis-HONO	gas	3426	1640	1292	856	—	637	249–251
trans-HONO	gas	3590	1696	1260	794	598	543	
cis-DONO	gas	2530	1616	—	816	—	508	
trans-DONO	gas	2650	1690	1018	739	591	416	

frequencies of some molecules of these types. Of the two isomers of *nitrous acid* (HONO), the *trans* form is more stable than the *cis* form.[249] Palm[252] has done a normal coordinate analysis of these two isomers. For the infrared spectra of X—SCN molecules (X: a halogen) and HNSO see Refs. 87 and 252*a*, respectively.

II-7. NITROGEN COMPOUNDS OF VARIOUS STRUCTURES

So far the normal vibrations have been discussed individually for each general type of molecular structure. It is more convenient, however, to group nitrogen compounds of various structures here and to discuss their group frequencies, since most of the structures rarely appear in the compounds of other elements.

(1) Oxides

The oxides of nitrogen are NO, N_2O, N_2O_2, $[N_2O_2]^{2-}$, N_2O_3, N_2O_4, N_2O_5, etc. NO and N_2O have already been described in Secs. II-1 and II-2. The structures of the other oxides are reported to be

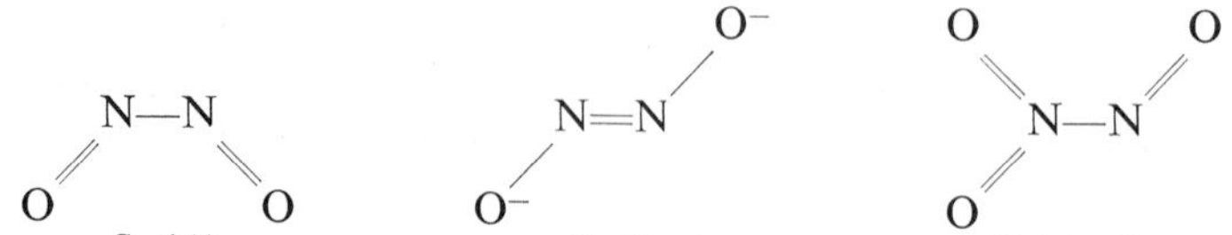

C_{2v} (*cis*)
C_{2h} (*trans*) C_{2h} (*trans*) C_s (planar)

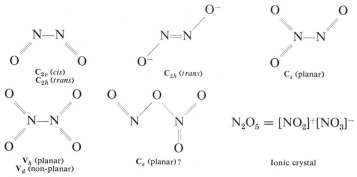

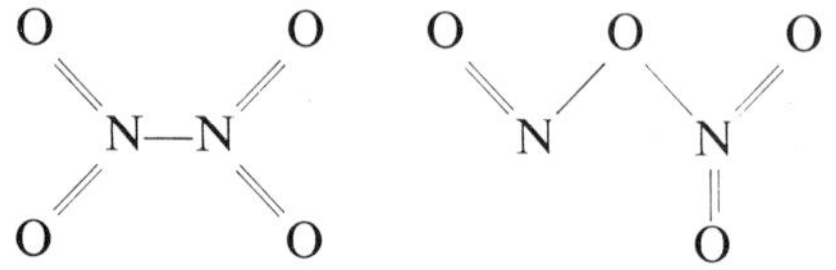

$N_2O_5 = [NO_2]^+[NO_3]^-$

V_h (planar)
V_d (non-planar) C_s (planar)? Ionic crystal

The observed fundamental frequencies and band assignments are given in Table II-20. Using the matrix isolation method, Fateley and colleagues[9]

TABLE II-20. VIBRATIONAL FREQUENCIES OF VARIOUS NITROGEN OXIDES (CM^{-1})

Molecule	State	Frequencies and Band Assignments	References
N_2O_2	$-190°C$ in CO_2 (IR)	*cis:* $\nu_{as}(NO)$, 1768; $\nu_s(NO)$, 1862 *trans:* $\nu_{as}(NO)$, 1740	9
N_2O_3	$-150°$ C (IR)	1863, 1589, 1297, 783, 627, 407, 313, 253(R)	253
$N_2{}^{14}O_4$ (V_h)	(IR) (R)	$\nu_1(A_g)-\nu(NO)$, 1380; $\nu_2(A_g)-\delta(NO_2)$, 808: $\nu_3(A_g)-\nu(NN)$, 266; $\nu_4(A_u)-\rho_t(NO_2)$?; $\nu_5(B_{1g})-\nu(NO)$, 1712; $\nu_6(B_{1g})-\rho_r(NO_2)$, 482; $\nu_7(B_{1u})-\rho_w(NO_2)$, 429; $\nu_8(B_{2g})-\rho_w(NO_2)$, 672; $\nu_9(B_{2u})-\nu(NO)$, 1748; $\nu_{10}(B_{2u})-\rho_r(NO_2)$, 381; $\nu_{11}(B_{3u})-\nu(NO)$, 1262; $\nu_{12}(B_{3u})-\delta(NO_2)$, 750	254–259
$N_2{}^{14}O_5$	$-190°$ (IR)	$NO_2{}^+$ ion: $\nu_1(1400)$, $\nu_2(538)$, $\nu_3(2375)$ $NO_3{}^-$ ion: $\nu_1(1050)$, $\nu_2(824)$, $\nu_3(1413)$, $\nu_4(722)$	260
$[N_2O_2]^{2-}$	(R)	$\nu_1(A_g)-\nu(NO)$, 1383; $\nu_2(A_g)-\nu(NN)$, 1115; $\nu_3(A_g)-\delta(NNO)$, (485);	261
	(IR)	$\nu_4(B_u)-\delta(NNO)$, (370); $\nu_5(B_u)-\nu(NO)$, 1020; $\nu_6(A_u)-\pi$, 504	262

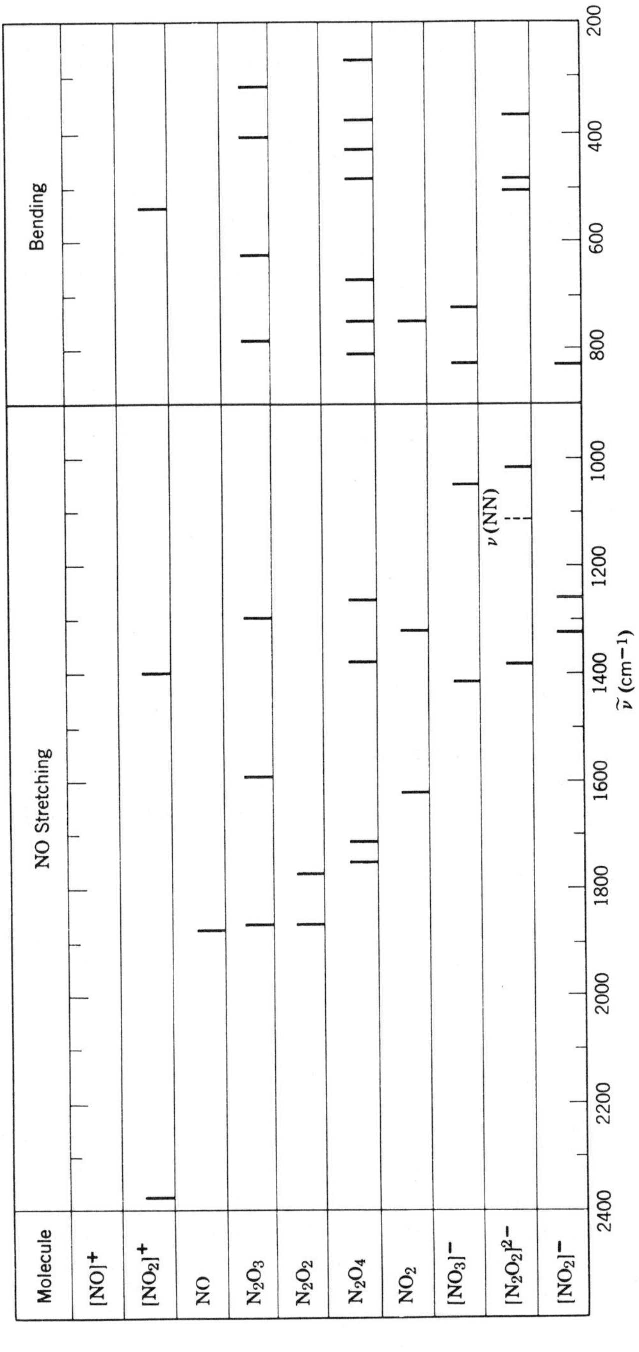

Fig. II-14. Distribution of stretching and bending frequencies in various nitrogen oxides.

have found that (1) NO exists as a monomer and as two dimers (*cis* and *trans*), (2) NO_2 exists as a monomer and as three dimers (planar, non-planar and asymmetrical ONO—NO_2) and (3) N_2O_3 exists as ON—NO_2 and ONONO. Teranishi and Decius[260] have shown that the spectrum of crystalline N_2O_5 can be interpreted on the basis of the ionic structure, $[NO_2]^+[NO_3]^-$, previously suggested by x-ray analysis. For normal coordinate analyses of N_2O_4 and $[N_2O_2]^{2-}$, see Refs. 258 and 261, respectively.

Figure II-14 illustrates the frequency distribution of the NO stretching and ONO bending vibrations in various oxides. It is interesting that the NO stretching frequency varies over a wide range (2400–1000 cm^{-1}) depending on the bond order. As a result, a narrow frequency range cannot be specified for the NO group.

(2) Fluorides

Dinitrogen difluoride (N_2F_2) exists as either one of the following two forms:

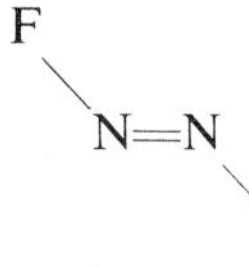

Trans-1,2-difluorodiazine (C_{2h})

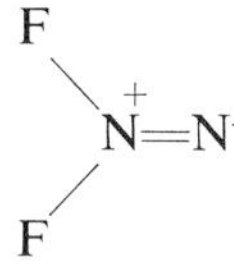

1,1-Difluorodiazine (C_{2v})

Sanborn[263] has confirmed these structures by infrared spectra.

(3) Hydrazine and Hydroxylamine

Owing to internal rotation, the hydrazine molecule may have conformation isomers such as those in Fig. II-15. The equilibria between these

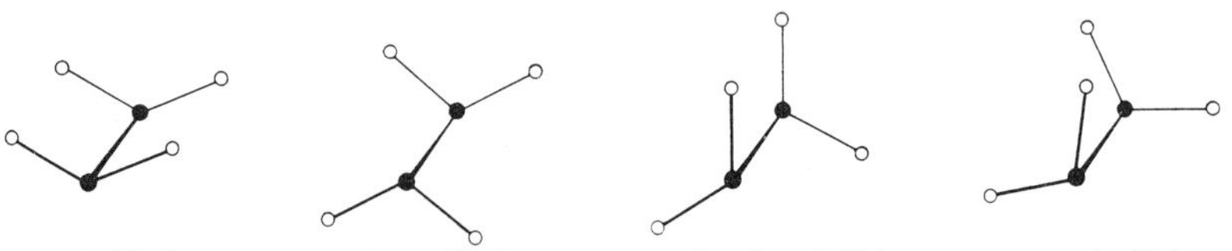

cis (C_{2v}) *trans* (C_{2h}) semi-eclipsed (C_2) *gauche* (C_2)

Fig. II-15. Various conformations of hydrazine.

isomers depend on the temperature at which the measurement is made. Table II-21 gives band assignments and fundamental frequencies of hydrazine and hydroxylamine based on $\mathbf{C}_2$ and $\mathbf{C}_s$ symmetry, respectively. The infrared spectra of *hydrazine dihalides* ($[N_2H_6]X_2$, X = F or Cl) have been studied by Snyder and Decius,[269] and of *hydroxylamine halides* ($[NH_3OH]X$, X = Cl, Br or I) by Frasco and Wagner.[270]

TABLE II-21. VIBRATIONAL FREQUENCIES AND BAND ASSIGNMENTS FOR HYDRAZINE AND HYDROXYLAMINE (CM^{-1})

$H_2N—NH_2$[264~266]			$H_2N—OH$[267,268]		
Gas (IR)	Assignments		Film (IR)	Assignments	
3325	$\nu_1(A)$	$\nu(NH)$	3245, 3173	$\nu_1(A')$	$\nu(NH)$
—	$\nu_2(A)$	$\nu(NH)$	2867	$\nu_2(A')$	$\nu(OH)$
1493	$\nu_3(A)$	$\delta(HNH)$	1515	$\nu_3(A')$	$\delta(HNH)$
1098	$\nu_4(A)$	$\rho_r(NH_2)$	1191	$\nu_4(A')$	$\delta(NOH)$
—	$\nu_5(A)$	$\nu(NN)$	912	$\nu_5(A')$	$\nu(NO)$
780	$\nu_6(A)$	$\rho_w(NH_2)$	950	$\nu_6(A')$	$\rho_r(NH_2)$
—	$\nu_7(A)$	$\rho_t(NH_2)$	3302	$\nu_7(A'')$	$\nu(NH)$
3350	$\nu_8(B)$	$\nu(NH)$	867	$\nu_8(A'')$	$\rho_w(NH_2)$
3280	$\nu_9(B)$	$\nu(NH)$	535	$\nu_9(A'')$	$\rho_t(NH_2)$
1587, 1628	$\nu_{10}(B)$	$\delta(HNH)$			
1275	$\nu_{11}(B)$	$\rho_r(NH_2)$			
966, 933	$\nu_{12}(B)$	$\rho_w(NH_2)$			

II-8. TETRAHEDRAL AND SQUARE-PLANAR FIVE-ATOM MOLECULES

(1) Tetrahedral XY_4 Molecules (T_d)

Figure II-16 illustrates the four normal modes of vibration of a tetrahedral XY_4 molecule. All the four vibrations are Raman active, whereas

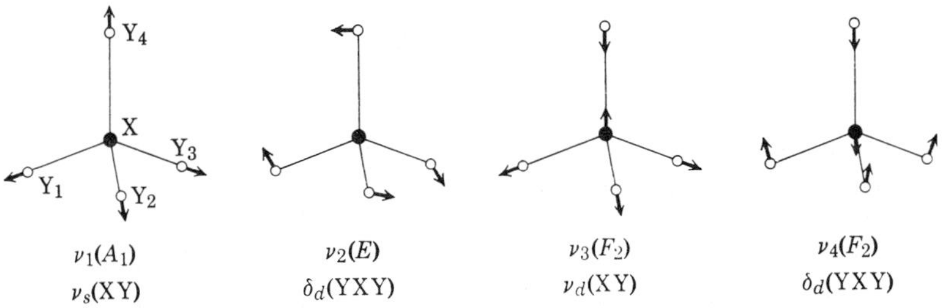

Fig. II-16. Normal modes of vibration of tetrahedral XY_4 molecules.

only ν_3 and ν_4 are infrared active. In Table II-22 are the fundamental frequencies of XH_4 molecules. Woodward and Roberts[284] have shown that the relationship kr^3 = a constant (k = stretching force constant;

r = bond distance) holds for a series of isoelectronic XH_4 molecules. Longuet-Higgins and Brown[285] have shown that the frequency, ν_2, is given by $4\pi^2\nu_2^2 = 9\sqrt{6}\, e^2/32mr^3$, where r is the bond distance and m and e are the mass and charge of the proton. Pistorius[286] has calculated the force constants of a number of XH_4 molecules. Among the many XH_4 molecules in Table II-20, the NH_4^+ ion is chemically the most important. The infrared spectrum of NH_4Cl is shown in Fig. II-17.

TABLE II-22. VIBRATIONAL FREQUENCIES OF TETRAHEDRAL XH_4 MOLECULES (CM^{-1})

Molecule	ν_1	ν_2	ν_3	ν_4	References
CH_4	2914	1520	3020	1305	271
SiH_4	2180	970	2183	910	271, 272
GeH_4	2106	931	2114	819	273, 271
SnH_4	(1910)	(829)	1860	677, 703, 760	274
CD_4	2085	1075	2259	996	275–277
SiD_4	(1545)	(689)	1597	681	278, 272
GeD_4	1504	665	1522	596	273
$[N^{14}H_4]^+$	3040	1680	3145	1400	271
$[N^{15}H_4]^+$	—	(1646)	3137	1399	279
$[PH_4]^+$	2304	1040	2370	930	271, 280
$[ND_4]^+$	2214	1215	2346	1065	271
$[PD_4]^+$	(1625)	777	1740, 1658	701, 683	280
$[NT_4]^+$	—	976	2022	913	279
$[B^{11}H_4]^-$	2264	1210	2244	1080	281–283
$[B^{10}H_4]^-$	2270	1208	2250	1093	
$[B^{11}D_4]^-$	(1570)	855	1696	823	
$[B^{10}D_4]^-$	1604	856	1707	827	
$[AlH_4]^-$	1790	799	1740	764	284

Hornig and his co-workers[287–290] have made an extensive study of the infrared spectra of ammonium halide crystals. One of their findings is that the combination band between $\nu_4(F_2)$ and ν_6 (torsional lattice vibration) is observed if the ammonium ion does not rotate freely in the crystal lattice. This holds for NH_4F, NH_4Cl and NH_4Br. In NH_4I (phase I), however, the band is not observed. Therefore the NH_4^+ ion may rotate more freely in this compound than in other halides. For other work concerning ammonium halides, see Refs. 291–296

Table II-23 lists the fundamental frequencies of tetrahalogen compounds. For $[CdCl_4]^{2-}$, $[HgCl_4]^{2-}$, $[HgBr_4]^{2-}$ and $[HgI_4]^{2-}$, see Ref. 322.

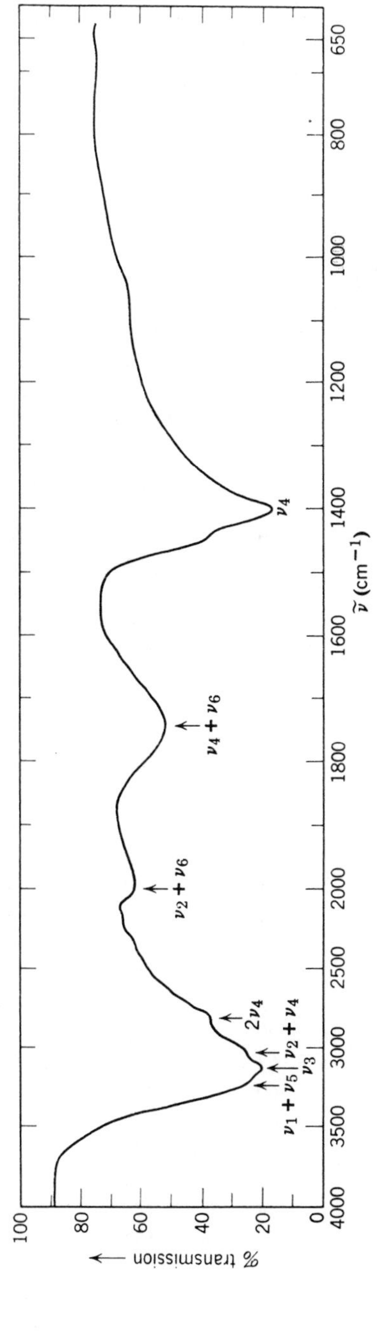

Fig. II-17. The infrared spectrum of NH_4Cl (ν_5, ν_6; lattice modes).[287]

TABLE II-23. VIBRATIONAL FREQUENCIES OF TETRAHALOGEN MOLECULES (cm^{-1})

Molecule	ν_1	ν_2	ν_3	ν_4	References
$C^{12}F_4$	908	435	1281	628	297, 298
$C^{13}F_4$	908	435	1240	(627)	297
SiF_4	800	268	1010	390	299
GeF_4	738	205	800	260	300, 301
ZrF_4	(600–725)	(200–150)	668	190	301*a*
$[B^{11}F_4]^-$	769	353	984	524	302, 303
$[B^{10}F_4]^-$	769	353	1016	529	302, 303
CCl_4	459	218	790, 762	314	304
$SiCl_4$	424	150	608	221	305, 306
$TiCl_4$	388	119	490, 506	139	313
VCl_4	383	128	475	128 or 150	313*a*
$GeCl_4$	397	132	451	171	271, 307–309
$ZrCl_4$	388	102	421	112	310*a*
$SnCl_4$	368	106	403	131	304, 306, 310
$PbCl_4$	327	90	348	90	309
$[AlCl_4]^-$	349	146	575	180	311
$[GaCl_4]^-$	346	114	386	149	312
$[FeCl_4]^-$	330	106	385	133	312*a*
$[ZnCl_4]^{2-}$	282	82	—	116	314
$[InCl_4]^-$	321	89	337	112	312*a*
CBr_4	267	123	672	183	305
$SiBr_4$	249	90	487	137	305
$GeBr_4$	234	78	328	111	271
$SnBr_4$	220	64	279	88	271
$[GaBr_4]^-$	210	71	278	102	315
$[InBr_4]^-$	197	55	239	79	316
$[TlBr_4]^-$	190	51	209	64	317
$TiBr_4$	230	74	383	91	318
$[ZnBr_4]^{2-}$	172	61	210	82	314
$[CdBr_4]^{2-}$	166	53	183	62	319
CI_4	178	90	555	123	320
SiI_4	168	63	405	94	308
GeI_4	159	60	264	80	320*a*
SnI_4	149	47	216	63	320*a*
$[GaI_4]^-$	145	52	222	73	321
$[InI_4]^-$	139	42	185	58	321
$[ZnI_4]^{2-}$	122	44	170	62	314
$[CdI_4]^{2-}$	117	36	145	44	322

For $[PCl_4]^+$ and $[BCl_4]^-$, see Refs. 323 and 323*a*. It is interesting to note that molecules like $TeCl_4$,[324a] SF_4[324] and SeF_4[325] are not tetrahedral, but trigonal bipyramidal with one of the three equatorial positions unoccupied ($\mathbf{C}_{2v}$). If an oxygen atom occupies this vacant position, the structure of *thionyl tetrafluoride* (OSF_4) is obtained. The vibrational spectrum of this compound has been obtained by Goggin et al.[325a]

TABLE II-24. VIBRATIONAL FREQUENCIES OF XO_4, XS_4 AND $X(OH)_4$ MOLECULES (CM^{-1})

Molecule	ν_1	ν_2	ν_3	ν_4	References
$[SiO_4]^{2-}$	800	500	1050	625	271, 326
$[PO_4]^{3-}$	970	358	1080	500	271
$[SO_4]^{2-}$	983	450	1105	611	271
$[ClO_4]^-$	935	460	1050–1170	630	327
$[VO_4]^{3-}$	870	345	825	480	328
$[CrO_4]^{2-}$	847	348	884	368	329
$[MnO_4]^-$	840	—	900	500	330
$[AsO_4]^{3-}$	837	349	878	463	328
$[SeO_4]^{2-}$	833	335	875	432	271
$[MoO_4]^{2-}$	936	220	895	365	271
RuO_4	(880)	(293)	913	330	331*a*, 330
$[IO_4]^-$	791	256	853	325	332
$[WO_4]^{2-}$	928	320	833	405	328, 333
$[ReO_4]^-$	971	331	918	(343)	334, 333
OsO_4	971	328	960	328	335, 333
$[AsS_4]^{3-}$	386	171	419	216	328
$[SbS_4]^{3-}$	366	156	380	178	328
$[B(OH)_4]^-$	754, 749, 747	379	950, 947	533	336
$[Al(OH)_4]^-$	615	310	(720)	310	337
$[Zn(OH)_4]^{2-}$	470	300	(570)	300	337

Hydrogenic vibrations are not listed for the last three ions.

Table II-24 lists the fundamental frequencies of XO_4, XS_4 and $X(OH)_4$ molecules. Since this group includes a number of ions which are chemically important, the infrared spectra of some of the compounds are shown in Figs. II-18 and II-19. It is seen that ν_3 and ν_4 appear strongly in infrared spectra, and, because of lowering of the symmetry, degenerate vibrations often split and Raman active modes become infrared active in the crystalline state [Sec. II-5(1)]. Table II-25 gives the Raman frequencies of the $[SO_4]^{2-}$ ion in various crystalline environments.[338] Doubly and

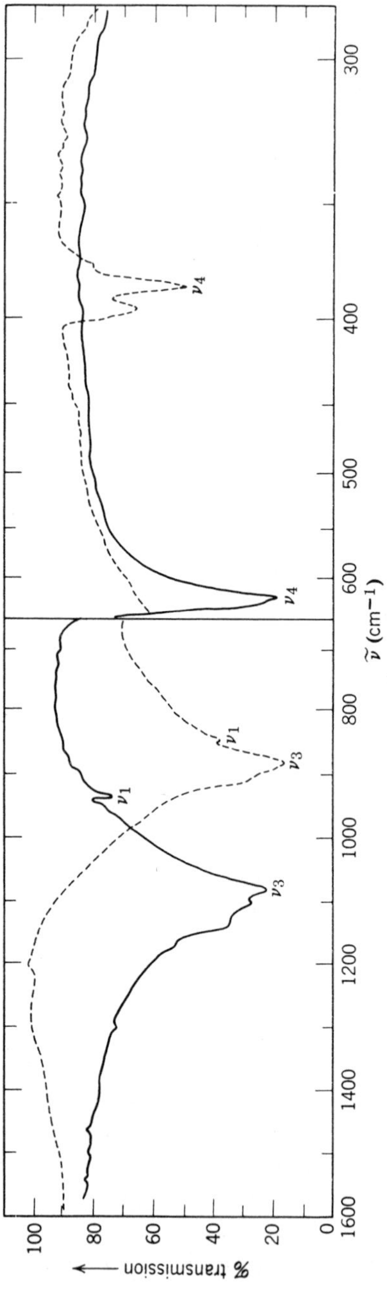

Fig. II-18. Infrared spectra of $KClO_4$ (solid line) and K_2CrO_4 (broken line).

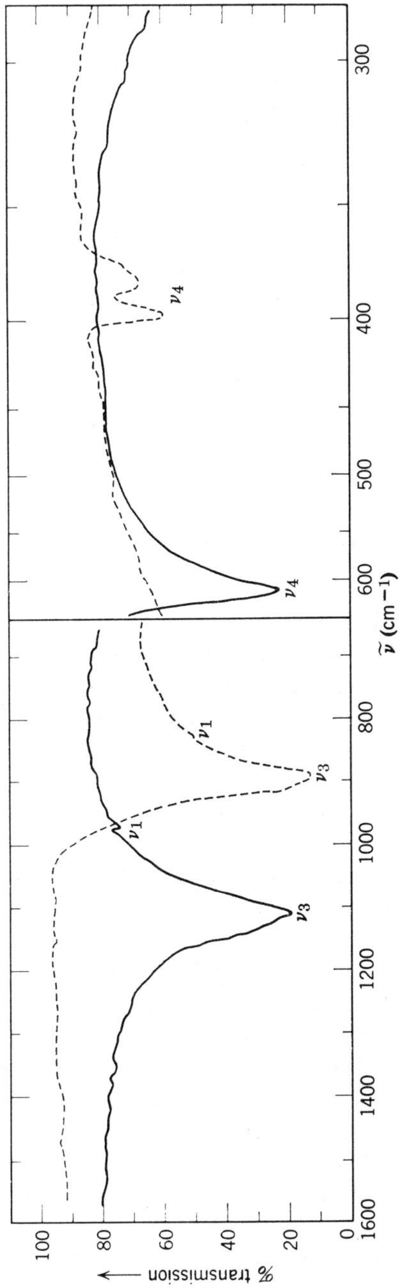

Fig. II-19. Infrared spectra of K_2SO_4 (solid line) and $KMnO_4$ (broken line).

triply degenerate vibrations split into two and three components, respectively.

TABLE II-25. RAMAN FREQUENCIES OF THE SO_4^{2-} ION IN VARIOUS COMPOUNDS (CM^{-1})[338]

Compound	ν_1	ν_2	ν_3	ν_4
Na_2SO_4	983	454	1106	622
$BaSO_4$	989	453, 462	1094, 1142, 1167	617, 630, 648
$CaSO_4$	1018	415, 499	1108, 1128, 1160	609, 628, 674
$CaSO_4 \cdot 2H_2O$[a]	1006	415, 499	1115, 1136, 1144	618, 622, 672

[a] For the H_2O bands, see Sec. III-3.

Hass and Sutherland[339] have made a detailed study of the crystal spectrum of *gypsum* ($CaSO_4 \cdot 2H_2O$). For the spectra of various *sulfates* in the crystalline state, see Refs. 340–349. The infrared and Raman spectra of *sulfuric acid* (H_2SO_4) and its deuterated compound have also been reported.[350,351] The spectra of sulfato complexes will be discussed in Sec. III-4(3). References 352–355*a* describe the spectra of *perchloric acid* and various *perchlorates*. For the spectra of $[PO_4]^{3-}$, $[HPO_4]^{2-}$, $[H_2PO_4]^-$, $[HPO_3]^{2-}$ and $[H_2PO_2]^-$, see Refs. 356–363. Duval and Lecomte[364] have measured the infrared spectra of a number of metal salts of XO_4^{2-} ions in the low frequency region.

(2) Tetrahedral $ZXY_3(C_{3v})$ and $Z_2XY_2(C_{2v})$ Molecules

If one of the Y atoms of an XY_4 molecule is replaced by a Z atom, the symmetry of the molecule is lowered to $\mathbf{C}_{3v}$. If two of the Y atoms are replaced, the symmetry becomes $\mathbf{C}_{2v}$. This lowering of symmetry splits the degenerate vibrations and activates infrared inactive vibrations, as Table II-26 shows. Thus the number of infrared active vibrations is increased to six in ZXY_3 and to nine in Z_2XY_2 molecules. Table II-27 lists the fundamental frequencies of hydrogen and halogen compounds of these types.

A good deal of experimental data on compounds of these types is available. Here only some references are given: $SiH_{4-n}X_n$ (X: a halogen)

TABLE II-26. CORRELATION TABLE FOR T_d, C_{3v} AND C_{2v}

Point Group	ν_1	ν_2	ν_3	ν_4
T_d	A_1(R)	E(R)	F_2(I,R)	F_2(I,R)
C_{3v}	A_1(I,R)	E(I,R)	A_1(I,R) + E(I,R)	A_1(I,R) + E(I,R)
C_{2v}	A_1(I,R)	A_1(I,R) + A_2(R)	A_1(I,R) + B_1(I,R) + B_2(I,R)	A_1(I,R) + B_1(I,R) + B_2(I,R)

TABLE II-27. VIBRATIONAL FREQUENCIES OF TETRAHEDRAL MOLECULES (CM^{-1})

$T_d(XY_4)$	A_1 ν_s(XY)	E δ_d(YXY)			F_2 ν_d(XY)			F_2 δ_d(YXY)			
$C_{3v}(ZXY_3)$	A_1 ν(XZ)	E δ(YXY)			A_1 ν(XY)		E ν_d(XY)	A_1 δ(YXY)		E $\rho_r(XY_3)$	
$C_{2v}(Z_2XY_2)$	A_1 ν(XZ)	A_1 δ(YXY)		A_2 $\rho_t(XY_2)$	A_1 ν(XY)	B_1 ν(XY)	B_2 ν(XZ)	A_1 δ(ZXZ)	B_1 $\rho_r(XY_2)$	B_2 $\rho_w(XY_2)$	References
CH_4	2914		1526			3020			1306		
DCH_3	2205		1477		2982		3030	1306		1156	
D_2CH_2	2139	1450		1286	2974	3030	2255	1034	1090	1235	365, 366
HCD_3	2992		1046		2141		2269	1299		982	
CD_4	2085		1054			2258			996		
SiH_4	2180		970			2183			910		
D_2SiH_2	1587	944		844	2189	2183	1601	683	743	862	278
$HSiD_3$	2182		683		1573		1598	851		683	
SiD_4	1545		689			1597			681		
GeH_4	2106		931			2114			819		
$DGeH_3$	1520		901		2106		2112	820		706	
D_2GeH_2	1512	881		807	2112	2112	1522	620	657	770	273
$HGeD_3$	2112		625		1504		1522	595		792	
GeD_4	1504		665			1522			596		
$FSiH_3$	872		943		2206		2196	990		728	
$ClSiH_3$	551		954		2201		2195	949		664	367
$BrSiH_3$	430		950		2200		2196	930		633	
$ISiH_3$	355		941		2192		2206	903		592	368
$SiCl_4$	424		150			610			221		
$BrSiCl_3$	368		135		545		610	191		205	
Br_2SiCl_2	326	111		122	563	605	508	182	191	174	
$ClSiBr_3$	579		101		288		498	159		173	
$SiBr_4$	249		90			487			137		
$TiCl_4$	389		120			≈500			140		
$BrTiCl_3$	326		105		439		508, 489	128		136	379
Br_2TiCl_2	294	87		—	462	492	401, 383	—	—	125	
$ClTiBr_3$	471		82		263		398, 388	110		123	
$TiBr_4$	235		74			393			94		
$GeCl_4$	396		132			453			172		
$BrGeCl_3$	309		116		417		450	160		—	
Br_2GeCl_2	281	94		—	420	444	338	146	155	—	308
$ClGeBr_3$	428		90		257		330	122		137	
$GeBr_4$	235		80			327			112		

Some of the band assignments given here were made by the author on an empirical basis and, accordingly, are subject to change.

(369–377); $SiX_{4-n}Y_n$ (X, Y: halogens) (308, 378); $GeH_{4-n}X_n$ (307, 380–383*a*); $GeX_{n-4}Y_n$ (306, 384–387); $SnX_{4-n}Y_n$ (308, 310); $[BClF_3]^-$ (323); TiX_3Y (388).

Tables II-28*a* and II-28*b* list the fundamental frequencies of compounds

TABLE II-28*a*. VIBRATIONAL FREQUENCIES OF ZXY_3 MOLECULES (CM^{-1})

Molecule (ZXY_3)	$\nu_1(A_1)$ $\nu(XY_3)$	$\nu_2(A_1)$ $\nu(XZ)$	$\nu_3(A_1)$ $\delta(XY_3)$	$\nu_4(E)$ $\nu(XY)_3$	$\nu_5(E)$ $\delta(XY_3)$	$\nu_6(E)$ $\rho_r(XY_3)$	References
$FClO_3$	1061	715	549	1315	589	405	389–391
$[SSO_3]^{2-}$	995	669	446	1123	541	335	328, 392
$[FSO_3]^-$	1082	786	566	1287	592	409	393, 394
$[ClCrO_3]^-$	907	438	295	954	365	209	401*b*
$[NOsO_3]^-$	897	1021	309	871	309	372	401*c*, 395
$ClReO_3$	1001	293	435	960	344	196	401*a*
$BrReO_3$	997	195	350	963	332	168	401*a*
$OVCl_3$	408	1035	165	504	249	129	396
$OVBr_3$	271	1025	120	400	83	212	151*a*
OPF_3	873	1415	473	900	485	345	397
$OPCl_3$	486	1290	267	581	337	193	398
$OPBr_3$	340	1261	173	488	267	118	399, 398
SPF_3	695	847	440	940	402	276	400
$SPCl_3$	435	753	250	542	250	167	401
$SPBr_3$	299	718	165	438	179	115	400

TABLE II-28*b*. VIBRATIONAL FREQUENCIES OF Z_2XY_2 MOLECULES (CM^{-1})

Molecule (Z_2XY_2)	$\nu_1(A_1)$ $\nu(XY)$	$\nu_2(A_1)$ $\nu(XZ)$	$\nu_3(A_1)$ $\delta(YXY)$	$\nu_4(A_1)$ $\delta(ZXZ)$	$\nu_5(A_2)$ $\rho_t(XY_2)$	$\nu_6(B_1)$ $\nu(XY)$	$\nu_7(B_1)$ $\rho_w(XY_2)$	$\nu_8(B_2)$ $\nu(XZ)$	$\nu_9(B_2)$ $\rho_r(XY_2)$	References
O_2SF_2	848	1269	544	545	360	885	545	1502	386	403*a*, 403, 402
O_2SCl_2	405	1182	218	560	388	362	380	1414	282	404, 405
O_2CrF_2	727	1006	(182)	304	(422)	789	(259)	1016	274	406
O_2CrCl_2	465	984	144	357	216	497	263	994	230	407, 408

containing oxygen and sulfur atoms. The *vanadyl group* (VO^{2+}), like the uranyl group, forms a number of chelate compounds with organic ligands such as acetylacetone. In all these complexes, the V=O stretching band is observed between 1050 and 950 cm^{-1}. The stretching vibrations of other metal-oxygen double bonds such as U=O and Mo=O[409] and Ru=O[409a] also appear in a similar frequency range. For other compounds only some references are given: $OAsF_3$ (409*b*); $FCrO_3$, $ClCrO_3$ (410); $[SPO_3]^-$ (410*a*); O_2SBrF (411); Cl_2POF, ClBrPOF and Br_2POF (412); Cl_2POBr and Br_2POCl (398); O_2CrFCl (413).

Normal coordinate analyses of tetrahedral XY_4, ZXY_3 and Z_2XY_2 molecules are common. References for some of these theoretical investigations are: XY_4 (414–418); ZXY_3 (419–424*a*).

(3) Square-Planar XY_4 Molecules (D_{4h})

Figure II-20 shows the seven normal modes of vibration of a square-planar XY_4 molecule. ν_3, ν_6 and ν_7 are infrared active, whereas ν_1, ν_2 and ν_4 are Raman active.

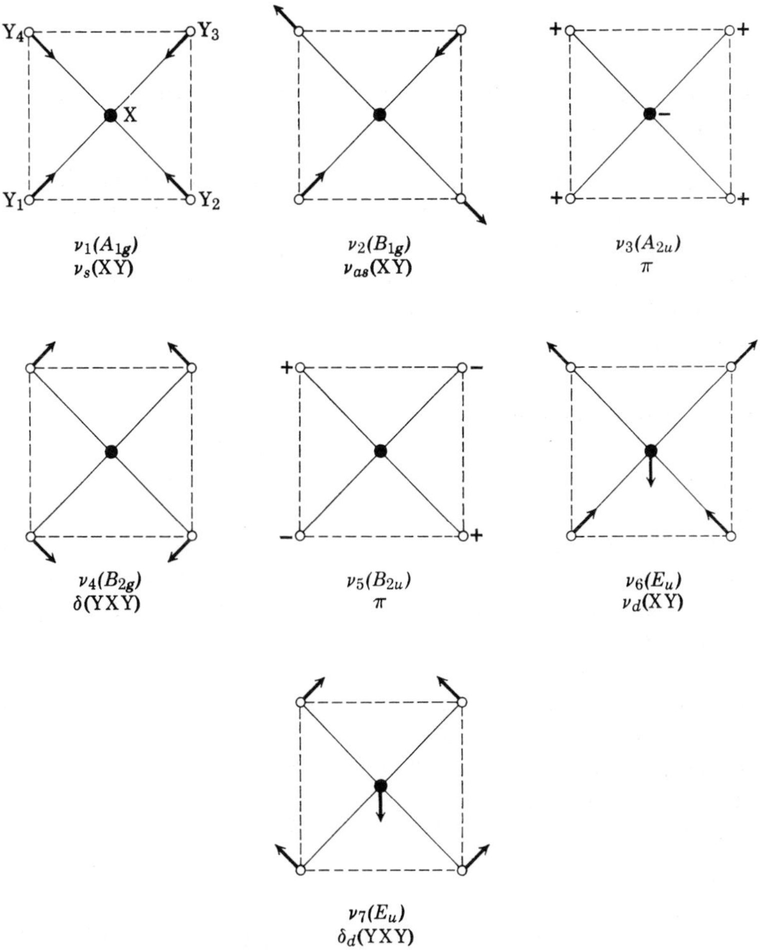

Fig. II-20. Normal modes of vibration of square-planar XY_4 molecules.

Table II-29 gives the observed Raman frequencies for some ions of this type. For normal coordinate analyses, see Refs. 425 and 427.

TABLE II-29. RAMAN FREQUENCIES OF SQUARE-PLANAR XY_4 MOLECULES (CM^{-1})

Ion	ν_1	ν_2	ν_4	References
$[ICl_4]^-$	288	128	261	425
$[AuCl_4]^-$	347	171	324	425, 426
$[AuBr_4]^-$	212	102	196	425
$[PtCl_4]^{2-}$	335	164	304	425

II-9. PHOSPHORUS AND SULFUR COMPOUNDS OF VARIOUS STRUCTURES

In addition to the phosphorus and sulfur compounds mentioned in previous sections, there are many more compounds of these elements and most of them contain tetrahedral phosphorus or sulfur. The band assignments given here are somewhat unreliable compared with those given in other sections, because most of the references provide only the observed frequencies or empirical band assignments.

(1) Phosphorus Compounds

From the measurements of infrared spectra of about sixty salts of phosphorus oxy-acids, Corbridge and Lowe[428] have made a chart of the characteristic absorptions of phosphorus compounds. The group frequency chart in Fig. II-21 is based on references cited in this book. In using a chart of this type, care must be taken because the frequency ranges are affected by many factors, such as the bond order, the nature of coupling with other modes, the kind of cation and the effect of hydrogen bonding in the crystalline state.

For individual molecules, only the references are given: P_4 (429–432); P_2H_4 (432, 432*a*); P_4O_6 (433); P_4O_{10} (434); $[P_2O_6]^{4-}$ and $[H_2P_2O_6]^{2-}$ (435, 435*a*); $[HP_2O_5]^{3-}$ (436); $[P_2O_7]^{4-}$ (435*a*, 437, 438); $[P_2O_8]^{4-}$ (439); $[P_3O_9]^{3-}$ (440–442); $[P_4O_{12}]^{4-}$ (443–444); $P_4O_6S_4$ (445); P_4S_3 (446); $(NH_2)_3PO$ (447); HPO_3NH_3 (447*a*); $[PNF_2]_n$ (447*b*, 447*c*).

(2) Sulfur Compounds

Simon and Kriegsmann[448] and Siebert[449] have made extensive studies of the vibrational spectra of sulfur compounds. Figure II-22 gives a group frequency chart obtained from the references appearing in this book. For individual molecules, only the references are listed: S_8 (450–453); $[S_2O_4]^{2-}$ (454); $[S_2O_5]^{2-}$ (455–457); $[SO_5]^{2-}$ (458); $[S_2O_6]^{2-}$ (435*a*);

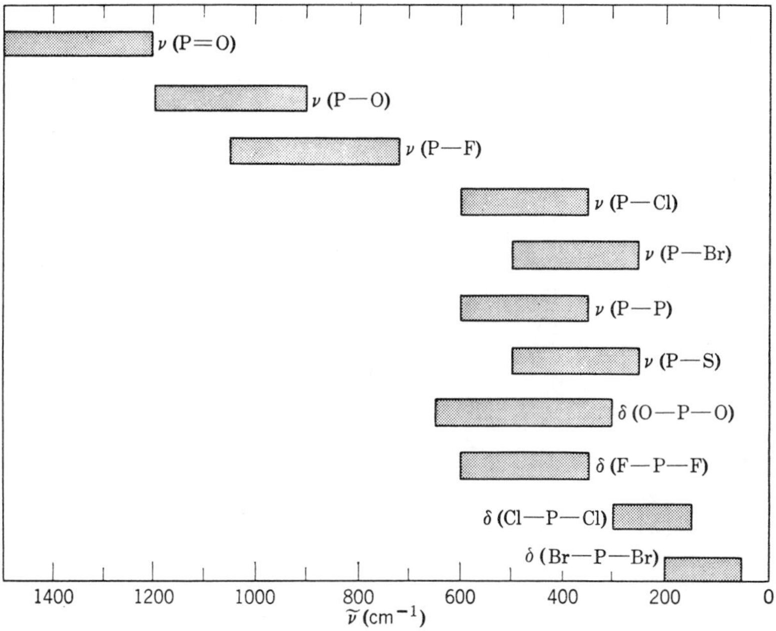

Fig. II-21. Characteristic frequencies of phosphorus compounds.

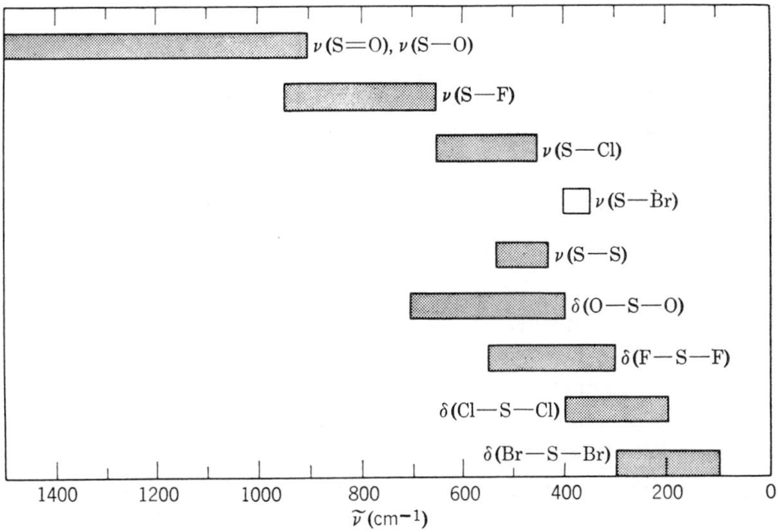

Fig. II-22. Characteristic frequencies of sulfur compounds.

$[S_2O_8]^{2-}$ (459); $[S_3O_6]^{2-}$ (460); $S_2O_5F_2$ and $S_2O_5Cl_2$ (461, 461*a*, 461*b*); $S_2O_6F_2$ (462); $S_3O_8F_2$ and $S_3O_8Cl_2$ (461*a*, 461*b*); S_2O_2 (463); $NH_3^+—SO_3^-$ (sulfamic acid) (464–466); $NH_3^+—OSO_3^-$ (467); N_4S_4 (468–469); $H_4N_4S_4$ (468); SNF, $S(NF)_2$ and SNF_3 (470, 470*a*); S_2F_{10} (471, 472).

II-10. XY_5, XY_6 AND XY_7 MOLECULES

(1) XY_5 Molecules ($\mathbf{D}_{3h}$ or $\mathbf{C}_{4v}$)

An XY_5 molecule may be a trigonal bipyramid ($\mathbf{D}_{3h}$) or a tetragonal pyramid ($\mathbf{C}_{4v}$). If it is trigonal bipyramidal, six of the eight normal

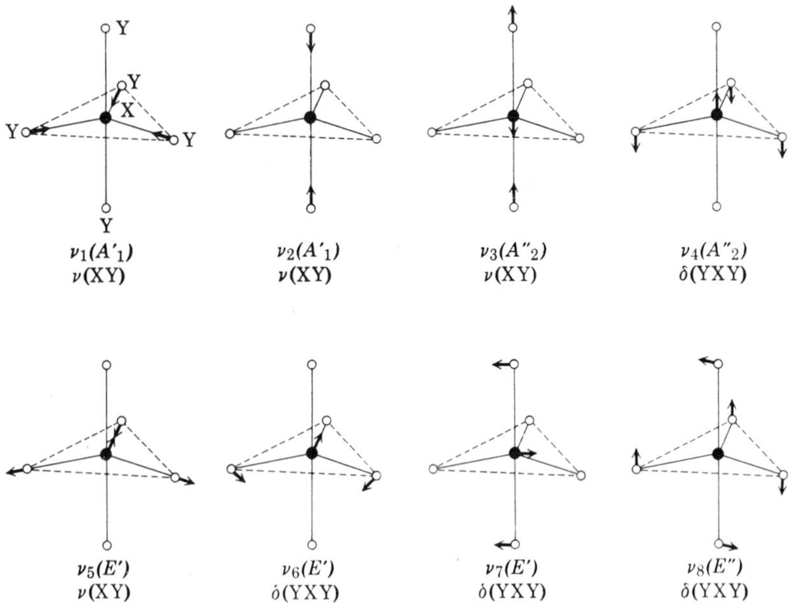

Fig. II-23. Normal modes of vibration of trigonal bipyramidal XY_5 molecules.[474]

vibrations (A_1', E' and E'') are Raman active, and five (A_2'' and E') are infrared active. If it is tetragonal pyramidal, all nine vibrations are Raman active, but only six (A_1 and E) are infrared active. Thus it is possible to distinguish between these two configurations through the infrared and Raman spectra.

Figure II-23 shows the eight normal modes of vibration of an XY_5 molecule having a trigonal bipyramidal structure. Table II-30 lists the observed fundamental frequencies of this type of molecule. It is interesting to note that in the gaseous and liquid states *phosphorus pentachloride* (PCl_5) exists as a trigonal bipyramidal molecule, whereas in the crystalline state it has an ionic structure consisting of $[PCl_4]^+[PCl_6]^-$ units. Gerding and Houtgraaf[480] have confirmed this structure from the Raman spectrum of crystalline PCl_5. The tetrahedral $[PCl_4]^+$ ion exhibits four Raman lines at 627, 451, 244 and 173 cm^{-1}, whereas the octahedral $[PCl_6]^-$ ion exhibits

TABLE II-30. VIBRATIONAL FREQUENCIES OF TRIGONAL BIPYRAMIDAL XY_5 MOLECULES (CM^{-1})

Molecule		ν_1	ν_2	ν_3	ν_4	ν_5	ν_6	ν_7	ν_8	References
PCl_5	IR	—	—	459 465 471	(176)	592	—	331 335 338	—	473, 468
	R	394	394	—	—	585	100	338	280	473, 474
$SbCl_5$	R	356	307	—	—	399	74	182	166	310*a*, 475
$NbCl_5$	R	412	355	—	—	497	153	396	106	476
SbF_5	R	667	264	—	—	716	90	491	228	477
PF_5	IR	—	—	938 948 957	565 576 585	1025	534	?	—	478, 479

three Raman lines at 358, 285 and 244 cm^{-1}, in agreement with theoretical predictions. Normal coordinate analyses for $\mathbf{D}_{3h}$-type molecules have been made by Ziomek and Mast[481] and Haarhoff and Pistorius.[482] In addition

TABLE II-31. VIBRATIONAL FREQUENCIES OF TETRAGONAL PYRAMIDAL XY_5 MOLECULES (CM^{-1})

Molecule		$\nu_1(A_1)$	$\nu_2(A_1)$	$\nu_3(A_1)$	$\nu_4(B_1)$	$\nu_5(B_1)$	$\nu_6(B_2)$	$\nu_7(E)$	$\nu_8(E)$	$\nu_9(E)$	References
BrF_5	R	683	572	365	536	315	481	626	415	244	490–492
	IR	690	583	—	—	—	—	645	418	—	491
IF_5	R	710	693	317	605	275	572	?	375	192	493
	IR	721	712 703	318	—	—	—	645	372	—	493

to the compounds listed in Table II-30, the $\mathbf{D}_{3h}$ structure has been reported for $MoCl_5$,[483] $NbCl_5$, $TaCl_5$ and others[484] in the gaseous state. In the crystalline state, however, $MoCl_5$[485] and $NbCl_5$[486] are dimerized through two chlorine bridges.

Tetragonal pyramidal XY_5 molecules are rare. So far this kind of structure has been reported for BrF_5, IF_5,[487] $[SbF_5]^{2-}$ [488] and $[SbCl_5]^{2-}$.[489] Table II-31 lists the fundamental frequencies observed for the first two of these molecules. Stephenson and Jones[490] have made a normal coordinate analysis of BrF_5.

(2) Octahedral XY_6 Molecules (O_h)

Figure II-24 indicates the six normal modes of vibration of an octahedral XY_6 molecule. ν_1, ν_2 and ν_5 are Raman active, whereas only ν_3 and ν_4 are

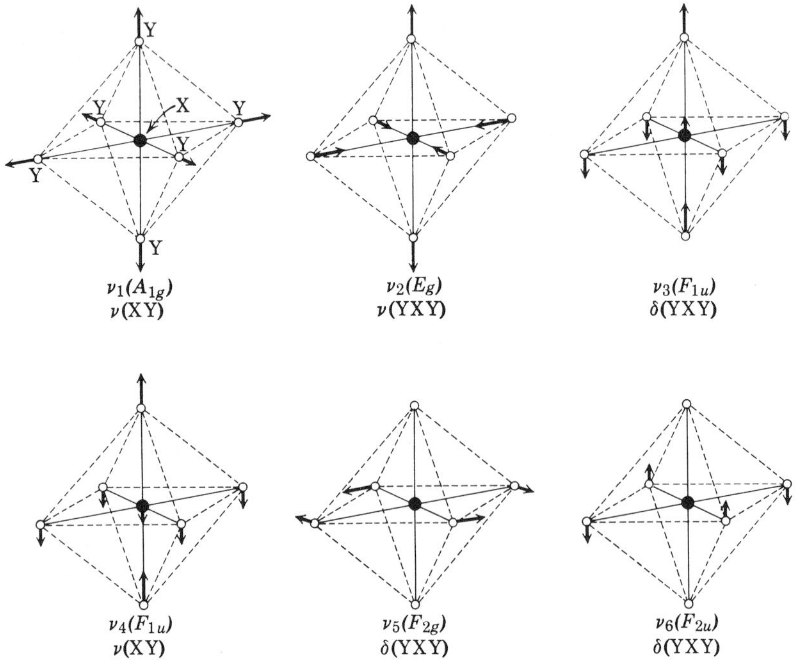

Fig. II-24. Normal modes of vibration of octahedral XY_6 molecules.

infrared active. Table II-32 gives the fundamental frequencies of molecules of this type. For $[AlF_6]^{3-}$, $[IO_6]^{5-}$ and $[TeO_6]^{6-}$, see Refs. 514, 515 and 516, respectively. Normal coordinate analyses for octahedral XY_6 molecules have been made by many investigators (Refs. 517–521). A spectrum of an XY_5Z molecule was first obtained by Cross et al[522] for SF_5Cl. Peacock and co-workers[522a] have measured the infrared spectra of a number of complex fluoroacid salts. Although a planar XY_6 molecule (D_{6h}) has not yet been found, Pistorius[523] has carried out a normal coordinate analysis of it.

TABLE II-32. VIBRATIONAL FREQUENCIES OF OCTAHEDRAL XY_6 MOLECULES (CM^{-1})

Molecule	ν_1	ν_2	ν_3	ν_4	ν_5	ν_6	References
SF_6	775	644	940	615	524	363	494–497
SeF_6	708	662	780	437	405	260	498, 499
TeF_6	701	674	752	327	313	197	498–500
MoF_6	741	643	741	264	306	190	503*a*, 503, 501
WF_6	769	670	712	256	322	216	501, 503
TcF_6	705	551	748	265	255	—	503*a*
ReF_6	755	596	715	257	246	193	504*a*, 504
OsF_6	733	632	720	268	252	230	505
IrF_6	696	643	718	276	260	205	506
PtF_6	655	601	705	273	242	211	505
UF_6	668	532	626	189	202	144	498, 501, 507
NpF_6	648	528	624	200	206	164	508
PuF_6	625	522	617	205	211	176	509, 510
$[SiF_6]^{2-}$	656	—	—	—	—	—	511
$[PF_6]^-$	741	—	—	—	—	—	511
$[TiCl_6]^{2-}$	463	340	—	—	252	—	512
$[SeCl_6]^{2-}$	346	273	—	—	166	—	273
$[SnCl_6]^{2-}$	311	229	—	—	158	—	513
$[SbCl_6]^-$	337	277	—	—	172	—	271
$[SnBr_6]^{2-}$	185	138	—	—	95	—	513
$[PtCl_6]^{2-}$	344	320	—	—	162	—	513*a*
$[PtBr_6]^{2-}$	207	190	—	—	97	—	513*a*
$[PdCl_6]^{2-}$	317	292	—	—	164	—	513*a*

(3) XY_7 Molecules ($\mathbf{D}_{5h}$)

Molecules of this type are very rare. Lord and colleagues[493] have studied the infrared and Raman spectra of the IF_7 molecule. If it is pentagonal bipyramidal ($\mathbf{D}_{5h}$), five vibrations should be Raman active and five should be infrared active. In fact, this structure for IF_7 was confirmed through these vibrations: Raman—678 (A_1'), 635 (A_1'), 360 (E_1''), 511 (E_2') and 313 (E_2') cm^{-1}; infrared—670 (A_2''), 368 (A_2''), 547 (E_1'), 426 (E_1') and 250 (E_1') cm^{-1}. The same conclusion has been obtained by nuclear magnetic resonance[487] and electron diffraction[524] studies of this molecule. Recently Khanna[524a] made a normal coordinate analysis of IF_7. The $\mathbf{D}_{5h}$ structure has also been reported for the $[UF_7]^{3-}$ ion in the crystalline state.[525]

No spectral data are yet available for the $[ZrF_7]^{3-}$ ion[526] or for the $[NbF_7]^{2-}$ and $[TaF_7]^{2-}$ ions,[527] which are less symmetrical than the $\mathbf{D}_{5h}$ structure.

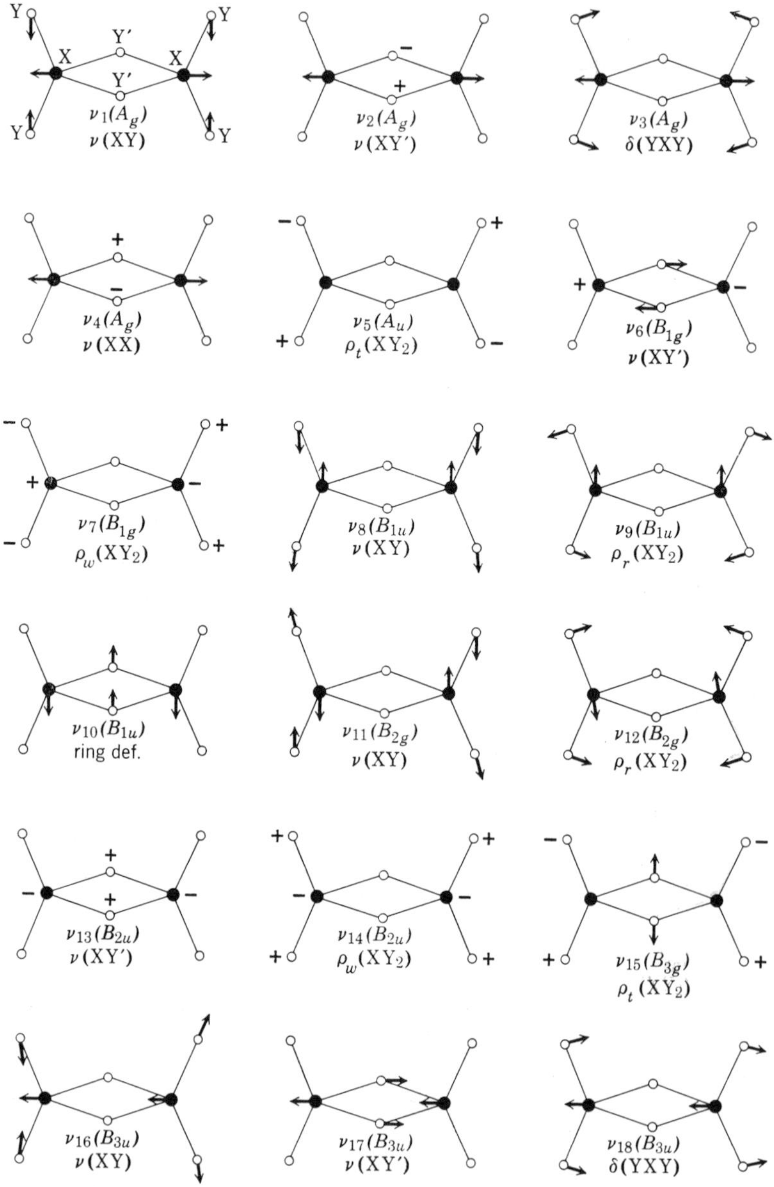

Fig. II-25. Normal modes of vibration of bridged X_2Y_6 molecules.[528]

II-11. X_2Y_6, X_2Y_7 AND XY_8 MOLECULES

(1) Bridged X_2Y_6 Molecules (V_h)

Figure II-25 indicates the eighteen normal modes of vibration[528] and band assignments for a bridged X_2Y_6 molecule. The vibrations of the A_g, B_{1g}, B_{2g} and B_{3g} species are Raman active, whereas those of the B_{1u}, B_{2u} and B_{3u} species are infrared active. Table II-33 lists the fundamental

TABLE II-33. VIBRATIONAL FREQUENCIES OF BRIDGED X_2Y_6 MOLECULES (CM^{-1})

	B_2H_6[a]	B_2D_6[b]	Al_2Cl_6[c]	Al_2Br_6[d]	Al_2I_6[d]
ν_1	2524	1850	506	491	406
ν_2	2104	1500	340	204	146
ν_3	1180	915	217	140	94
ν_4	794	700	112	73	53
ν_5	(829)	(592)	(75)	—	—
ν_6	1768	1270	438	(291)	(195)
ν_7	(1035)	(860)	164	176	—
ν_8	2612	1985	625	—	—
ν_9	(950)	730	(202)	—	—
ν_{10}	368	250	—	—	—
ν_{11}	2591	1975	606	407	344
ν_{12}	(920)	(725)	154	112	—
ν_{13}	1915	1460	420	—	—
ν_{14}	973	720	—	—	—
ν_{15}	1012	730	160	—	—
ν_{16}	2525	1840	484	—	—
ν_{17}	1606	1199	(301)	—	—
ν_{18}	1177	876	(177)	—	—

[a] Refs. 529–531.
[b] Refs. 529, 532, 533.
[c] Refs. 534–536,
[d] Refs. 535–536.

frequencies of five molecules of this type. The bridged XY′ stretching frequencies (ν_2, ν_6, ν_{13} and ν_{17}) are always lower than the terminal XY stretching frequencies (ν_1, ν_8, ν_{11} and ν_{16}) in these compounds. *Aluminum chloride* exists as a dimer in the gaseous and liquid phases, whereas it consists of an $[AlCl_6]^{3-}$ unit in the crystalline state. *Gallium chloride* exists as a dimer even in the solid state.[537] For the dimer of $FeCl_3$, see Ref. 310*a*. A normal coordinate analysis of B_2H_6 has been done by Brown and Longuet-Higgins[538] and by Venkateswarlu and Thirugnanasambandam.[539]

A number of boron compounds have unusual structures. Only the references are cited for these compounds: $M(BH_4)$ (540); B_5H_9 (541, 542); $B_{10}H_{14}$ (543); $B_3H_3N_3$ (borazole) (544); B_2O_2 and B_2O_3 (545); HBO_2 (546); B_2Cl_4 (547, 548); and B_2S_3 (549).

(2) Ethane-Type X_2Y_6 Molecules

The conformation of ethane-type molecules may be staggered ($\mathbf{D}_{3d}$) or eclipsed ($\mathbf{D}_{3h}$). The twelve normal modes of vibration of the staggered

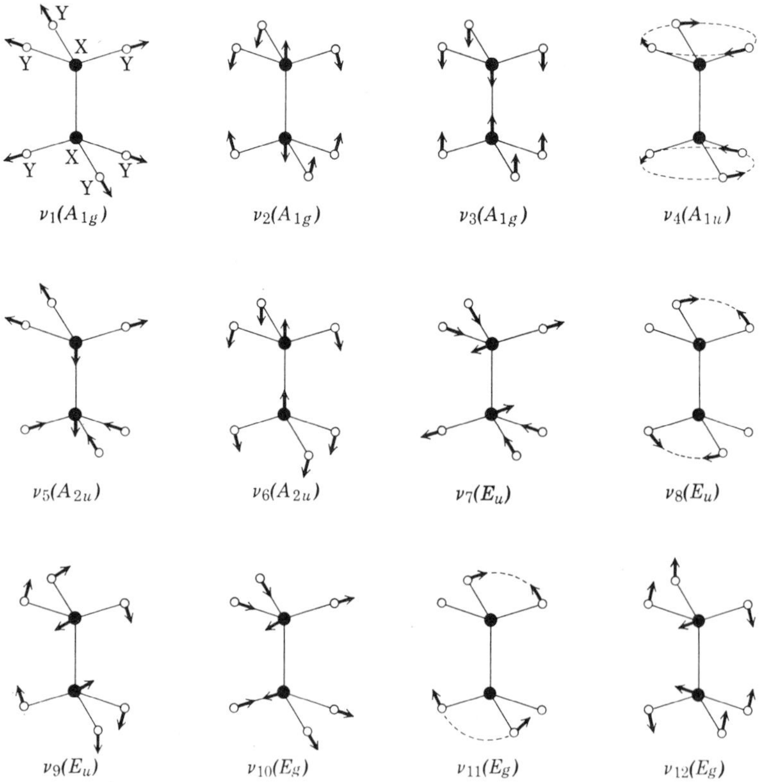

Fig. II-26. Normal modes of vibration of ethane-type X_2Y_6 molecules.

molecule are illustrated in Fig. II-26. The vibrations of the A_{1g} and E_g species are Raman active, and those of the A_{2u} and E_u species are infrared active. Table II-34 gives the fundamental frequencies and band assignments based on $\mathbf{D}_{3d}$ symmetry.

A large number of references on silicon compounds are available. Most of these compounds have rather complicated structures which have not been included in the preceding sections. References are given here for some of them. *Disiloxane*, $(H_3Si)_2O$, has been studied by Lord et al.,[555] Curl and Pitzer[556] and McKean.[557] It was found that the Si—O—Si angle of this compound differs slightly from 180°. *Disilyl sulfide*, $(H_3Si)_2S$, has been studied by Linton et al.[558] and Ebsworth et al.[559] The Si—S—Si angle is expected to be near 100°. Robinson[560] and Kriegsmann and Forster[561] have shown that the spectrum of *trisilylamine*, $(H_3Si)_3N$, can be explained by using a trigonal planar model. For a correlation between the Si—H stretching frequency and the inductive effect or the structure, see Ref. 562 or 563.

TABLE II-34. VIBRATIONAL FREQUENCIES OF ETHANE-TYPE X_2Y_6 MOLECULES (CM^{-1})

Molecule	C_2H_6[a]	C_2D_6[a]	Si_2H_6[b]	Si_2D_6[c]	Ge_2H_6[d]
ν_1 $\nu(XY)$	2899	2083	2152	1548	(2070)
ν_2 $\delta(XY_3)$	(1375)	1158	909	683	765
ν_3 $\nu(XX)$	993	852	434	408	229
ν_4 $\rho_t(XY_3)$	275	200	—	—	144
ν_5 $\nu(XY)$	2954	2111	2154	1549	2078
ν_6 $\delta(XY_3)$	1379	1072	844	625	755
ν_7 $\nu(XY)$	2994	2236	2179	1585	2114
ν_8 $\delta(XY_3)$	1486	1102	940	683	898
ν_9 $\rho_r(XY_3)$	821	601	379	277	407
ν_{10} $\nu(XY)$	2963	2225	2155	1569	2150
ν_{11} $\delta(XY_3)$	1460	1055	929	667	875
ν_{12} $\rho_r(XY_3)$	(1155)	970	625	475	417

[a] Refs. 550, 551.
[b] Refs. 552, 553.
[c] Ref. 552.
[d] Ref. 554.

(3) X_2Y_7 Molecules

Ions such as $[S_2O_7]^{2-}$, $[Se_2O_7]^{2-}$, $[Si_2O_7]^{2-}$, $[As_2O_7]^{4-}$, $[Cr_2O_7]^{2-}$ and $[Mn_2O_7]^{2-}$ belong to the $Y_3X—Y—XY_3$ type. Although a normal coordinate analysis has not yet been done for this type, Stammreich et al.[564] and Simon and Wagner[564a] have made empirical band assignments for the spectra of the $[Cr_2O_7]^{2-}$ and $[S_2O_7]^{2-}$ ions, respectively, based on $\mathbf{C}_{2v}$ symmetry.

(4) XY_8 Molecules

The XY_8 molecule may take the form of (I) a cube ($\mathbf{O}_h$), (II) an Archimedean antiprism ($\mathbf{D}_{4h}$), (III) a dodecahedron ($\mathbf{D}_{2d}$) or (IV) a face-centered trigonal prism ($\mathbf{C}_{2v}$). Although XY_8 molecules are rare, x-ray analysis indicates that the $[TaF_8]^{3-}$ and $[CrO_8]^{3-}$ ions have structures II and III, respectively.[565,566] Recently, Weinstock and Malm[567] have shown that the compound previously suggested to be OsF_8 is OsF_6. Dove[567a] has shown from infrared and x-ray studies that the compounds of the type $M_3{}^{I}HM^{IV}F_8$ (M^I = Na, K; M^{IV} = Nb, Pb, Ti, Sn) consist of M^{I+}, $[M^{IV}F_6]^{2-}$ and $[HF_2]^-$ ions in the crystalline state. Little work has been done on the vibrational spectra of XY_8 molecules. Pistorius[568] has calculated the G and F matrix elements for a cubic XY_8 molecule.

The infrared spectra of the $[Mo(CN)_8]^{4-}$ and $[W(CN)_8]^{4-}$ ions have been obtained (see Table III-10). Stammreich and Sala (Ref. 88 of Part III) have studied the Raman spectrum of the $[Mo(CN)_8]^{4-}$ ion and have suggested structure II, although structure III was found in the crystalline state.[569]

II-12. MINERALS

A large amount of literature on the vibrational spectra of minerals is available. Some of these investigations are classified here, and only the references are given for each group.

(1) Theoretical Analysis

Vibrational spectra of minerals which occur as *giant molecules* can be investigated by using the method of factor group analysis.[195,203] Minerals which do not occur as giant molecules can be studied by using the method of site group analysis.[202] Some references are: α-quartz (570); β-quartz (571); silicon carbide (572); rutile (573); and silicates (574–574*b*).

(2) Location of the Position of Hydrogen through Measurement of Infrared Dichroism

The position of hydrogen is rather difficult to determine from x-ray analysis. Studies of the infrared dichroism of, for example, the OH stretching band is useful in the elucidation of the orientation of the OH bond in minerals. Some references are: muscovite (575); afwillite (576); and silicates (577).

(3) Identification of Minerals

The differences in the spectra of calcite and aragonite have been discussed in Sec. II-5. Minerals having different crystal structures (modifications) can be distinguished by means of their spectra. Some references are: diamonds (578, 578*a*); silicas (579–582); carbonates (583–584); hydrated aluminas (585); micas (586–587); serpentine minerals (588); and talcs (589). For a collection of infrared spectra of various minerals, see Ref. 590.

(4) Infrared Reflection Spectra

The reflection method is useful in obtaining the infrared spectra of minerals. Reflection spectra have been obtained for silicas (591, 592), carborundum (593) and titanates (594).

References

1. S. A. Rice and W. Klemperer, *J. Chem. Phys.*, **27,** 573 (1957); W. Klemperer and S. A. Rice, *ibid.*, **26,** 618 (1957); W. Klemperer, W. G. Norris, A. Büchler and A. G. Emslie, *ibid.*, **33,** 1534 (1960); W. Klemperer and W. G. Norris, *ibid.*, **34,** 1071 (1961).
2. D. F. Smith, *J. Chem. Phys.*, **28,** 1040 (1958).
3. R. M. Adams and J. J. Katz, *J. Opt. Soc. Am.*, **46,** 895 (1956).
4. P. A. Giguère and N. Zengin, *Can. J. Chem.*, **36,** 1013 (1958).
5. D. F. Hornig and W. E. Osberg, *J. Chem. Phys.*, **23,** 662 (1955); G. L. Hiebert and D. F. Hornig, *ibid.*, **28,** 316 (1958).
6. M. L. Josien, G. Sourisseau and C. Castinel, *Bull. soc. chim. France*, **1955,** 1539; M. L. Josien and G. Sourisseau, *ibid.*, **1955,** 178; P. Grange, J. Lascombe and M. L. Josien, *Spectrochim. Acta*, **16,** 981 (1960).
7. J. Berkowitz, *J. Chem. Phys.*, **29,** 1386 (1958); **32,** 1519 (1960).
8. A. L. Smith, W. E. Keller and H. L. Johnston, *J. Chem. Phys.*, **19,** 189 (1951).
9. W. G. Fateley, H. A. Bent and B. L. Crawford, *J. Chem. Phys.*, **31,** 204 (1959).
10. D. J. Millen and D. Watson, *J. Chem. Soc.*, **1957,** 1369; J. D. S. Goulden and D. J. Millen, *ibid.*, **1950,** 2620.
11. W. B. Person, R. E. Humphrey, W. A. Deskin and A. I. Popov, *J. Am. Chem. Soc.*, **80,** 2049 (1958); W. B. Person, R. E. Erickson and R. E. Buckes, *ibid.*, **82,** 29 (1960); A. I. Popov, R. E. Humphrey and W. B. Person, *ibid.*, **82,** 1850 (1960).
12. W. D. Stalleup and D. Williams, *J. Chem. Phys.*, **10,** 199 (1942).
13. R. A. Penneman and L. H. Jones, *J. Chem. Phys.*, **24,** 293 (1956).
14. R. A. Penneman and L. H. Jones, *J. Chem. Phys.*, **28,** 169 (1958).
15. J. Goubeau, H. Haeberle and H. Ulmer, *Z. anorg. u. allgem. Chem.*, **311,** 110 (1961).
15*a*. J. Guy and M. Chaigneau, *Bull. soc. chim. France*, **1956,** 257.
16. A. Langseth and C. K. Møller, *Acta. Chem. Scand.*, **4,** 725 (1950); *Nature*, **166,** 147 (1950).
17. L. H. Jones, *J. Chem. Phys.*, **22,** 217 (1954).
18. K. A. Wickersheim, *J. Chem. Phys.*, **31,** 863 (1959).
18*a*. R. M. Hexter, *J. Chem. Phys.*, **34,** 941 (1961).
19. E. Drouard, *Compt. rend.*, **249,** 665 (1959); **247,** 68 (1958).
20. W. R. Busing, *J. Chem. Phys.*, **23,** 933 (1955).
21. J. A. Ibers, J. Kumamoto and R. G. Snyder, *J. Chem. Phys.*, **33,** 1164 (1960); R. G. Snyder, J. Kumamoto and J. A. Ibers, *ibid.*, **33,** 1171 (1960).
22. R. A. Buchanan, *J. Chem. Phys.*, **31,** 870 (1959).
23. W. R. Busing and H. W. Morgan, *J. Chem. Phys.*, **28,** 998 (1958).

24. R. M. Hexter, *J. Opt. Soc. Am.*, **48,** 770 (1958).
25. H. A. Benesi, *J. Chem. Phys.*, **30,** 852 (1959).
26. R. T. Mara and G. B. B. M. Sutherland, *J. Opt. Soc. Am.*, **43,** 1100 (1953).
27. B. A. Phillips and W. R. Busing, *J. Phys. Chem.*, **61,** 502 (1957).
28. C. Duval and J. Lecomte, *Bull. soc. chim. France*, **8,** 713 (1941).
29. C. Cabannes-Ott, *Compt. rend.*, **242,** 355 (1956).
30. D. Krishnamurti, *Proc. Indian Acad. Sci.*, **50A,** 223 (1959).
31. C. Cabannes-Ott, *Compt. rend.*, **242,** 2825 (1956).
32. R. West and R. H. Baney, *J. Phys. Chem.*, **64,** 822 (1960).
33. A. V. Stuart and G. B. B. M. Sutherland, *J. Chem. Phys.*, **24,** 559 (1956).
33*a*. M. Falk and E. Whalley, *J. Chem. Phys.*, **34,** 1554 (1961).
34. O. Glemser and E. Hartert, *Naturwiss.*, **40,** 552 (1953).
35. O. Glemser, *Nature*, **183,** 1476 (1959).
36. V. A. Kolesov and Y. I. Ryskin, *Optika i Spektroskopiya*, **7,** 261 (1959).
37. T. Dupuis, *Rec. trav. chim.*, **79,** 518 (1960).
38. D. E. Bethell and N. Sheppard, *Trans. Faraday Soc.*, **51,** 9 (1955).
39. P. Natalis, *Ann. soc. sci. Bruxelles, Sér. I*, **73,** 261 (1959).
40. E. Hartert and O. Glemser, *Z. Elektrochem.*, **60,** 746 (1956).
41. R. L. Williams and R. J. Page, *J. Chem. Soc.*, **1957,** 4143.
42. J. H. Taylor, W. S. Benedict and J. Strong, *J. Chem. Phys.*, **20,** 1884 (1952).
43. W. E. Osberg and D. F. Hornig, *J. Chem. Phys.*, **20,** 1345 (1952).
43*a*. M. E. Jacox and D. E. Milligan, *Spectrochim. Acta*, **17**, 1196 (1961).
44. L. H. Jones and E. McLaren, *J. Chem. Phys.*, **28,** 995 (1958).
45. A. H. Nielsen and R. T. Lagemann, *J. Chem. Phys.*, **22,** 36 (1954).
46. T. Wentink, *J. Chem. Phys.* **29,** 188 (1958).
47. W. Klemperer and L. Lindeman, *J. Chem. Phys.* **25,** 397 (1956); W. Klemperer, *ibid.*, **25,** 1066 (1956).
48. P. Gray and T. C. Waddington, *Trans. Faraday Soc.*, **53,** 901 (1957).
48*a*. H. A. Papazian, *J. Chem. Phys.*, **34,** 1614 (1961).
49. D. A. Dows, E. Whittle and G. C. Pimentel, *J. Chem. Phys.*, **23,** 1475 (1955); D. A. Dows, G. C. Pimentel and E. Whittle, *ibid.*, **23,** 1606 (1955); D. E. Milligan, H. W. Brown and G. C. Pimentel, *ibid.*, **25,** 1080 (1956).
50. L. H. Jones and R. A. Penneman, *J. Chem. Phys.*, **22,** 781 (1954); R. Newman and R. M. Badger, *ibid.*, **19,** 1207 (1951).
51. T. C. Waddington, *J. Chem. Soc.*, **1958,** 1708.
52. R. A. Marcus and J. M. Fresco, *J. Chem. Phys.*, **27,** 564 (1957).
53. S. K. Deb and A. D. Yoffe, *Trans. Faraday Soc.*, **55,** 106 (1959).
54. G. K. T. Conn and C. K. Wu, *Trans. Faraday Soc.*, **34,** 1483 (1938).
55. D. A. Long, F. S. Murfin and R. L. Williams, *Proc. Roy. Soc.* (*London*), **A223,** 251 (1954).
56. H. D. Rix, *J. Chem. Phys.*, **22,** 429 (1954).
57. A. Büchler and W. Klemperer, *J. Chem. Phys.*, **29,** 121 (1958).
58. R. E. Rundle and P. H. Lewis, *J. Chem. Phys.*, **20,** 132 (1952).
59. C. K. Ingold, D. J. Millen and H. G. Poole, *Nature*, **158,** 480 (1946); *J. Chem. Soc.*, **1950,** 2576; C. K. Ingold and D. J. Millen, *ibid.*, **1950,** 2612.
60. J. Prigent, *Compt. rend.*, **247,** 1739 (1958).
61. J. Sutton, *Nature*, **169,** 235 (1952).
62. L. H. Jones and R. A. Penneman, *J. Chem. Phys.*, **21,** 542 (1953); L. H. Jones, *ibid.*, **23,** 2105 (1955).
63. L. H. Jones, *Spectrochim. Acta*, **6,** 409 (1959).

64. J. Lecomte and R. Freymann, *Bull soc. chim. France*, **8,** 622 (1941).
65. P. Jolibois, *Compt. rend.*, **217,** 426 (1943).
66. H. W. Crandall, *J. Chem. Phys.*, **17,** 602 (1949).
67. B. M. Gatehouse and A. E. Comyns, *J. Chem. Soc.*, **1958,** 3965.
68. G. L. Caldow, A. B. V. Cleave and R. L. Eager, *Can. J. Chem.*, **38,** 772 (1960).
68*a*. S. P. McGlynn, J. K. Smith and W. C. Neely, *J. Chem. Phys.*, **35,** 105 (1961).
68*b*. R. Tsuchida, *Bull. Chem. Soc. Japan*, **13,** 388, 438 (1938).
69. H. C. Allen, E. D. Tidwell and E. K. Plyler, *J. Chem. Phys.*, **25,** 302 (1956).
70. W. S. Richardson, *J. Chem. Phys.*, **19,** 1213 (1951).
71. P. A. Staats, H. W. Morgan and J. H. Goldstein, *J. Chem. Phys.*, **25,** 582 (1956).
72. R. E. Dodd and R. Little, *Spectrochim. Acta*, **16,** 1083 (1960).
72*a*. W. J. Orville-Thomas, *J. Chem. Phys.*, **20,** 920 (1952).
73. W. O. Freitag and E. R. Nixon, *J. Chem. Phys.*, **24,** 109 (1956).
74. J. Wagner, *Z. physik. Chem.*, **B48,** 309 (1941).
75. J. Wagner, *Z. physik. Chem.*, **A193,** 55 (1943).
76. W. West and M. Farnsworth, *J. Chem. Phys.*, **1,** 402 (1933).
77. G. M. Begun and W. H. Fletcher, *J. Chem. Phys.*, **28,** 414 (1958).
78. D. A. Dows, *J. Chem. Phys.*, **26,** 745 (1957).
79. H. J. Callomon, D. C. McKean and H. W. Thompson, *Proc. Roy. Soc.* (*London*), **A208,** 341 (1951).
80. P. O. Kinell and B. Strandberg, *Acta Chem. Scand.*, **13,** 1607 (1959).
81. L. H. Jones, *J. Chem. Phys.*, **25,** 1069 (1956); **28,** 1234 (1958).
81*a*. H. W. Morgan, *J. Inorg. & Nuclear Chem.*, **16,** 368 (1960).
82. A. Maki and J. C. Decius, *J. Chem. Phys.*, **31,** 772 (1959).
82*a*. T. C. Waddington, *J. Chem. Soc.*, **1959,** 2499.
83. R. L. Webb, S. Frank and W. C. Schneider, *J. Am. Chem. Soc.*, **77,** 3491 (1955).
84. T. Wadsten and S. Andersson, *Acta Chem. Scand.*, **13,** 1069 (1959).
84*a*. B. R. Penfold and W. N. Lipscomb, *Acta Cryst.*, **14,** 589 (1961).
85. W. B. Person, R. E. Humphrey, W. A. Deskin and A. I. Popov, *J. Am. Chem. Soc.*, **81,** 273 (1959).
86. F. Fehér and H. Weber, *Z. Naturforsch.*, **11b,** 426 (1956).
86*a*. R. G. R. Bacon, R. S. Irwin, J. M. Pollock and A. D. E. Pullin, *J. Chem. Soc.*, **1958,** 764.
87. M. J. Nelson and A. D. E. Pullin, *J. Chem. Soc.*, **1960,** 604.
87*a*. D. B. Sowerby, *J. Inorg. & Nuclear Chem.*, **22,** 205 (1961).
88. T. Wentink, *J. Chem. Phys.*, **30,** 105 (1959).
88*a*. W. J. Jones, W. J. Orville-Thomas and U. Opik, *J. Chem. Soc.*, **1959,** 1625.
88*b*. W. B. Person, G. R. Anderson, J. N. Fordemwalt, H. Stammreich and R. Forneris, *J. Chem. Phys.*, **35,** 908 (1961).
89. W. S. Benedict, N. Gailar and E. K. Plyler, *J. Chem. Phys.*, **24,** 1139 (1956).
90. J. H. Hibben, *J. Chem. Phys.*, **5,** 166 (1937).
91. C. Haas and D. F. Hornig, *J. Chem. Phys.*, **32,** 1763 (1960); D. F. Hornig, H. F. White and F. P. Reding, *Spectrochim. Acta*, **12,** 338 (1958).
92. G. Gompertz and W. J. Orville-Thomas, *J. Phys. Chem.*, **63,** 1331 (1959).
93. R. D. Waldron, *J. Chem. Phys.*, **26,** 809 (1957).
94. S. Pinchas and M. Halmann, *J. Chem. Phys.*, **31,** 1692 (1959).
95. P. A. Staats, H. W. Morgan and J. H. Goldstein, *J. Chem. Phys.*, **24,** 916 (1956).
96. H. C. Allen and E. K. Plyler, *J. Chem. Phys.*, **25,** 1132 (1956).
97. F. P. Reding and D. F. Hornig, *J. Chem. Phys.*, **27,** 1024 (1957).
98. A. H. Nielsen and H. H. Nielsen, *J. Chem. Phys.*, **5,** 277 (1937).

99. D. M. Cameron, W. C. Sears and H. H. Nielsen, *J. Chem. Phys.*, **7,** 994 (1939).
100. M. K. Wilson and R. M. Badger, *J. Chem. Phys.*, **16,** 741 (1948).
101 H. J. Bernstein and J. Powling, *J. Chem. Phys.*, **18,** 685 (1950).
102. K. Hedberg, *J. Chem. Phys.*, **19,** 509 (1951).
103. A. H. Nielsen and P. J. H. Woltz, *J. Chem. Phys.*, **20,** 1878 (1952).
104. J. P. Mathieu, *Compt. rend.*, **234,** 2272 (1952).
105. E. T. Arakawa and A. H. Nielsen, *J. Mol. Spectroscopy*, **2,** 413 (1958).
106. R. E. Weston and T. F. Brodasky, *J. Chem. Phys.*, **27,** 683 (1957).
107. R. D. Shelton, A. H. Nielsen and W. H. Fletcher, *J. Chem. Phys.*, **21,** 2178 (1953).
108. R. N. Wiener and E. R. Nixon, *J. Chem. Phys.*, **25,** 175 (1956).
109. S. R. Polo and M. K. Wilson, *J. Chem. Phys.*, **22,** 900 (1954).
110. P. A. Giguère and M. Falk, *Spectrochim. Acta*, **16,** 1 (1960).
111. H. Stammreich, R. Forneris and K. Sone, *J. Chem. Phys.*, **23,** 972 (1955).
112. K. Hedberg and R. M. Badger, *J. Chem. Phys.*, **19,** 508 (1951).
113. P. J. H. Woltz, E. A. Jones and A. H. Nielsen, *J. Chem. Phys.*, **20,** 378 (1952).
114. L. Landau, *J. Mol. Spectroscopy*, **4,** 276 (1960).
115. W. H. Eberhardt, *J. Chem. Phys.*, **20,** 529 (1952).
116. W. G. Burns and H. J. Bernstein, *J. Chem. Phys.*, **18,** 1669 (1950).
117. E. Greinacher, W. Lüttke and R. Mecke, *Z. Elektrochem.*, **59,** 23 (1955).
118. E. R. Lippincott, C. E. Weir and A. Van Valkenburg, *J. Chem. Phys.*, **32,** 612 (1960).
119. M. L. Josien and P. Saumagne, *Bull. soc. chim. France*, **1956,** 937.
120. M. Anbar, M. Halmann and S. Pinchas, *J. Chem. Soc.*, **1960,** 1242.
121. C. Duval, J. Lecomte and M. J. Morandat, *Bull. soc. chim. France*, **1951,** 745.
122. H. Y. Sheng, E. F. Barker and D. M. Dennison, *Phys. Rev.*, **60,** 786 (1941).
123. C. M. Lewis and W. V. Houston, *Phys. Rev.*, **44,** 903 (1933).
124. F. P. Reding and D. F. Hornig, *J. Chem. Phys.*, **19,** 594 (1951); **22,** 1926 (1954).
125. M. V. Migeotte and E. F. Barker, *Phys. Rev.*, **50,** 418 (1936).
126. H. W. Morgan, P. A. Staats, J. H. Goldstein, *Phys. Rev.*, **27,** 1212 (1957).
127. S. Sundaram and F. F. Cleveland, *J. Mol. Spectroscopy*, **5,** 61 (1960).
128. E. Lee and C. K. Wu, *Trans. Faraday Soc.*, **35,** 1366 (1939).
129. W. H. Haynie and H. H. Nielsen, *J. Chem. Phys.*, **21,** 1839 (1953).
130. R. C. Taylor and G. L. Vidale, *J. Am. Chem. Soc.*, **78,** 5999 (1956).
131. R. E. Weston, *J. Am. Chem. Soc.*, **76,** 2645 (1954).
132. C. C. Ferriso and D. F. Hornig, *J. Chem. Phys.*, **23,** 1464 (1955): J. T. Mullhaupt and D. F. Hornig, *ibid.*, **24,** 169 (1956).
133. D. E. Bethell and N. Sheppard, *J. Chem. Phys.*, **21,** 1421 (1953).
134. D. J. Millen and E. G. Vaal, *J. Chem. Soc.*, **1956,** 2913.
135. W. J. Biermann and J. B. Gilmour, *Can. J. Chem.*, **37,** 1249 (1959).
136. J. Kinumaki and K. Aida, *Sci. Repts. Research Insts., Tohoku Univ., Ser. A*, **6,** 186 (1954); K. Aida, *Bull. Chem. Research Inst. Non-aqueous Solutions, Tohoku Univ.*, **4,** 126 (1954).
137. C. A. Plint, R. M. B. Small and H. L. Welsh, *Can. J. Phys.*, **32,** 653 (1954).
138. R. D. Waldron and D. F. Hornig, *J. Am. Chem. Soc.*, **75,** 6079 (1953).
139. F. P. Reding and D. F. Hornig, *J. Chem. Phys.*, **23,** 1053 (1955).
140. J. S. Burgess. *Phys. Rev.*, **76,** 1267 (1949).
141. R. E. Weston, *J. Chem. Phys.*, **20,** 1820 (1952).
142. S. Sundaram, F. Suszek and F. F. Cleveland, *J. Chem. Phys.*, **32,** 251 (1960).
143. J. Duchesne and I. Ottelet, *J. phys. radium*, **11,** 119 (1950).
144. I. Gamo, *Compt. rend.*, **236,** 911 (1953); **238,** 2305 (1954); **239,** 1478 (1954).
145. M. K. Wilson and S. R. Polo, *J. Chem. Phys.*, **20,** 1716 (1952); **21,** 1426 (1953).

146. E. L. Pace and L. Pierce, *J. Chem. Phys.*, **23,** 1248 (1955).
147. H. S. Gutowsky and A. D. Liehr, *J. Chem. Phys.*, **20,** 1652 (1952).
148. D. M. Yost and J. E. Sherborne, *J. Chem. Phys.*, **2,** 125 (1934).
149. P. W. Davis and R. A. Oetjen, *J. Mol. Spectroscopy*, **2,** 253 (1958).
150. L. Giulotto, *Nuovo cimento*, **18,** 367 (1941).
151. M. L. Delwaulle, *Compt. rend.*, **228,** 1585 (1949).
151*a*. F. A. Miller and W. K. Baer, *Spectrochim. Acta*, **17,** 114 (1961).
152. J. C. Evans, *J. Mol. Spectroscopy*, **4,** 435 (1960).
152*a*. L. A. Woodward and M. J. Taylor, *J. Chem. Soc.*, **1962,** 407.
153. H. Stammreich, R. Forneris and Y. Tavares, *J. Chem. Phys.*, **25,** 580 (1956).
154. G. E. Moore, *J. Am. Chem. Soc.*, **74,** 6076 (1952).
155. P. N. Schatz, *J. Chem. Phys.*, **29,** 481 (1958).
156. A. K. Ramdas, *Proc. Indian Acad. Sci.*, **37A,** 451 (1953): **36A,** 55 (1952).
157. C. Rocchiccioli, *Compt. rend.*, **242,** 2922 (1956).
158. N. Duveau, *Bull. soc. chim. France*, **10,** 374 (1943).
158*a*. J. L. Hollenberg and D. A. Dows, *Spectrochim. Acta*, **16,** 1155 (1960).
159. M. Rolla, *Gazz. chim. ital.*, **69,** 779 (1939).
160. C. Rocchiccioli, *Compt. rend.*, **249,** 236 (1959).
161. W. E. Dasent and T. C. Waddington, *J. Chem. Soc.*, **1960,** 2429, 3350.
162. N. R. Rao, *Indian J. Phys.*, **16,** 71 (1942).
163. J. C. Evans and H. J. Bernstein, *Can. J. Chem.*, **33,** 1270 (1955).
164. A. Simon and K. Waldmann, *Z. physik. Chem.*, **204,** 235 (1955).
165. C. Rocchiccioli, *Compt. rend.*, **244,** 2704 (1957).
166. H. Siebert, *Z. anorg. u. allgem. Chem.*, **275,** 225 (1955).
167. C. Rocchiccioli, *Compt. rend.*, **247,** 1108 (1958).
168. A. Depaigne-Delay, C. Duval and J. Lecomte, *Bull. soc. chim. France*, **1946,** 54.
169. J. T. Last, *Phys. Rev.*, **105,** 1740 (1957).
170. J. K. O'Loane and M. K. Wilson, *J. Chem. Phys.*, **23,** 1313 (1955).
171. C. A. McDowell, *Trans. Faraday Soc.*, **49,** 371 (1953).
172. H. Gerding, E. Smit and R. Westrik, *Rec. trav. chim.*, **60,** 513 (1941).
173. G. Allen and C. A. McDowell, *J. Chem. Phys.*, **23,** 209 (1955).
174. H. Stammreich, R. Forneris and Y. Tavares, *J. Chem. Phys.*, **25,** 1277 (1956).
175. J. A. Rolfe and L. A. Woodward, *Trans. Faraday Soc.*, **51,** 779 (1955).
176. A. Simon and R. Paetzold, *Z. anorg. u. allgem. Chem.*, **301,** 246 (1959); *Naturwiss.*, **44,** 108 (1957).
177. M. Falk and P. A. Giguère, *Can. J. Chem.*, **34,** 1680 (1958).
178. A. Simon and R. Paetzold, *Z. anorg. u. allgem. Chem.*, **303,** 39, 46, 53, 72, 79, (1960); *Z. Elektrochem.*, **64,** 209 (1960).
179. F. A. Cotton and W. D. Horrocks, *Spectrochim. Acta*, **16,** 358 (1960).
180. J. Vanderryn, *J. Chem. Phys.*, **30,** 331 (1959).
181. D. A. Dows, *J. Chem. Phys.*, **31,** 1637 (1959).
182. A. H. Nielsen, *J. Chem. Phys.*, **22,** 659 (1954).
183. R. E. Scruby, J. R. Lacher and J. D. Park, *J. Chem. Phys.*, **19,** 386 (1951).
183*a*. D. A. Dows and G. Bottger, *J. Chem. Phys.*, **34,** 689 (1961).
184. T. Wentink and V. H. Tiensuu, *J. Chem. Phys.*, **28,** 826 (1958).
185. H. Gerding and J. Lecomte, *Physica*, **6,** 737 (1939).
185*a*. R. W. Lovejoy, J. H. Colwell, D. F. Eggers and G. D. Halsey, *J. Chem. Phys.*, **36,** 612 (1962).
186. W. C. Steele and J. C. Decius, *J. Chem. Phys.*, **25,** 1184 (1956).
187. L. P. Lindeman and M. K. Wilson, *J. Chem. Phys.*, **24,** 242 (1956).

188. J. Goubeau, D. E. Richter and H. J. Becher, *Z. anorg. u. allgem. Chem.*, **278,** 12 (1955).
189. W. R. Heslop and J. W. Linnett, *Trans. Faraday Soc.*, **49,** 1262 (1953).
190. H. Gerding and W. J. Nijveld, *Rec. trav. chim.*, **59,** 1206 (1940); *Z. physik. Chem.*, **B35,** 193 (1937).
190*a*. R. J. Gillespie and E. A. Robinson, *Can. J. Chem.*, **39,** 2189 (1961).
191. C. Duval and J. Lecomte, *Bull. soc. chim. France*, **1952,** 101.
192. R. R. Servoss and H. M. Clark, *J. Chem. Phys.*, **26,** 1175 (1957).
193. D. F. Hornig and R. C. Plumb, *J. Chem. Phys.*, **26,** 637 (1957).
194. C. W. F. T. Pistorius, *J. Chem. Phys.*, **31,** 1454 (1959).
194*a*. J. L. Parsons, *J. Chem. Phys.*, **33,** 1860 (1960).
195. S. Bhagavantam and T. Venkatarayudu, *Proc. Indian Acad. Sci.*, **9A,** 224 (1939).
196. D. Krishnamurti, *Proc. Indian Acad. Sci.*, **43A,** 210 (1956).
197. T. S. Krishnan, *Proc. Indian Acad. Sci.*, **44A,** 96 (1956).
198. M. Anbar, M. Halmann and S. Pinchas, *J. Chem. Soc.*, **1960,** 1242, 1246.
199. B. S. R. Rao, *Proc. Indian Acad. Sci.*, **10A,** 167 (1939); **19A,** 93 (1944).
200. R. Newman and R. S. Halford, *J. Chem. Phys.*, **18,** 1276, 1291 (1950).
201. W. E. Keller and R. S. Halford, *J. Chem. Phys.*, **17,** 26 (1949).
202. R. S. Halford, *J. Chem. Phys.*, **14,** 8 (1946).
203. S. Bhagavantam, *Proc. Indian Acad. Sci.*, **13A,** 543 (1941).
204. R. Duval, C. Duval and J. Lecomte, *Bull. soc. chim. France*, **10,** 517 (1943).
205. J. Louisfert, *Compt. rend.*, **233,** 381 (1951); **235,** 287 (1952).
205*a*. K. Buijs and C. J. H. Schutte, *Spectrochim. Acta*, **17,** 917, 921, 927 (1961); **18,** 307 (1962).
206. J. C. Decius, *J. Chem. Phys.*, **22,** 1941 (1954); **23,** 1290 (1955).
207. J. R. Ferraro, *J. Mol. Spectroscopy*, **4,** 99 (1960).
208. C. C. Addison and B. M. Gatehouse, *J. Chem. Soc.*, **1960,** 613.
209. H. Cohn, C. K. Ingold and H. G. Poole, *J. Chem. Soc.*, **1952,** 4272.
210. O. Redlich and L. E. Nielsen, *J. Am. Chem. Soc.*, **65,** 654 (1943).
211. R. E. Dodd, J. A. Rolfe and L. A. Woodward, *Trans. Faraday Soc.*, **52,** 145 (1956).
212. R. Ryason and M. K. Wilson, *J. Chem. Phys.*, **22,** 2000 (1954).
213. T. A. Hariharan, *Proc. Indian Acad. Sci.*, **48A,** 49 (1958).
214. J. Overend and J. C. Evans, *Trans. Faraday Soc.*, **55,** 1817 (1959).
215. A. H. Nielsen, T. G. Burke, P. J. H. Woltz and E. A. Jones, *J. Chem. Phys.*, **20,** 596 (1952).
216. P. J. H. Woltz and E. A. Jones, *J. Chem. Phys.*, **17,** 502 (1949).
217. E. Catalano and K. S. Pitzer, *J. Am. Chem. Soc.*, **80,** 1054 (1958).
218. E. A. Jones and T. G. Burke, *J. Chem. Phys.*, **18,** 1308 (1950).
219. R. R. Patty and R. T. Lagemann, *Spectrochim. Acta*, **15,** 60 (1959).
220. R. F. Stratton and A. H. Nielsen, *J. Mol. Spectroscopy*, **4,** 373 (1960).
221. H. H. Claassen, B. Weinstock and J. G. Malm, *J. Chem. Phys.*, **28,** 285 (1958).
222. C. W. F. T. Pistorius, *J. Chem. Phys.*, **30,** 332 (1959).
222*a*. J. P. Devlin and I. C. Hisatsune, *Spectrochim. Acta*, **17,** 206 (1961).
223. K. Venkateswarlu and S. Sundaram, *J. chim. phys.*, **54,** 202 (1957); *J. Chem. Phys.*, **23,** 2368 (1955).
223*a*. J. W. Linnett and D. F. Heath, *Trans. Faraday Soc.*, **48,** 592 (1952).
223*b*. G. J. Janz and Y. Mikawa, *J. Mol. Spectroscopy*, **5,** 92 (1960).
224. O. Bain and P. A. Giguère, *Can. J. Chem.*, **33,** 527 (1955).
225. P. A. Giguère and O. Bain, *J. Phys. Chem.*, **56,** 340 (1952).
226. P. A. Giguère, *J. Chem. Phys.*, **18,** 88 (1950).

227. R. C. Taylor, *J. Chem. Phys.*, **18,** 898 (1950).
228. R. C. Taylor and P. C. Cross, *J. Chem. Phys.*, **24,** 41 (1956).
229. A. Simon and H. Kriegsmann, *Naturwiss.*, **42,** 12 (1955).
229*a*. R. L. Miller and D. F. Hornig, *J. Chem. Phys.*, **35,** 265 (1961).
230. N. Zengin and P. A. Giguère, *Can. J. Chem.*, **37,** 632 (1959).
231. M. K. Wilson and R. M. Badger, *J. Chem. Phys.*, **17,** 1232 (1949).
232. F. Fehér, W. Lane and G. Winkhaus, *Z. anorg. u. allgem. Chem.*, **288,** 113 (1956).
233. F. Fehér and M. Baudler, *Z. Elektrochem.*, **47,** 844 (1941).
234. J. R. B. Matutano and C. Otero, *Anales real soc. españ. fís. y quím.*, **51B,** 223 (1955).
235. F. N. Hooge and J. A. A. Ketelaar, *Rec. trav. chim.*, **77,** 902 (1958).
236. H. J. Bernstein and J. Powling, *J. Chem. Phys.*, **18,** 1018 (1950).
237. H. Gerding and R. Westrik, *Rec. trav. chim.*, **60,** 701 (1941).
238. J. A. A. Ketelaar, F. N. Hooge and G. Blasse, *Rec. trav. chim.*, **75,** 220 (1956); **76,** 529 (1957).
239. H. Stammreich and R. Forneris, *Spectrochim. Acta*, **8,** 46 (1956).
240. A. Simon and H. Kriegsmann, *Naturwiss.*, **42,** 14 (1955).
241. O. Knop and P. A. Giguère, *Can. J. Chem.*, **37,** 1794 (1959).
242. F. Fehér and M. Baudler, *Z. anorg. u. allgem. Chem.*, **254,** 289 (1947); F. Fehér and M. Baudler, *ibid.*, **258,** 132 (1949); F. Fehér and G. Winkhaus, *ibid.*, **288,** 123 (1956).
243. E. G. Brame, S. Cohen, J. L. Margrave and V. W. Meloche, *J. Inorg. & Nuclear Chem.*, **4,** 90 (1957).
244. D. A. Dows and G. C. Pimentel, *J. Chem. Phys.*, **23,** 1258 (1955).
245. G. Herzberg and C. Reid, *Disc. Faraday Soc.*, **9,** 92 (1952).
246. L. H. Jones, J. N. Shoolery and R. G. Shulman, *J. Chem. Phys.*, **18,** 990 (1950).
247. C. Reid, *J. Chem. Phys.*, **18,** 1512 (1950).
248. L. H. Jones and R. M. Badger, *J. Chem. Phys.*, **18,** 1511 (1950).
249. L. H. Jones, R. M. Badger and G. E. Moore, *J. Chem. Phys.*, **19,** 1599 (1951).
250. L. d'Or and P. Tarte, *Bull. soc. roy. sci. Liège*, **20,** 478 (1951).
251. P. Tarte, *Bull. soc. roy. sci. Liège*, **20,** 16 (1951).
252. A. Palm, *J. Chem. Phys.*, **26,** 855 (1957).
252*a*. H. Richert, *Z. anorg. u. allgem. Chem.*, **309,** 171 (1960).
253. I. C. Hisatsune and J. P. Devlin, *Spectrochim. Acta*, **16,** 401 (1960); **17,** 218 (1961).
254. G. M. Begun, *J. Mol. Spectroscopy*, **4,** 388 (1960).
255. R. N. Wiener and E. R. Nixon, *J. Chem. Phys.*, **26,** 906 (1957).
256. R. G. Snyder and I. C. Hisatsune, *J. Mol. Spectroscopy*, **1,** 139 (1957); *J. Chem. Phys.*, **26,** 960 (1957).
257. I. C. Hisatsune and R. V. Fitzsimmons, *Spectrochim. Acta*, **15,** 206 (1959).
258. I. C. Hisatsune, J. P. Devlin and S. Califano, *Spectrochim. Acta*, **16,** 450 (1960).
259. I. C. Hisatsune, J. P. Devlin and Y. Wada, *J. Chem. Phys.*, **33,** 714 (1960).
260. R. Teranishi and J. C. Decius, *J. Chem. Phys.*, **22,** 896 (1954); **21,** 1116 (1953).
261. D. J. Millen, C. N. Polydoropoulous and D. Watson, *J. Chem. Soc.*, **1960,** 687.
262. R. J. W. LeFèvre, W. T. Oh, I. H. Reece and R. L. Werner, *Australian J. Chem.*, **10,** 361 (1957).
263. R. H. Sanborn, *J. Chem. Phys.*, **33,** 1855 (1960).
264. P. A. Giguère and I. D. Liu, *J. Chem. Phys.*, **20,** 136 (1952).
265. E. L. Wagner and E. L. Bulgozdy, *J. Chem. Phys.*, **19,** 1210 (1951).
266. A. Yamaguchi, *J. Chem. Soc. Japan*, **80,** 1109 (1959).
267. R. E. Nightingale and E. L. Wagner, *J. Chem. Phys.*, **22,** 203 (1954).
268. P. A. Giguère and I. D. Liu, *Can. J. Chem.*, **30,** 948 (1952).

269. R. G. Snyder and J. C. Decius, *Spectrochim. Acta*, **13**, 280 (1959).
270. D. L. Frasco and E. L. Wagner, *J. Chem. Phys.*, **30**, 1124 (1959).
271. Landolt-Börnstein, *Physikalisch-chemische Tabellen*, 2 Teil, 1951.
272. I. F. Kovalev, *Optika i Spectroskopiya*, **2**, 310 (1957).
273. L. P. Lindeman and M. K. Wilson, *Z. physik. Chem.*, **9**, 29 (1956).
274. L. May and C. R. Dillard, *J. Chem. Phys.*, **34**, 694 (1961).
275. G. E. MacWood, *J. Chem. Phys.*, **4**, 402 (1936).
276. H. M. Kaylor and A. H. Nielsen, *J. Chem. Phys.*, **23**, 2139 (1955).
277. A. H. Nielsen, *Phys. Rev.*, **54**, 118 (1938).
278. J. H. Meal and M. K. Wilson, *J. Chem. Phys.*, **24**, 385 (1956).
279. H. W. Morgan, P. A. Staats and J. H. Goldstein, *J. Chem. Phys.*, **27**, 1212 (1957).
280. J. V. Martinez and E. L. Wagner, *J. Chem. Phys.*, **27**, 1110 (1957).
281. A. R. Emery and R. C. Taylor, *J. Chem. Phys.*, **28**, 1029 (1958).
282. E. R. Lippincott, *J. Chem. Phys.*, **17**, 1351 (1949).
283. C. J. H. Schutte, *Spectrochim. Acta*, **16**, 1054 (1960); J. A. A. Ketelaar and C. J. H. Schutte, *ibid.*, **17**, 1240 (1961).
284. L. A. Woodward and H. L. Roberts, *Trans. Faraday Soc.*, **52**, 1458 (1956).
285. H. C. Longuet-Higgins and D. A. Brown, *J. Inorg. & Nuclear Chem.*, **1**, 60 (1955); D. A. Brown, *J. Chem. Phys.*, **29**, 451 (1958).
286. C. W. F. T. Pistorius, *J. Chem. Phys.*, **27**, 965 (1957).
287. E. L. Wagner and D. F. Hornig, *J. Chem. Phys.*, **18**, 296, 305 (1950).
288. R. C. Plumb and D. F. Hornig, *J. Chem. Phys.*, **21**, 366 (1953).
289. R. C. Plumb and D. F. Hornig, *J. Chem. Phys.*, **23**, 947 (1955).
290. W. Vedder and D. F. Hornig, *J. Chem. Phys.*, **35**, 1560 (1961).
291. T. C. Waddington, *J. Chem. Soc.*, **1958**, 4340.
292. J. P. Mathieu, R. M. Aguirre and L. C. Mathieu, *Compt. rend.*, **232**, 318 (1951); J. P. Mathieu, *ibid.*, **233**, 1595 (1951).
293. J. P. Mathieu and H. Poulet, *Spectrochim. Acta*, **16**, 696 (1960).
294. L. C. Mathieu and J. P. Mathieu, *J. chim. phys.*, **49**, 226 (1952).
295. J. P. Mathieu, *Compt. rend.*, **240**, 2508 (1955).
296. D. Penot, H. Poulet and J. P. Mathieu, *Compt. rend.*, **243**, 1303 (1956).
297. J. Goubeau, W. Bues and F. W. Kampmann, *Z. anorg. u. allgem. Chem.*, **283**, 123 (1956).
298. P. J. H. Woltz and A. H. Nielsen, *J. Chem. Phys.*, **20**, 307 (1952).
299. E. A. Jones, J. S. Kirby-Smith, P. J. H. Woltz and A. H. Nielsen, *J. Chem. Phys.*, **19**, 242 (1951).
300. A. D. Caunt, L. N. Short and L. A. Woodward, *Trans. Faraday Soc.*, **48**, 873 (1952).
301. A. D. Caunt, L. N. Short and L. A. Woodward, *Nature*, **168**, 557 (1951).
301*a*. A. Büchler, J. B. Berkowitz-Mattuck and D. H. Dugre, *J. Chem. Phys.*, **34**, 2202 (1961).
302. J. Goubeau and W. Bues, *Z. anorg. u. allgem. Chem.*, **268**, 221 (1952).
303. N. N. Greenwood, *J. Chem. Soc.*, **1959**, 3811.
304. H. L. Welsh, M. F. Crawford and G. D. Scott, *J. Chem. Phys.*, **16**, 97 (1948).
305. R. R. Haun, and W. D. Harkins, *J. Am. Chem. Soc.*, **54**, 3917 (1932).
306. D. A. Long, T. V. Spencer, D. N. Waters and L. A. Woodward, *Proc. Roy. Soc. (London)*, **A240**, 499 (1957).
307. L. P. Lindeman and M. K. Wilson, *Spectrochim. Acta*, **9**, 47 (1957).
308. M. L. Delwaulle, F. François, M. B. Delhaye-Buisset and M. Delhaye, *J. phys. radium*, **15**, 206 (1954).

309. J. T. Neu and W. D. Gwinn, *J. Am. Chem. Soc.*, **70,** 3463 (1948).
310. M. L. Delwaulle and F. François, *Compt. rend.*, **219,** 64 (1944).
310*a*. J. K. Wilmshurst, *J. Mol. Spectroscopy*, **5,** 343 (1960).
311. H. Gerding and H. Hautgraaf, *Rec. trav. chim.*, **72,** 21 (1953).
312. L. A. Woodward and A. A. Nord, *J. Chem. Soc.*, **1956,** 3721.
312*a*. L. A. Woodward and M. J. Taylor, *J. Chem. Soc.*, **1960,** 4473.
313. N. J. Hawkins and D. R. Carpenter, *J. Chem. Phys.*, **23,** 1700 (1955).
313*a*. M. F. A. Dove, J. A. Creighton and L. A. Woodward, *Spectrochim. Acta*, **18,** 267 (1962).
314. M. L. Delwaulle, *Compt. rend.*, **240,** 2132 (1955).
315. L. A. Woodward and A. A. Nord, *J. Chem. Soc.*, **1955,** 2655.
316. L. A. Woodward and P. T. Bill, *J. Chem. Soc.*, **1955,** 1699.
317. M. L. Delwaulle, *Compt. rend.*, **238,** 2522 (1954).
318. F. A. Miller and G. L. Carlson, *Spectrochim. Acta*, **16,** 6 (1960).
319. J. A. Rolfe, D. E. Sheppard and L. A. Woodward, *Trans. Faraday Soc.*, **50,** 1275 (1954).
320. H. Stammreich, Y. Tavares and D. Bassi, *Spectrochim. Acta*, **17,** 661 (1961).
320*a*. H. Stammreich, R. Forneris and Y. Tavares, *J. Chem. Phys.*, **25,** 1278 (1956).
321. L. A. Woodward and G. H. Singer, *J. Chem. Soc.*, **1958,** 716.
322. M. L. Delwaulle, *Bull. soc. chim. France*, **1955,** 1294.
323. T. C. Waddington and F. Klanberg, *J. Chem. Soc.*, **1960,** 2339.
323*a*. W. Kynaston, B. E. Larcombe and H. S. Turner, *J. Chem. Soc.*, **1960,** 1772.
324. R. E. Dodd, L. A. Woodward and H. L. Roberts, *Trans. Faraday Soc.*, **52,** 1052 (1956).
324*a*. D. P. Stevenson and V. Schomaker, *J. Am. Chem. Soc.*, **62,** 1267 (1940).
325. J. A. Rolfe, L. A. Woodward and D. A. Long, *Trans. Faraday Soc.*, **49,** 1388 (1953).
325*a*. P. L. Goggin, H. L. Roberts and L. A. Woodward, *Trans. Faraday Soc.*, **57,** 1877 (1961).
326. D. Fortnum and J. O. Edwards, *J. Inorg. & Nuclear Chem.*, **2,** 264 (1956).
327. H. Colm, *J. Chem. Soc.*, **1952,** 4282.
328. H. Siebert, *Z. anorg. u. allgem. Chem.*, **275,** 225 (1954).
329. D. Bassi and O. Sala, *Spectrochim. Acta*, **12,** 403 (1958).
330. F. A. Miller and C. H. Wilkins, *Anal. Chem.*, **24,** 1253 (1952).
331. M. H. Ortner, *J. Chem. Phys.*, **34,** 556 (1961).
331*a*. R. E. Dodd, *Trans. Faraday Soc.*, **55,** 1480 (1959).
332. H. Siebert, *Z. anorg. u. allgem. Chem.*, **273,** 21 (1953).
333. L. A. Woodward and H. L. Roberts, *Trans. Faraday Soc.*, **52,** 615 (1956).
334. H. H. Claassen and A. J. Zielen, *J. Chem. Phys.*, **22,** 707 (1954).
335. N. J. Hawkins and W. W. Sabol, *J. Chem. Phys.*, **25,** 775 (1956).
336. J. O. Edwards, G. C. Morrison, V. F. Ross and J. W. Schultz, *J. Am. Chem. Soc.*, **77,** 266 (1955).
337. E. R. Lippincott, J. A. Psellos and M. C. Tobin, *J. Chem. Phys.*, **20,** 536 (1952).
338. R. S. Krishnan, *Proc. Indian. Acad. Sci.*, **23A,** 288 (1946).
339. M. Hass and G. B. B. M. Sutherland, *Proc. Roy. Soc.* (*London*), **A236,** 427 (1956).
340. D. Krishnamurti, *Proc. Indian Acad. Sci.*, **48A,** 355 (1958).
341. L. C. Mathieu, *J. phys. radium*, **84,** (1949).
342. C. Shantakumari, *Proc. Indian Acad. Sci.*, **37A,** 393 (1953).
343. C. Duval and J. Lecomte, *Compt. rend.*, **248,** 1977 (1959).
344. T. S. Krishnan and P. S. Narayanan, *Proc. Indian Acad. Sci.*, **41A,** 121 (1955).

345. J. P. Mathieu, L. C. Mathieu and H. Poulet, *J. phys. radium*, **16**, 781 (1955).
346. D. Krishnamurti, *Proc. Indian Acad. Sci.*, **42A**, 77 (1955).
347. T. S. Krishnan, *J. Indian Inst. Sci.*, **38A**, 207 (1956).
348. R. S. Krishnan and C. S. Kumari, *Proc. Indian Acad. Sci.*, **32A**, 105 (1950).
349. R. Lafont, *Compt. rend.*, **242**, 1154 (1956).
350. P. A. Giguère and R. Savoie, *Can. J. Chem.*, **38**, 2467 (1961).
351. R. J. Gillespie and E. A. Robinson, *Can. J. Chem.*, **40**, 644 (1962).
352. A. Weil and J. P. Mathieu, *Compt. rend.*, **238**, 2510 (1954).
353. R. M. Ansidei, *Atti accad. nazl. Lincei, Rend., Classe sci. fis., mat. e nat.*, [7] **1**, 459 (1940).
354. R. M. Ansidei, *Boll. sci. fac. chim. ind. Bologna*, **18**, 116 (1940).
354*a*. P. A. Giguère and R. Savoie, *Can. J. Chem.*, **40**, 495 (1962).
355. O. Redlich, E. K. Holt and J. Bigeleisen, *J. Am. Chem. Soc.*, **55**, 13 (1944).
355*a*. S. D. Ross, *Spectrochim. Acta*, **18**, 225 (1962).
356. A. Galy, *J. phys. radium.*, **12**, 827 (1951).
357. J. V. Pustinger, W. T. Cave and M. L. Nielsen, *Spectrochim. Acta*, **11**, 909 (1959).
358. J. A. A. Ketelaar, *Acta Cryst.*, **7**, 691 (1954).
359. M. Tsuboi, *J. Am. Chem. Soc.*, **79**, 1351 (1957).
359*a*. J. S. Ziomek, J. R. Ferraro and D. F. Peppard, *J. Mol. Spectroscopy*, **8**, 212 (1962).
360. A. Mutschin and K. Maenuchen, *Z. anal. Chem.*, **156**, 241 (1957).
361. C. Duval and J. Lecomte, *Microchim. Acta*, **1956**, 454; *Compt. rend.*, **240**, 66 (1955).
362. J. Lecomte, A. Boulle and M. Lang-Dupont, *Compt. rend.*, **241**, 1927 (1955).
363. L. W. Daasch and D. C. Smith, *Anal. Chem.*, **23**, 853 (1951).
364. C. Duval and J. Lecomte, *Compt. rend.*, **239**, 249 (1954); *Z. Elektrochem.*, **64**, 582 (1960).
365. W. S. Benedict, K. Morikawa, R. B. Barnes and H. S. Taylor, *J. Chem. Phys.*, **5**, 1 (1937).
366. G. E. MacWood and H. C. Urey, *J. Chem. Phys.*, **4**, 402 (1936).
367. C. Newman, J. K. O'Loane, S. R. Polo and M. K. Wilson, *J. Chem. Phys.*, **25**, 855 (1956).
368. R. N. Dixon and N. Sheppard, *Trans. Faraday Soc.*, **53**, 282 (1957).
369. F. François and M. B. Delhaye-Buisset, *Compt. rend.*, **230**, 1946 (1950).
370. D. W. Mayo, H. E. Opitz and J. S. Peake, *J. Chem. Phys.*, **23**, 1344 (1955).
371. A. Monfils, *J. Chem. Phys.*, **19**, 138 (1951).
372. A. Monfils, *Compt. rend.*, **236**, 795 (1953).
373. C. Newman, *Spectrochim. Acta*, **15**, 793 (1959).
374. J. A. Hawkins, S. R. Polo and M. K. Wilson, *J. Chem. Phys.*, **21**, 1122 (1953).
375. F. A. Andersen and B. Bak, *Acta Chem. Scand.*, **8**, 738 (1954).
376. J. A. Hawkins, *J. Chem. Phys.*, **21**, 360 (1953).
377. T. G. Gibian and D. S. McKinney, *J. Am. Chem. Soc.*, **73**, 1431 (1951).
378. Y. Kakiuchi, *Bull. Chem. Soc. Japan*, **26**, 260 (1953).
379. M. L. Delwaulle and F. François, *Compt. rend.*, **219**, 335 (1944); **220**, 173 (1945).
380. R. C. Lord and C. M. Steese, *J. Chem. Phys.*, **22**, 542 (1954).
381. S. L. N. G. Krishnamachari, *Indian J. Phys.*, **29**, 384 (1955).
382. M. L. Delwaulle, *Compt. rend.*, **230**, 1945 (1950).
383. M. L. Delwaulle and F. Francois, *Compt. rend.*, **230**, 743 (1950).
383*a*. J. E. Griffiths, T. N. Srivastava and M. Onyszchuk, *Can. J. Chem.*, **40**, 579 (1962).
384. M. L. Delwaulle, *Compt. rend.*, **238**, 84 (1954).

385. I. N. Godnev, A. S. Sverklin and N. I. Ushanova, *Optika i Spektroskopia*, **2,** 704 (1957).
386. R. Dupeyrat, *Compt. rend.*, **241,** 932 (1955).
387. O. Hálová, *Chem. listy*, **49,** 640 (1955).
388. M. L. Delwaulle and F. François, *Compt. rend.*, **224,** 1422 (1947).
389. R. P. Madden and W. S. Benedict, *J. Chem. Phys.*, **25,** 594 (1956).
390. F. X. Powell and E. R. Lippincott, *J. Chem Phys.*, **32,** 1883 (1960).
391. D. R. Linde and D. E. Mann, *J. Chem. Phys.*, **25,** 1128 (1956).
392. R. Duval and J. Lecomte, *Compt. rend.*, **213,** 998 (1941).
393. H. Siebert, *Z. anorg. u. allgem. Chem.*, **289,** 15 (1957).
394. D. W. A. Sharp, *J. Chem. Soc.*, **1957,** 3761.
395. J. Lewis and G. Wilkinson, *J. Inorg. & Nuclear Chem.*, **6,** 12 (1958).
396. F. A. Miller and L. R. Cousins, *J. Chem. Phys.*, **26,** 329 (1957).
397. H. S. Gutowsky and A. D. Liehr, *J. Chem. Phys.*, **20,** 1652 (1952).
398. M. L. Delwaulle and F. François, *Compt. rend.*, **220,** 817 (1945).
399. H. Gerding and M. van Driel, *Rec. trav. chim.*, **61,** 419 (1942).
400. M. L. Delwaulle and F. François, *Compt. rend.*, **226,** 896 (1948).
401. H. Gerding and R. Westrik, *Rec. trav. chim.*, **61,** 842 (1942).
401*a*. F. A. Miller and G. L. Carlson, *Spectrochim. Acta*, **16,** 1148 (1960).
401*b*. H. Stammreich, O. Sala and K. Kawai, *Spectrochim. Acta*, **17,** 226 (1961).
401*c*. L. A. Woodward, J. A. Creighton and K. A. Taylor, *Trans. Faraday Soc.*, **56,** 1267 (1960).
402. W. D. Perkins and M. K. Wilson, *J. Chem. Phys.*, **20,** 1791 (1952); G. R. Hunt and M. K. Wilson, *Spectrochim. Acta*, **16,** 570 (1960).
403. P. Bender and J. M. Wood, *J. Chem. Phys.*, **23,** 1316 (1955).
403*a*. R. J. Gillespie and E. A. Robinson, *Can. J. Chem.*, **39,** 2171 (1961).
404. R. Vogel-Hogler, *Acta Phys. Austriaca*, **1,** 311(1947).
405. D. E. Martz and R. T. Langeman, *J. Chem. Phys.*, **22,** 1193 (1954).
406. W. E. Hobbs, *J. Chem. Phys.*, **28,** 1220 (1958).
407. H. Stammreich, K. Kawai and Y. Tavares, *Spectrochim. Acta*, **15,** 438 (1959).
408. F. A. Miller, G. L. Carlson and W. B. White, *Spectrochim. Acta*, **15,** 709 (1959).
409. C. G. Barraclough, J. Lewis and R. S. Nyholm, *J. Chem. Soc.*, **1959,** 3552.
409*a*. F. S. Martin, J. M. Fletcher, P. G. M. Brown and B. M. Gatehouse, *J. Chem. Soc.*, **1959,** 76.
409*b*. G. Mitra, *J. Am. Chem. Soc.*, **80,** 5639 (1958).
410. T. Dupuis, *Compt. rend.*, **246,** 3332 (1958).
410*a*. E. Steger and K. Martin, *Z. anorg. u. allgem. Chem.*, **308,** 330 (1960).
411. T. T. Crow and R. T. Lagemann, *Spectrochim. Acta*, **12,** 143 (1958).
412. M. L. Delwaulle and F. François, *Compt. rend.*, **222,** 1193 (1946).
413. G. D. Flesch and H. J. Svec, *J. Am. Chem. Soc.*, **80,** 3189 (1958).
414. J. W. Linnett, *Quart. Revs. (London)*, **1,** 73 (1947).
415. L. A. Woodward, *Trans. Faraday Soc.*, **54,** 1271 (1958).
416. C. W. F. T. Pistorius, *J. Chem. Phys.*, **28,** 514 (1958).
417. K. Venkateswarlu and S. Sundaram, *J. Chem. Phys.*, **23,** 2365 (1955).
418. S. Sundaram, *J. Chem. Phys.*, **33,** 708 (1960).
419. H. Murata and K. Kawai, *J. Chem. Phys.*, **23,** 2451 (1955).
420. K. Kawai and H. Murata, *J. Chem. Soc. Japan*, **77,** 504 (1956).
421. S. L. N. G. Krishnamachari, *Indian J. Phys.*, **29,** 147 (1955).
422. H. Siebert, *Z. anorg. u. allgem. Chem.*, **275,** 210 (1954).
423. K. Venkateswarlu and S. Sundaram, *J. phys. radium*, **17,** 905 (1956).

424. L. S. Mayants, E. M. Popov and M. I. Kabachnik, *Optika i Spektroskopia*, **6,** 589 (1959).
424*a*. J. S. Ziomek and E. A. Piotrowski, *J. Chem. Phys.*, **34,** 1087 (1961).
425. H. Stammreich and R. Forneris, *Spectrochim. Acta*, **16,** 363 (1960).
426. J. D. S. Goulden, A. Maccoll and D. J. Millen, *J. Chem. Soc.*, **1950,** 1635.
427. A. Maccoll, *J. Proc. Roy. Soc. N. S. Wales*, **77,** 130 (1943).
428. D. E. C. Corbridge and E. J. Lowe, *J. Chem. Soc.*, **1954,** 493, 4555.
429. H. J. Bernstein and J. Powling, *J. Chem. Phys.*, **18,** 1018 (1950).
430. N. B. Slater, *Trans. Faraday Soc.*, **50,** 207 (1954).
431. C. W. F. T. Pistorius, *J. Chem. Phys.*, **29,** 1421 (1958).
432. E. R. Nixon, *J. Phys. Chem.*, **60,** 1054 (1956).
432*a*. M. Baudler and L. Schmidt, *Z. anorg. u. allgem. Chem.*, **289,** 219 (1957).
433. H. Gerding, H. van Brederode and H. C. J. de Decker, *Rec. trav. chim.*, **61,** 549 (1942).
434. H. Gerding and H. C. J. de Decker, *Rec. trav. chim.*, **64,** 191 (1945).
435. M. Baudler, *Z. anorg. u. allgem. Chem.*, **279,** 115 (1955).
435*a*. W. G. Palmer, *J. Chem. Soc.*, **1961,** 1552.
436. M. Baudler, *Z. anorg. u. allgem. Chem.* **292,** 325 (1957).
437. A. Simon and H. Richter, *Z. anorg. u. allgem. Chem.*, **301,** 154 (1959).
438. E. Steger and G. Leukroth, *Z. anorg. u. allgem. Chem.*, **303,** 169 (1960).
439. A. Simon and H. Richter, *Z. anorg. u. allgem. Chem.*, **304,** 1 (1960).
440. E. Steger, *Z. anorg. u. allgem. Chem.*, **296,** 305 (1958).
441. A. Simon and E. Steger, *Z. anorg. u. allgem. Chem.*, **277,** 209 (1954).
442. J. Lecomte, A. Boulle and M. Dominé-Bergès, *Compt. rend.*, **226,** 575 (1948); *Bull. soc. chim. France*, **1948,** 764.
443. E. Steger and A. Simon, *Z. anorg. u. allgem. Chem.*, **291,** 76 (1957).
444. E. Steger and A. Simon, *Z. anorg. u. allgem. Chem.*, **294,** 1, 147 (1958).
445. H. Gerding and H. van Brederode, *Rec. trav. chim.*, **64,** 183 (1945).
446. H. Gerding, J. W. Maarsen and P. C. Nobel, *Rec. trav. chim.*, **76,** 757 (1957).
447. E. Steger, *Z. Elektrochem.*, **61,** 1004 (1957); *Z. anorg. u. allgem. Chem.*, **310,** 114 (1961).
447*a*. E. Steger, *J. anorg. u. allgem. Chem.*, **309,** 304 (1961).
447*b*. H. J. Becher and F. Seel, *Z. anorg. u. allgem. Chem.*, **305,** 148 (1960).
447*c*. A. C. Chapman and N. L. Paddock, *J. Chem. Soc.*, **1962,** 635.
448. A. Simon and H. Kriegsmann, *Z. physik. Chem.*, **204,** 369 (1955).
449. H. Siebert, *Z. anorg. u. allgem. Chem.*, **275,** 225 (1954).
450. K. Venkateswarlu and P. Thirugnanasambandam, *Trans. Faraday Soc.*, **55,** 1993 (1959).
451. G. M. Barrow, *J. Chem. Phys.*, **21,** 219 (1953).
451*a*. D. W. Scott and J. P. McCullough, *J. Mol. Spectroscopy*, **6,** 372 (1961).
452. K. Venkateswarlu, *Proc. Indian Acad. Sci.*, **12A,** 453 (1940).
453. H. Gerding and R. Westrik, *Rec. trav. chim.*, **62,** 68 (1944).
453*a*. V. D. Neff and T. H. Walnut, *J. Chem. Phys.*, **35,** 1723 (1961).
454. A. Simon, *Z. anorg. u. allgem. Chem.*, **260,** 161 (1949).
455. A. Simon and K. Waldmann, *Z. anorg. u. allgem. Chem.*, **281,** 135 (1955).
456. A. Simon, K. Waldmann and E. Steger, *Z. anorg. u. allgem. Chem.*, **288,** 131 (1956).
457. A. Simon and K. Waldmann, *Z. anorg. u. allgem. Chem.*, **283,** 359 (1956); **284,** 36 (1956).
458. A. Simon and G. Kratzsch, *Z. anorg. u. allgem. Chem.*, **242,** 369 (1939).
459. A. Simon and H. Richter, *Naturwiss.* **44,** 178 (1957).

460. A. Meuwsen and G. Heinze, *Z. anorg. u. allgem. Chem.*, **269,** 86 (1952).
461. H. Gerding and A. C. V. D. Linden, *Rec. trav. chim.*, **61,** 735 (1942).
461*a*. G. J. Gillespie and E. A. Robinson, *Can. J. Chem.*, **39,** 2179 (1961).
461*b*. A. Simon and R. Lehmann, *Z. anorg. u. allgem. Chem.*, **311,** 212, 224 (1961).
462. F. B. Dudley and G. H. Cady, *J. Am. Chem. Soc.*, **79,** 513 (1957).
463. A. V. Jones, *J. Chem. Phys.*, **18,** 1263 (1950).
464. I. Nakagawa, S. Mizushima, A. J. Saraceno, T. J. Lane and J. V. Quagliano, *Spectrochim. Acta*, **12,** 239 (1958).
465. A. M. Vuagnat and E. L. Wagner, *J. Chem. Phys.*, **26,** 77 (1957).
466. T. Dupuis, *Compt. rend.*, **243,** 1621 (1956).
467. V. Wannagat and R. Pfeiffenschneider, *Z. anorg. u. allgem. Chem.*, **297,** 151 (1958).
468. E. R. Lippincott and M. C. Tobin, *J. Chem. Phys.*, **21,** 1559 (1953); *J. Am. Chem. Soc.*, **73,** 4990 (1951).
469. H. Garcia-Fernandy, *Bull. soc. chim. France*, **1959,** 760.
470. G. A. Gallup and J. L. Koenig, *J. Phys. Chem.*, **64,** 395 (1960).
470*a*. O. Glemser and H. Richert, *Z. anorg. u. allgem. Chem.*, **307,** 313, 328 (1960).
471. R. E. Dodd, L. A. Woodward and H. L. Roberts, *Trans. Faraday Soc.*, **53,** 1545, 1557 (1957).
472. J. K. Wilmshurst and H. J. Bernstein, *Can. J. Chem.*, **35,** 191 (1957).
473. J. K. Wilmshurst and H. J. Bernstein, *J. Chem. Phys.*, **27,** 661 (1957).
474. H. Siebert, *Z. anorg. u. allgem. Chem.*, **265,** 303 (1951).
475. K. A. Jensen, *Z. anorg. u. allgem. Chem.*, **250,** 257 (1943).
476. J. Gaunt and J. B. Ainscough, *Spectrochim. Acta*, **10,** 52 (1957).
477. J. Gaunt and J. B. Ainscough, *Spectrochim. Acta*, **10,** 57 (1957).
478. H. S. Gutowsky and A. D. Liehr, *J. Chem. Phys.*, **20,** 1652 (1952).
479. J. P. Pemsler and W. G. Planet, *J. Chem. Phys.*, **24,** 920 (1956).
480. H. Gerding and H. Houtgraaf, *Rec. trav. chim.*, **74,** 5 (1955).
481. J. S. Ziomek and C. B. Mast, *J. Chem. Phys.*, **21,** 862 (1953); J. S. Ziomek, *ibid.*, **22,** 1001 (1954).
482. P. C. Haarhoff and C. W. F. T. Pistorius, *Z. Naturforsch.*, **14A,** 972 (1959).
483. R. V. G. Ewens and M. W. Lister, *Trans. Faraday Soc.*, **34,** 1358 (1938).
484. H. A. Skinner and L. E. Sutton, *Trans. Faraday Soc.*, **36,** 668 (1940).
485. D. E. Sands and A. Zalkin, *Acta Cryst.*, **12,** 723 (1959).
486. A. Zalkin and D. E. Sands, *Acta Cryst.*, **11,** 615 (1958).
487. H. S. Gutowsky and C. J. Hoffmann, *J. Chem. Phys.*, **19,** 1259 (1951).
488. A. Byström and K. A. Wilhelm, *Arkiv Kemi*, **3,** 461 (1951).
489. M. Edstrand, M. Inge and N. Ingri, *Acta Chem. Scand.*, **9,** 122 (1955).
490. C. V. Stephenson and E. A. Jones, *J. Chem. Phys.*, **20,** 1830 (1952).
491. T. G. Burke and E. A. Jones, *J. Chem. Phys.*, **19,** 1611 (1951).
492. L. Stein, *J. Am. Chem. Soc.*, **81,** 1273 (1959).
493. R. C. Lord, M. A. Lynch, W. C. Schumb and E. J. Slowinski, *J. Am. Chem. Soc.*, **72,** 522 (1950).
494. R. T. Lagemann and E. A. Jones, *J. Chem. Phys.*, **19,** 534 (1951).
495. A. de Lattre, *J. Chem. Phys.*, **20,** 520 (1952).
496. D. Edelson and K. B. McAfee, *J. Chem. Phys.*, **19,** 1311 (1951).
497. C. W. Gullikson, J. R. Nielsen and A. T. Stair, *J. Mol. Spectroscopy*, **1,** 151 (1957).
498. J. Gaunt, *Trans. Faraday Soc.*, **49,** 1122 (1953).
499. T. G. Burke, *J. Chem. Phys.*, **25,** 791 (1956).
500. J. Gaunt, *Trans. Faraday Soc.*, **51,** 893 (1955).
501. T. G. Burke, D. F. Smith and A. H. Nielsen, *J. Chem. Phys.*, **20,** 447 (1952).
502. T. G. Burke and D. F. Smith, *Phys. Rev.*, **83,** 485 (1951).

503. K. N. Tanner and A. B. F. Duncan, *J. Am. Chem. Soc.*, **73,** 1164 (1951).
503*a*. H. H. Claassen, H. Selig and J. G. Malm, private communication.
504. J. Gaunt, *Trans. Faraday Soc.*, **50,** 209 (1954).
504*a*. H. H. Claassen, J. G. Malm and H. Selig, private communication.
505. B. Weinstock, H. H. Claassen and J. G. Malm, *J. Chem. Phys.*, **32,** 181 (1960).
506. H. C. Mattraw, N. J. Hawkins, D. R. Carpenter and W. W. Sabol, *J. Chem. Phys.*, **23,** 985 (1955).
507. H. H. Claassen, B. Weinstock and J. G. Malm, *J. Chem. Phys.*, **25,** 426 (1956).
508. J. G. Malm, B. Weinstock and H. H. Claassen, *J. Chem. Phys.*, **23,** 2192 (1955).
509. N. J. Hawkins, H. C. Mattraw and W. W. Sabol, *J. Chem. Phys.*, **23,** 2191 (1955).
510. B. Weinstock and J. G. Malm, *J. Inorg. & Nuclear Chem.*, **2,** 380 (1956).
511. L. A. Woodward and L. E. Anderson, *J. Inorg. & Nuclear Chem.*, **3,** 326 (1956).
512. K. W. F. Kohlrausch, "Raman-Spektren," *Hand- und Jahrbuch der chemische Physik*, 1943.
513. L. A. Woodward and L. E. Anderson, *J. Chem. Soc.*, **1957,** 1284.
513*a*. L. A. Woodward and J. A. Creighton, *Spectrochim. Acta*, **17,** 594 (1961).
514. A. de Lattre, *J. Chem. Phys.*, **19,** 1610 (1951).
515. H. Siebert, *Z. anorg. u. allgem. Chem.*, **303,** 162 (1960).
516. H. Siebert, *Z. anorg. u. allgem. Chem.*, **301,** 161 (1959).
517. J. Gaunt, *Trans. Faraday Soc.*, **50,** 546 (1954).
518. K. Venkateswarlu and S. Sundaram, *Z. physik. Chem.*, **9,** 174 (1956).
519. C. W. F. T. Pistorius, *J. Chem. Phys.*, **29,** 1328 (1958).
520. H. H. Claassen, *J. Chem. Phys.*, **30,** 968 (1959).
521. J. W. Linnett and C. J. S. M. Simpson, *Trans. Faraday Soc.*, **55,** 857 (1959).
522. L. H. Cross, H. L. Roberts, P. Goggin and L. A. Woodward, *Trans. Faraday Soc.*, **56,** 945 (1960); *Spectrochim. Acta*, **17,** 344 (1961).
522*a*. R. D. Peacock and D. W. A. Sharp, *J. Chem. Soc.*, **1959,** 2762; A. J. Edwards and R. D. Peacock, *J. Chem. Soc.*, **1959,** 4126.
522*b*. D. F. Eggers, H. E. Wright and D. W. Robinson, *J. Chem. Phys.*, **35,** 1045 (1961).
523. C. W. F. T. Pistorius, *J. Mol. Spectroscopy*, **2,** 287 (1958).
524. R. E. LaVilla and S. H. Bauer, *J. Chem. Phys.*, **33,** 182 (1960).
524*a*. R. K. Khanna, *J. Mol. Spectroscopy*, **8,** 134 (1962).
525. W. H. Zachariasen, *Acta Cryst.*, **7,** 792 (1954).
526. G. C. Hampson and L. Pauling, *J. Am. Chem. Soc.*, **60,** 2702 (1938).
527. J. L. Hoard, *J. Am. Chem. Soc.*, **61,** 1252 (1939).
528. R. P. Bell and H. C. Longuet-Higgins, *Proc. Roy. Soc. (London)*, **A183,** 357 (1945).
529. W. J. Lehmann, J. F. Ditter and I. Shapiro, *J. Chem. Phys.*, **29,** 1248 (1958).
530. A. N. Webb, J. T. Neu and K. S. Pitzer, *J. Chem. Phys.*, **17,** 1007 (1949).
531. W. E. Anderson and E. F. Barker, *J. Chem. Phys.*, **18,** 698 (1950).
532. R. C. Taylor and A. R. Emery, *Spectrochim. Acta*, **10,** 419 (1958).
533. R. C. Lord and E. Nielsen, *J. Chem. Phys.*, **19,** 1 (1951).
534. W. Klemperer, *J. Chem. Phys.*, **24,** 353 (1956).
535. H. Gerding and E. Smit, *Z. physik. Chem.*, **B50,** 171 (1941).
536. H. Gerding and E. Smit, *Z. physik. Chem.*, **B51,** 217 (1942).
537. H. Gerding, H. G. Haring and P. A. Renes, *Rec. trav. chim.*, **72,** 78 (1953).
538. D. A. Brown and H. C. Longuet-Higgins, *J. Inorg. & Nuclear Chem.*, **1,** 352 (1955).
539. K. Venkateswarlu and P. Thirugnanasambandam, *Proc. Indian Acad. Sci.*, **48A,** 344 (1958).
540. W. C. Price, *J. Chem. Phys.*, **17,** 1044 (1949); W. C. Price, H. C. Longuet-Higgins, B. Rice and T. F. Young, *ibid.*, **17,** 217 (1949).
541. H. J. Hrostowski and G. C. Pimentel, *J. Am. Chem. Soc.*, **76,** 998 (1954).

542. W. J. Taylor, C. W. Beckett, J. Y. Tung, R. B. Holden and H. L. Johnston, *Phys. Rev.*, **79,** 234 (1950).
543. W. E. Keller and H. L. Johnston, *J. Chem. Phys.*, **20,** 1749 (1952).
544. W. C. Price, R. D. B. Fraser, T. S. Robinson, H. C. Longuet-Higgins, *Discussions Faraday Soc.*, **9,** 131 (1950).
545. D. White, D. E. Mann, P. N. Walsh and A. Sommer, *J. Chem. Phys.*, **32,** 481 (1960); D. White, P. N. Walsh and D. E. Mann, *ibid.*, **28,** 508 (1958).
546. D. White, D. E. Mann, P. N. Walsh and A. Sommer, *J. Chem. Phys.*, **32,** 488 (1960).
547. M. J. Linevsky, E. R. Shull, D. E. Mann and T. Wartik, *J. Am. Chem. Soc.*, **75,** 3287 (1953).
548. D. E. Mann and L. Fano, *J. Chem. Phys.*, **26,** 1665 (1957).
549. F. T. Green and J. L. Margrave, *J. Am. Chem. Soc.*, **81,** 5555 (1959).
550. F. Stitt, *J. Chem. Phys.*, **7,** 297 (1939).
551. B. L. Crawford, W. H. Avery and J. W. Linnett, *J. Chem. Phys.*, **6,** 682 (1938).
552. G. W. Bethke and M. K. Wilson, *J. Chem. Phys.*, **26,** 1107 (1957).
553. H. S. Gutowsky and E. O. Stejskal, *J. Chem. Phys.*, **22,** 939 (1954).
554. D. A. Dows and R. M. Hexter, *J. Chem. Phys.*, **24,** 1029, 1117 (1956).
555. R. C. Lord, D. W. Robinson and W. C. Schumb, *J. Am. Chem. Soc.*, **78,** 1327 (1956).
556. R. F. Curl and K. S. Pitzer, *J. Am. Chem. Soc.*, **80,** 2371 (1958).
557. D. C. McKean, *Spectrochim. Acta*, **13,** 38 (1958).
558. H. R. Linton and E. R. Nixon, *J. Chem. Phys.*, **29,** 921 (1958).
559. E. A. V. Ebsworth, R. Taylor and L. A. Woodward, *Trans. Faraday Soc.*, **55,** 211 (1959).
560. D. W. Robinson, *J. Am. Chem. Soc.*, **80,** 5924 (1958).
561. H. Kriegsmann and W. Forster, *Z. anorg. u. allgem. Chem.*, **298,** 212 (1959); **299,** 78, 223, 232 (1959).
562. H. W. Thompson, *Spectrochim. Acta*, **16,** 239 (1960).
563. A. L. Smith and N. C. Angelotti, *Spectrochim. Acta*, 412 (1959).
564. H. Stammreich, D. Bassi, O. Sala and H. Siebert, *Spectrochim. Acta*, **13,** 192 (1958).
564*a*. A. Simon and H. Wagner, *Z. anorg. u. allgem. Chem.*, **311,** 102 (1961).
565. J. L. Hoard, W. G. Martin, M. E. Smith and J. E. Whitney, *J. Am. Chem. Soc.*, **76,** 3820 (1954).
566. R. Stomberg and C. Brosset, *Acta Chem. Scand.*, **14,** 441 (1960).
567. B. Weinstock and J. G. Malm, *J. Am. Chem. Soc.*, **80,** 4466 (1958).
567*a*. M. F. A. Dove, *J. Chem. Soc.*, **1959,** 3722.
568. C. W. F. T. Pistorius, *Bull. soc. chim. Belges*, **68,** 630 (1959).
569. J. L. Hoard and H. H. Nordsieck, *J. Am. Chem. Soc.*, **61,** 2853 (1939).
570. B. D. Saksena, *Proc. Indian Acad. Sci.*, **12A,** 93 (1940); **30A,** 308 (1949).
571. B. D. Saksena, *Proc. Indian Acad. Sci.*, **30A,** 128 (1949).
572. A. K. Ramdas, *Proc. Indian Acad. Sci.*, **37A,** 571 (1953).
573. F. Matossi, *J. Chem. Phys.*, **19,** 1543 (1951).
574. F. Matossi, *J. Chem. Phys.*, **17,** 679 (1949).
574*a*. B. D. Saksena, *Trans. Faraday Soc.*, **57,** 242 (1961).
574*b*. V. Stubičan and B. Roy, *Z. Krist.*, **115,** 200 (1961).
575. M. Tsuboi, *Bull. Chem. Soc. Japan*, **23,** 83 (1950).
576. H. E. Petch, *Acta Cryst.*, **9,** 29 (1956).
577. J. M. Serratosa and W. F. Bradley, *J. Phys. Chem.*, **62,** 1164 (1958).
578. G. B. B. M. Sutherland and H. A. Willis, *Trans. Faraday Soc.*, **41,** 289 (1945); D. E. Blackwell and G. B. B. M. Sutherland, *J. chim. phys.*, **46,** 9 (1949).

578*a*. J. J. Charette, *J. Chem. Phys.*, **35,** 1906 (1961).
579. M. Haccuria, *Bull. soc. chim. Belges*, **62,** 428 (1953).
580. P. J. Launer, *Am. Mineralogist*, **37,** 764 (1952).
581. W. D. Keller and E. E. Pickett, *Am. Mineralogist*, **34,** 855 (1949); **37,** 764 (1952); **38,** 725 (1953); **39,** 256 (1954).
582. J. J. Kirkland, *Anal. Chem.*, **27,** 1537 (1955).
582*a*. R. Soda, *Bull. Chem. Soc. Japan*, **34,** 1491 (1961).
583. C. K. Huang and P. F. Kerr, *Am. Mineralogist*, **45,** 311 (1960).
584. J. Louisfert and T. Pobegiun, *Compt. rend.*, **235,** 287 (1953).
585. L. D. Fredrickson, *Anal. Chem.*, **26,** 1883 (1954).
586. J. M. Serratosa and W. F. Bradley, *Nature*, **181,** 111 (1958).
587. A. M. Vergnoux, S. Théron and M. Pouzol, *Compt. rend.*, **238,** 467 (1954).
588. G. W. Brindley and J. Zussman, *Am. Mineralogist*, **44,** 185 (1959).
589. V. C. Farmer, *Mineral. Mag.*, **31,** 829 (1958).
590. J. M. Hunt, M. P. Wisherd and L. C. Bonham, *Anal. Chem.*, **22,** 1478 (1950).
591. I. Simon and H. O. McMahon, *J. Chem. Phys.*, **21,** 23 (1953); I. Simon, *J. Opt. Soc. Am.*, **41,** 336 (1951).
592. J. Reitzel, *J. Chem. Phys.*, **23,** 2407 (1955).
593. J. P. Mathieu and H. Poulet, *Compt. rend.*, **244,** 2794 (1957).
594. P. Turlier, L. Eyraud and C. Eyraud, *Compt. rend.*, **243,** 659 (1956).

Coordination Compounds

Part III

III-1. AMMINE AND AMIDO COMPLEXES

(1) Ammine (NH_3) Complexes

Figure III-1 shows the infrared spectra of some typical ammine complexes. Although the structure of the ammine complex as a whole is highly complicated, the vibrational spectrum may be understood if a simple 1:1 model (i.e., M—NH_3) is used. The normal modes of vibration of such a simple model may be represented by those of a tetrahedral ZXY_3 molecule, shown in Fig. III-2. Thus the following six vibrations are expected for the 1:1 complex model: antisymmetric and symmetric NH_3 stretching, NH_3 degenerate deformation, NH_3 symmetric deformation, NH_3 rocking and M—N stretching. According to the selection rule for the point group $\mathbf{C}_{3v}$, these vibrations are both infrared and Raman active. Of these six vibrations, the NH_3 stretching bands can be assigned empirically since they always appear between 3400 and 3000 cm^{-1}. The three bending modes were first assigned by Nakagawa and Mizushima[1,2] from a normal coordinate analysis based on a 1:1 complex model like that in Fig. III-2. The band assignment for the M—N stretching mode is, however, still a subject of controversy. Each mode of vibration will be discussed.

(a) NH_3 Stretching Bands

Table III-1 lists the vibrational frequencies of typical ammine complexes. The NH_3 stretching bands in the complexes are usually broader, and their

TABLE III-1. VIBRATIONAL FREQUENCIES OF TYPICAL AMMINE COMPLEXES (CM^{-1})[3]

Compound	$\nu(NH_3)$	$\delta_d(NH_3)$	$\delta_s(NH_3)$	$\rho_r(NH_3)$
NH_3	3414, 3336	1628	950	—
$[Ni(NH_3)_6](ClO_4)_2$	3397, 3312	1618	1236	(620)
$[Cr(NH_3)_6](ClO_4)_3$	3330, 3280	1622	1334	718
$[Co(NH_3)_6]ClO_4)_3$	3320, 3240	1630	1352	803
$[Co(NH_3)_6](NO_3)_3$	3290, 3200	1618	—	—
$[Co(NH_3)_6]I_3$	3150	1590	1323	792
$[Co(NH_3)_6]Br_3$	3120	1578	1318	797
$[Co(NH_3)_6]Cl_3$	3070	1603	1325	818
$[NH_4]Cl$	3138, 3041	1710	1403	—

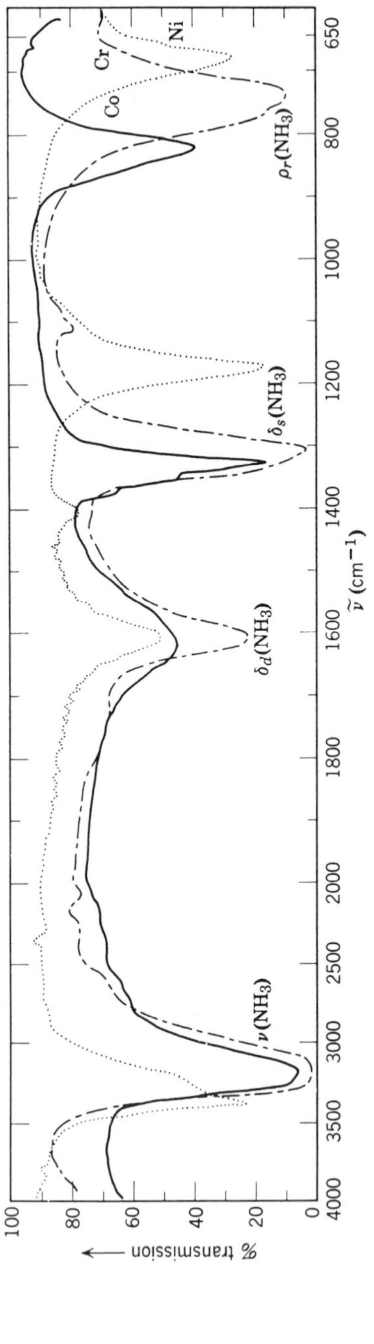

Fig. III-1. Infrared spectra of hexammine complexes: $[Co(NH_3)_6]Cl_3$, solid line; $[Cr(NH_3)_6]Cl_3$, dot-dash line; $[Ni(NH_3)_6]Cl_2$, dotted line.

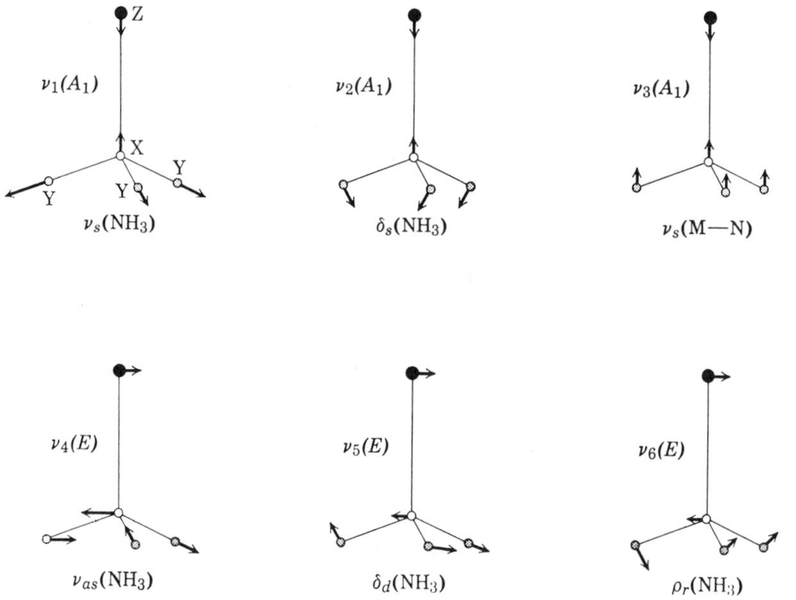

Fig. III-2. Normal modes of vibration of tetrahedral ZXY_3 molecules. (The band assignment is given for an M—NH_3 group.)

frequencies lower, than those of the free NH_3 molecule. Several factors may be responsible for the frequency shift. One is the *effect of coordination*.[3] The NH_3 stretching frequency decreases in the series $NH_3 >$ $[Ni(NH_3)_6]^{2+} > [Cr(NH_3)_6]^{3+} > [Co(NH_3)_6]^{3+} > [NH_4]^+$, if the perchlorates are compared. On the other hand, the stability order of these compounds is known to be Co(III) > Cr(III) > Ni(II). Therefore it is reasonable to conclude that the N—H bond order decreases (and the NH_3 stretching frequency decreases) as the M—N bond order increases in the stability order mentioned. Since the NH_3 stretching frequencies of the ammine complexes are intermediate between those of free NH_3 and the $[NH_4]^+$ ion, the M—N bond of the ammine complexes is probably partially ionic.

The NH_3 stretching frequency is also sensitive to changes in the anion. As seen in Table III-1, the frequency of the NH_3 stretching band of the $[Co(NH_3)_6]^{3+}$ ion decreases by about 230 cm^{-1} when $[ClO_4]^-$ is replaced by Cl^-. There is ample evidence of the presence of hydrogen bonding between the N—H of ammine complex ions and anions such as halogens.[4] Therefore it is evident that *hydrogen bonding*[3] weakens the N—H bond and shifts the band to a lower frequency. It should be noted that the magnitude of the shift due to hydrogen bonding is even greater than the difference in the NH_3 stretching frequencies between $[Ni(NH_3)_6](ClO_4)_2$ and $[Co(NH_3)_6](ClO_4)_3$. In addition to these two factors, Svatos et al.[5] cite the effects of *hydration* and *configuration* (*cis*, *trans*, etc.).

The broadening of the NH_3 stretching band in Fig. III-1 may also be the result of hydrogen bonding as well as overlapping of the individual N—H stretching bands of the whole complex ion.

(b) NH_3 Deformation and Rocking Bands

As Table III-1 shows, the effects of coordination and hydrogen bonding shift the three bending bands to higher frequencies. The direction of the band shifts of these bending modes is opposite to that of the stretching modes. Svatos and co-workers[6] have examined the frequencies of these three bending modes in a series of ammine complexes and have found that the NH_3 rocking frequency is most sensitive and the degenerate deformation frequency least sensitive to the metal. These results can be reasonably explained by the conclusions drawn from normal coordinate analysis.[1,2] Recently, Wilmshurst[7] has found a linear relation between the electronegativity of the metal and the square of either the symmetric deformation or the rocking frequency.

(c) Metal-Nitrogen (M—N) Stretching Bands

The M—N stretching frequency is of particular interest since it provides direct information about the coordinate bond. Because of the relatively heavy mass of the metal and the low bond order of the coordinate bond, the M—N stretching vibration may appear in the lower frequency region. Hill and Rosenberg[8] and Kobayashi and Fujita[9] previously suggested that the bands between 850 and 650 cm^{-1} in the ammine complexes may be due to the M—N stretching vibration. It has been shown, however, that these bands are due to the NH_3 rocking modes.[1,2]

As mentioned earlier, there are no definite band assignments for the M—N stretching vibrations of the Co(III) ammine complexes at present. Powell and Sheppard[10] have assigned an extremely weak band at 502 cm^{-1} to the M—N stretching vibration in $[Co(NH_3)_6]Cl_3$. Although the reason for the weakness of this band is not obvious, the corresponding bands are clearly seen in $[Co(NH_3)_5Cl]Cl_2$ (493 cm^{-1}), $[Pd(NH_3)_4]Cl_2 \cdot H_2O$ (498 cm^{-1}) and $[Pt(NH_3)_4]Cl_2$ (511 cm^{-1}). Figure III-3 shows the infrared spectra of $[Co(NH_3)_6]Cl_3$ and $[Co(NH_3)_5X]X_2$ (X: a halogen) in the CsBr region.[11] Additional evidence to support this assignment is the existence of a linear relation between the Raman active M—N stretching frequency or the NH_3 rocking frequency and the stability constant in a series of ammine complexes of various metals, illustrated in Fig. III-4. If the Raman active M—N stretching frequency in the $[Co(NH_3)_6]^{3+}$ ion is 575 cm^{-1}, it is not unreasonable to expect the infrared active M—N stretching mode to be near 500 cm^{-1}. Following the assignments made by Powell and Sheppard, Nakamoto et al.[12] have assigned the bands near 500 cm^{-1} observed in various nitroammine complexes to Co(III)—N stretching

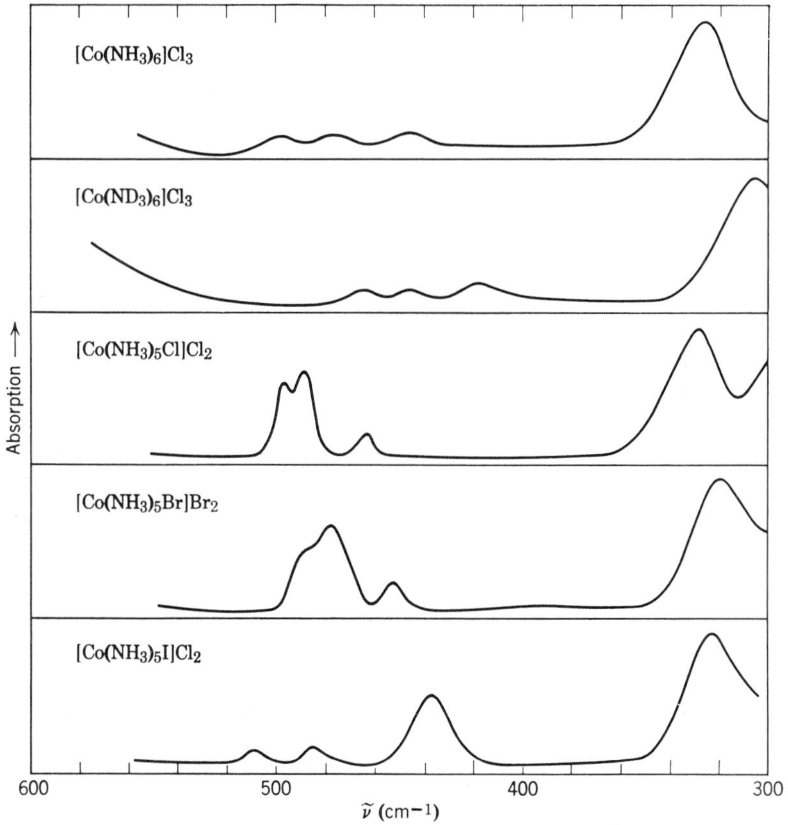

Fig. III-3. Infrared spectra of Co(III) ammine complexes in the CsBr region.[11] (Curves are only schematic.)

modes. Recently, Block[13] made a normal coordinate analysis for the $[Co(NH_3)_6]^{3+}$ ion and obtained fairly good agreement between the calculated (542 cm^{-1}) and observed (502 cm^{-1}) frequencies for the infrared active M—N stretching mode. The value of the Co—N stretching force constant (GVF) used in this calculation was 2×10^5 dynes/cm, which is reasonable in view of the stability of the complex.

On the other hand, Barrow and colleagues[14] assigned a strong band at 330 cm^{-1} in $[Co(NH_3)_6]Cl_3$ to the Co(III)—N stretching mode. This assignment was followed by Bertin et al.,[15] whose results are shown in Table III-2 together with those of Barrow and co-workers. According to these results, the Co(III)—N and Co(II)—N stretching bands are located in almost the same range. This seems to contradict the fact that the heat of formation of the Co(III) ammine complex is twice that of the Co(II) ammine complex.[16] Furthermore, the relationship between stability and

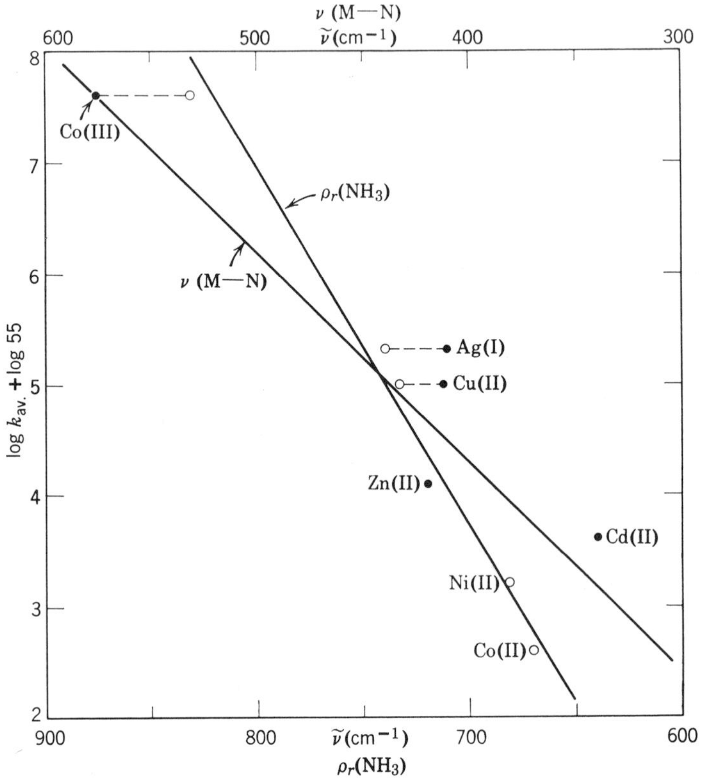

Fig. III-4. Relation between stability constant and NH_3 rocking and M—N stretching frequencies (from data of Powell and Sheppard[10]). ○ for $\rho_r(NH_3)$ and ● for ν(M—N).

M—N stretching frequency found by Powell and Sheppard will break down completely if the band at 328 cm^{-1} of the $[Co(NH_3)_6]^{3+}$ ion is adopted as the Co(III)—N stretching frequency.

Although the band assignment of the Co(III)—N stretching mode is still a subject of discussion, the author personally prefers the assignments made by Powell and Sheppard for the reasons mentioned above. Table III-3 summarizes the observed frequencies and the band assignments made recently by Nakamoto and Fujita.[11] Recently Shimanouchi and Nakagawa[16a] made a normal coordinate analysis of the $[Co(NH_3)_6]^{3+}$ ion, taking the NH_3 group as a single atom. They have also assigned to the Co—N stretching and N—Co—N bending modes of the F_{1u} species a weak band at 464 cm^{-1} and a strong band at 325 cm^{-1}, respectively. The Co—N stretching force constant (UBF) was estimated to be 1.07×10^5 dynes/cm.

TABLE III-2. VIBRATIONAL FREQUENCIES AND BAND ASSIGNMENTS OF AMMINE COMPLEXES (CM^{-1})[14,15]

Compound	$\nu(NH_3)$	$\delta_d(NH_3)$	$\delta_s(NH_3)$	$\rho_r(NH_3)$	$\nu(MN)$
$[Co(NH_3)_6]Cl_3$	3080	1600	1325	827	328
$[Co(NH_3)_6]Br_3$	3090	1590	1322	813	322
$[Co(NH_3)_6]I_3$	3080	1600	1325	808	320
$[Co(NH_3)_6]Cl_2$	3130	1605	1160	634	318
$[Co(NH_3)_6]Br_2$	3080	1590	1165	634	317
$[Co(NH_3)_6]I_2$	3220	1600	1190	622	308
$[Pt(NH_3)_4]Cl_2 \cdot H_2O$	3200	1587	1340, 1326	880, 842	497
$[Zn(NH_3)_4]I_2$	3290	1600	1242	693	410
$[Cu(NH_3)_4]Cl_2$	3270	1596	1245	709	420
$[Cd(NH_3)_4]Cl_2$	3360, 3260	1608	1207	561	381

There is much more agreement on the assignment of the M—N stretching band of other ammine complexes. The bands near 500 cm^{-1} observed in various Pt(II) and Pd(II) ammine complexes were assigned to the M—N stretching modes by Powell and Sheppard[10] and Mizushima et al.[17] Powell[18] has shown that the band is shifted to a lower frequency as a ligand of stronger *trans effect*† is introduced in a position *trans* to the Pt—N bond. The Hg(II)—N stretching bands in the $[Hg(NH_3)_2]^{2+}$ ion were found near 500 cm^{-1} by Bertin et al.[15] The results obtained by normal coordinate analyses for the skeletal vibrations of some ammine complexes are summarized in Table III-4. Recently, Leonard and co-workers[19] have demonstrated the existence of the $[Na(NH_3)_4]^+$ ion from a study of the

† The reactivity of a group in a square-planar complex depends on the nature of the group coordinated in a position *trans* to it. A group which is *trans* to Cl^- is much more labile than the same group *trans* to H_2O. In this respect Cl^- is said to have a stronger *trans* effect than H_2O. The order of increasing *trans* effect is $H_2O < [OH]^- < NH_3 \sim RNH_2 < Cl^- < Br^- < I^- < [NO_2]^- < CO < C_2H_4 < [CN]^-$. For details, see Refs. 24, I-39 and I-40.

TABLE III-3. INFRARED FREQUENCIES OF AMMINE COMPLEXES IN THE CsBr REGION (CM^{-1})[11]

Compound	ν(M—N)[a]	δ(N—M—N)
$[Co(NH_3)_6]Cl_3$	500, 476, 448	327
$[Co(ND_3)_6]Cl_3$	465, 446, 419	306
$[Co(NH_3)_5Cl]Cl_2$	496, 488, 464	329
$[Co(NH_3)_5Br]Br_2$	488, 478, 458	320
$[Co(NH_3)_5I]Cl_2$	509, 485, 437	324
$[Cr(NH_3)_6]Cl_3$	492, 474, 459	—
$[Ni(NH_3)_6]Cl_2$	334	—

[a] If only the metal-nitrogen skeleton is considered, these hexammine complexes belong to the point group $\mathbf{O}_h$. Since the infrared active M—N stretching mode belongs to the F_{1u} species, it is not unreasonable to expect that this band will split into three peaks as a result of the crystal field effect.

TABLE III-4. OBSERVED SKELETAL FREQUENCIES AND FORCE CONSTANTS IN AMMINE COMPLEXES (CM^{-1})[15,17]

Compound	Symmetry	ν(M—N)	δ(N—M—N)	UBF Force Constant (10^5 dynes/cm)
$[Pt(NH_3)_4]Cl_2$	$\mathbf{D}_{4h}$	538 (A_{1g}) 526 (B_{2g}) (577) (E_{1u})	270 (B_{1g}) (204) (E_{1u})	K(Pt—N) = 2.804 H(N—Pt—N) = 0.147 F(N ··· N) = 0.05
$[Hg(NH_3)_2]Cl_2$	$\mathbf{D}_{3h}'$	513 ($\bar{A}_2$) (493) (A_1)	(159) (E)	K(Hg—N) = 1.695 H(N—Hg—N) = 0.119 F(Hg ··· H) = 0.30

Raman spectrum. The Raman spectra of a number of ammine complexes have been obtained by Damaschun[20] and Mathieu and Cornevin.[21]

(2) Amido (NH_2) Complexes

As for the ammine complexes, the vibrational modes of the coordinated amido group may be approximated by the normal modes of vibration of a pyramidal ZXY_2 molecule. Mizushima and colleagues[22] have carried out a normal coordinate analysis for an infinite linear polymer, $[Hg(NH_2)_2]_\infty^+$. The results are given in Table III-5. Brodersen and Becher[23] have also

TABLE III-5. VIBRATIONAL FREQUENCIES AND BAND ASSIGNMENTS OF AMIDO COMPLEXES (CM^{-1})[22]

Compound	$\delta(NH_2)$	$\rho_w(NH_2)$	$\rho_t(NH_2)$	$\rho_r(NH_2)$	ν(Hg—N)
$[Hg(NH_2)]_\infty^+(Cl^-)_\infty$	1534	1022	(978)	668	573
$[Hg(NH_2)]_\infty^+(Br^-)_\infty$	1528, 1505	1005, 950	(978), (978)	647, 620	560, 510

studied the infrared spectra of a number of compounds containing Hg—N bonds and have found the Hg—N stretching bands in the range 700 to 400 cm^{-1}. Brodersen[24] also studied the infrared spectra of *hydrazine complexes* of mercury.

Chatt and co-workers[25] have studied the effect of hydrogen bonding on the N—H stretching frequencies of complexes of the type $[PtRNH_2Cl_2L]$ [R = CH_3, C_2H_5, etc.; L = C_2H_4, $P(C_2H_5)_3$], in organic solvents such as chloroform and dioxane. Their study revealed that the complexes of primary amines have a strong tendency to associate through intermolecular hydrogen bonds of the N—H · · · Cl type, whereas those of secondary amines have little tendency to associate. Recently, this difference was explained on the basis of steric repulsion and intramolecular interaction between the NH hydrogen and the non-bonding *d*-electrons of the metal.[26] Adams and colleagues[26a] have obtained the infrared spectra of compounds of the types $[PtR_2(PR_3')_2]$ and $[PtXR(PR_3')_2]$, where R and R′ are alkyl groups and X is a univalent acid radical. They have discussed the effect of varying R, R′ and X on the Pt—C stretching (700–500 cm^{-1}) and the methyl symmetric deformation (1230–1170 cm^{-1}) bands.

III-2. NITRO AND NITRITO COMPLEXES

(1) Nitro (NO_2) Complexes

The infrared spectrum of a typical nitro complex is shown in Fig. III-5. The normal modes of vibration of the nitro group coordinated to a metal

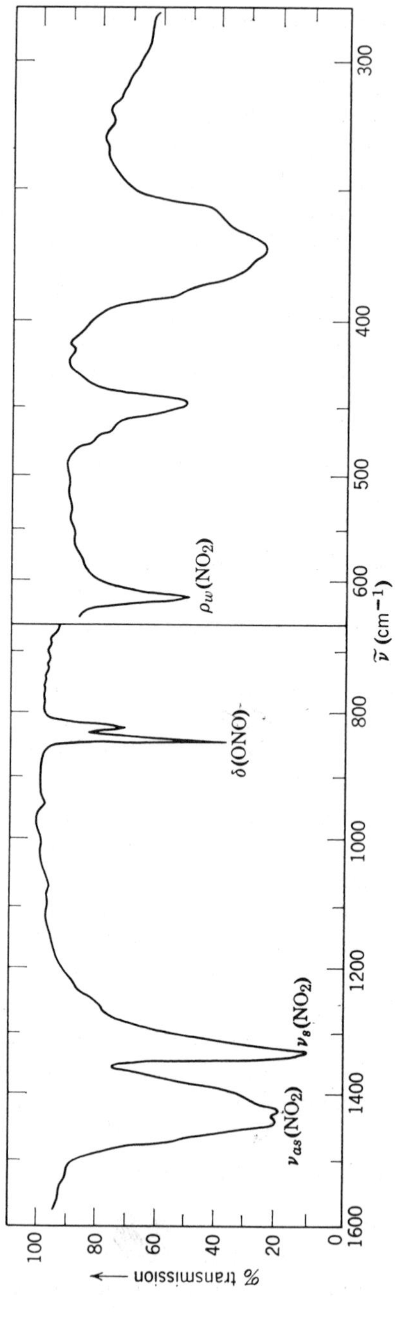

Fig. III-5. The infrared spectrum of $Na_3[Co(NO_2)_6]$.

may be approximated by those of a planar ZXY_2 molecule, illustrated in Fig. III-6. In addition, the NO_2 twisting mode may become infrared active, if X represents a relatively heavy group of atoms.

In order to assign these vibrational modes, Nakamoto et al.[12] made a normal coordinate analysis of the $[Pt(NO_2)_4]^{2-}$ ion. The results are given

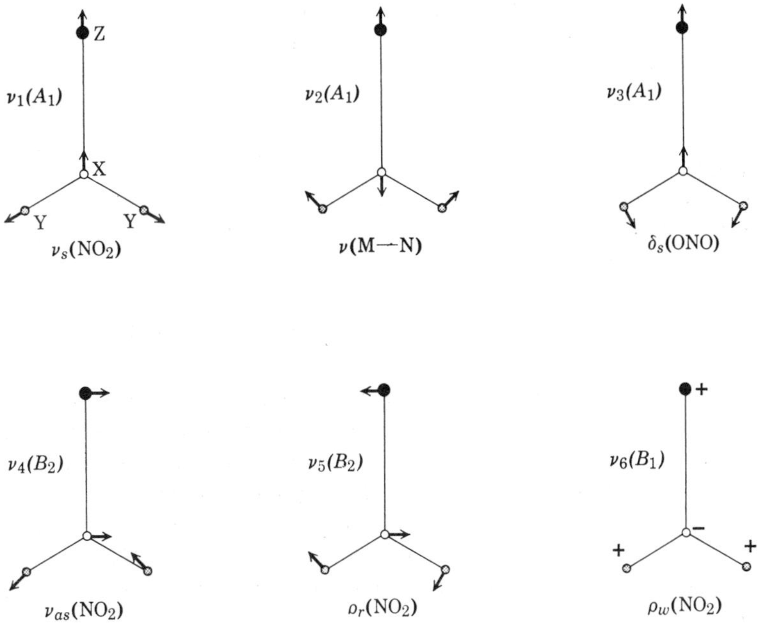

Fig. III-6. Normal modes of vibration of planar ZXY_2 molecules. (The band assignment is given for an M—NO_2 group.)

in Table III-6. The antisymmetric and symmetric NO_2 stretching, NO_2 wagging and M—N stretching bands are shifted to higher frequencies in the order $[Ni(NO_2)_6]^{4-} < [Co(NO_2)_6]^{3-} < [Pt(NO_2)_4]^{2-}$. As for hexammine complexes, this result may be interpreted as an indication of increasing bond order of the M—N bond in the preceding series. Recently, Puget and Duval[27] have measured the infrared spectra of a number of *hexanitrites*.

The spectra of *nitroammine* complexes may be interpreted as a superposition of the spectrum of the M—NO_2 group and that of the M—NH_3 group, which was discussed in Sec. III-1. Practically, however, this approach cannot be utilized, because band overlapping as well as vibrational coupling between these two groups is extensive. As a result, Beattie and Tyrrell[28] have found it difficult to correlate the stereochemistry and the number of nitro groups with the spectra. It is possible, however, to distinguish the *cis* and *trans* isomers spectrally. Since the *cis* isomer has lower symmetry than the *trans* isomer, the former exhibits more bands than the latter. This was demonstrated by Faust and Quagliano[29] and Merritt and Wiberley,[30] and later confirmed by Chatt et al.[31] Recently, Morris and Busch[32] have shown that the *cis* and *trans* isomers of nitro-ethylenediamine complexes can be distinguished on a similar basis.

TABLE III-6.   VIBRATIONAL FREQUENCIES OF NITRO COMPLEXES (CM^{-1})[12]

Compound	$\nu_{as}(NO_2)$	$\nu_s(NO_2)$	$\delta(ONO)$	$\rho_w(NO_2)$	$\nu(M-N)$
[ONO]$^-$ ion	1335	1250	830	—	—
K$_2$Ca[Ni(NO$_2$)$_6$]	1335	1325	833	462	—
K$_3$[Co(NO$_2$)$_6$]	1396, 1381	1332	834	630	413
K$_2$[Pt(NO$_2$)$_4$]	1436, 1410 1386	1350	838, 832 828	636, 613	450
CH$_3$NO$_2$	1582	1384	647	599, 476	—

Majumdar and co-workers,[33] using infrared spectra, have detected the presence of two stereo isomers of trinitrotriamine Co(III). Nakamoto and colleagues[12] have suggested that the M—NH$_3$ stretching bands near 500 cm^{-1} may be useful for distinguishing these stereo isomers.

Although the nitro group may form a bridge between two metal atoms, the structure of the bridge was unknown for a long time. Nakamoto and co-workers[12] have suggested that, of the three possible structures, structure

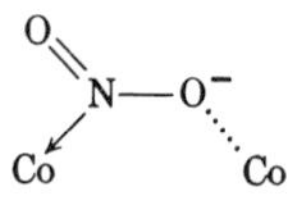

I   II   III

I is most probable, since the observed NO stretching frequencies (1516 and 1200 cm^{-1}) in the

$$\left[(NH_3)_3Co \underset{NO_2}{\overset{OH}{\diagup \diagdown}} OH-Co(NH_3)_3 \right]^{3+}$$

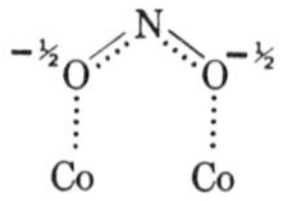

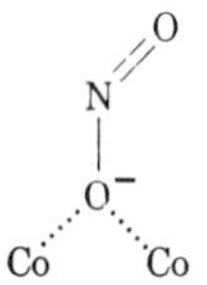

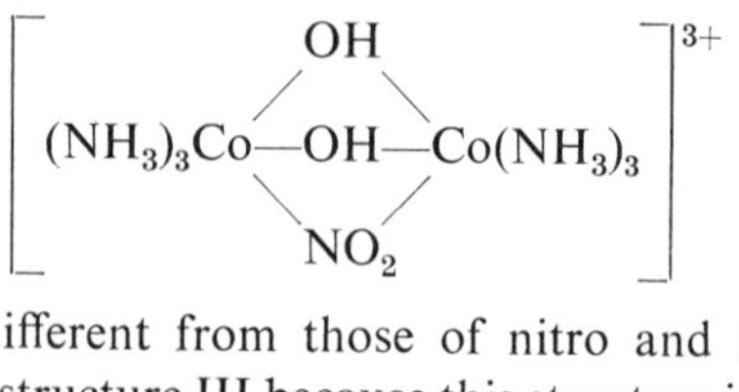

ion are markedly different from those of nitro and nitrito complexes. This result rules out structure III because this structure is expected to show some similarity to that of the nitrito complexes. The high antisymmetric stretching frequency of the bridged complex is also difficult to explain on the basis of structure II. Structure I is also supported by Chatt et al.[31] on the basis of their experimental data.

(2) Nitrito (ONO) Complexes

The stable nitropentammine Co(III) complex has an isomer in which the oxygen of the nitro group is coordinated to the metal. This nitrito-pentammine complex is unstable and is gradually converted to the nitro complex. Penland et al.[34] followed the conversion by observing the disappearance of the characteristic bands of the nitrito group in KBr pellets. Table III-7 compares the infrared frequencies of these two isomers. The

TABLE III-7. VIBRATIONAL FREQUENCIES OF NITROAMMINE AND NITRITOAMMINE COMPLEXES (cm^{-1})[12]

Compound	$\delta_d(NH_3)$	$\nu_{as}(NO_2)$	$\delta_s(NH_3)$	$\nu_s(NO_2)$	$\rho_r(NH_3)$	$\delta(NO_2)$	$\rho_w(NO_2)$	ν(Co—N)	ν(Cr—N)
$[Co(NH_3)_5NO_2]Cl_2$	1595	1428	1310	1310	850	824	594	513, 499, 488	—
$[Co(NH_3)_5ONO]Cl_2$	1595	1468	1325	1065	850	825	—	?	—
$[Cr(NH_3)_5ONO]Cl_2$	1613	1460	1300	1048	766	839	—	—	476, 466 444

ν(Co—N) and ν(Cr—N) denote metal—NH_3 stretching modes.

NO_2 stretching frequencies are markedly different in these two isomers, and, furthermore, the nitrito complexes lack wagging vibrations. Nakamoto and colleagues[12] have also shown that the corresponding Cr(III) complex exists only as a nitrito complex [the nitropentammine complex of Cr(III) has not yet been prepared]. Beattie and Satchell[35] have studied the kinetics of the conversion of the Co(III) complexes mentioned above, using infrared spectra. Recently, Basolo and Hammaker[36] have attempted a similar study of the nitrito-nitro conversion for the pentammine complexes of Ir(III) and Rh(III). For a general survey of the infrared spectra of nitro complexes, see Ref. 37. Reference 21 lists Raman spectral data for some nitro complexes.

III-3. LATTICE WATER, AQUO AND HYDROXO COMPLEXES

Water in inorganic salts may be classified either as *lattice water* or *coordinated water*. There is, however, no definite borderline between the two. The former term denotes water molecules trapped in the crystal lattice, either by weak hydrogen bonds to the anion or by weak coordinate bonds to the metal, or by both, whereas the latter denotes water molecules in the first coordination sphere of the metal. Although bond distances and angles obtained from x-ray and neutron diffraction data provide direct information concerning the geometry of the water molecule in the crystal lattice, studies of vibrational spectra are also useful for this purpose.

(1) Lattice Water

In general, lattice water absorbs at 3550–3200 cm^{-1} (antisymmetric and symmetric O—H stretching modes)[38] and at 1630–1600 cm^{-1} (H—O—H bending mode). If the spectrum is examined under higher resolution, the fine structure of these bands is observed. For example, Hass and Sutherland (Ref. II-339) found eight peaks between 3500 and 3400 cm^{-1} in $CaSO_4 \cdot 2H_2O$. Such a result may indicate the presence of an interaction between the water molecules through hydrogen bonding of the type $OH_2 \cdots [SO_4]^{2-} \cdots H_2O$. Detailed studies of the vibrational spectra of compounds having lattice water have been made for a number of compounds by the method of site group or factor group analysis (Sec. II-5). Some of the references are: $Li_2SO_4 \cdot H_2O$ (39, 40); $K_2HgCl_4 \cdot H_2O$ (40); $CaSO_4 \cdot 2H_2O$ (41); $BaCl_2 \cdot 2H_2O$ (42); $LiClO_4 \cdot 3H_2O$ (43); $MnCl_2 \cdot 4H_2O$ (44); $CaCl_2 \cdot 6H_2O$ (45); $MgSO_4 \cdot 7H_2O$ (46); $WO_3 \cdot nH_2O$ (46*a*).

Lattice water also absorbs the low frequency region (600–300 cm^{-1}) owing to *librational modes*.† Recently van der Elsken and Robinson[46b] studied these modes in a number of hydrates of alkali and alkaline earth halides.

(2) Aquo (H_2O) Complexes

Besides the three fundamental modes of the free water molecule, coordinated water is expected to show other vibrational modes such as those in Fig. III-6. The wagging, twisting and rocking modes are activated by coordination to the metal. In order to locate the bands due to these vibrations, Fujita et al.[47] have examined the infrared spectra of typical aquo complexes. Figure III-7 shows the infrared spectra of $[Ni(gly)_2] \cdot 2H_2O$ and the anhydrous compound. The bands characteristic of coordinated water are seen near 795 cm^{-1} in $[Ni(gly)_2] \cdot 2H_2O$, near 875 cm^{-1} in $CuSO_4 \cdot 5H_2O$ and near 1012 and 965 cm^{-1} in $K[Cr(ox)_2(H_2O)_2] \cdot 3H_2O$.‡ It is interesting to note that $K_3[Cr(ox)_3] \cdot 3H_2O$ does not exhibit these characteristic bands. Recently, Gamo[47a] assigned the bands observed between 880 and 650 cm^{-1} in various inorganic salts to the wagging or rocking mode of coordinated water. Sartori and co-workers[48] have calculated the vibrational frequencies of coordinated water using the model shown in Fig. III-6. According to their calculations, the rocking, wagging and the metal-oxygen stretching vibrations appear at 900, 768 and 673 cm^{-1},

† The rotational motions of the water molecule are restricted in the crystal lattice because of hydrogen bonding to neighboring atoms. The resulting rotational oscillations of the whole molecule are called "librational modes."

‡ gly: glycinate anion; ox: oxalate anion. In this respect, formulas such as $[Ni(gly)_2(H_2O)_2]$ and $[Cu(H_2O)_4]SO_4 \cdot H_2O$ are better representations of the structures of these compounds.

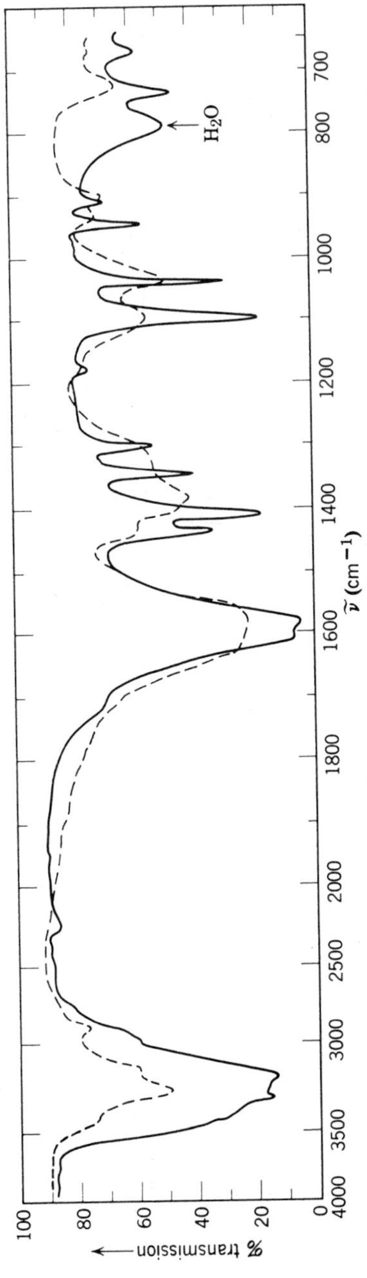

Fig. III-7. Infrared spectra of $Ni(gly)_2 \cdot 2H_2O$ (solid line) and its anhydrous compound (broken line).

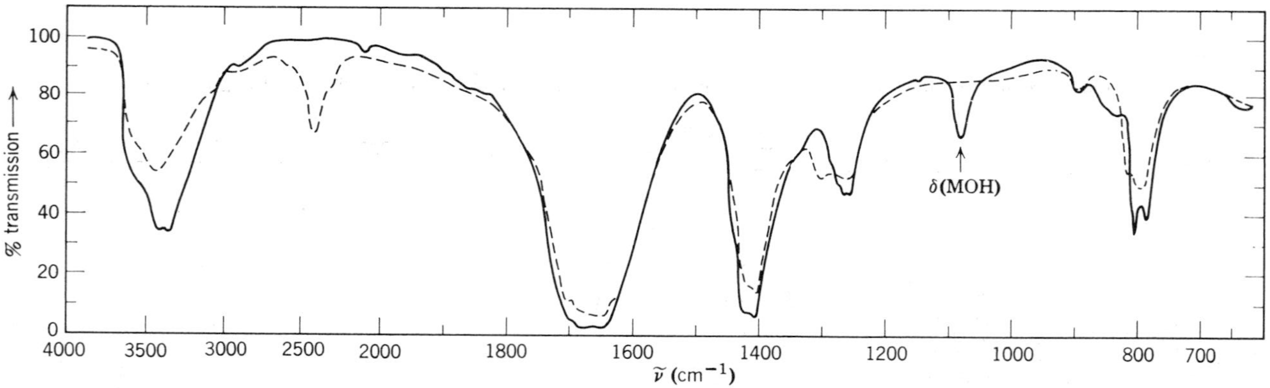

Fig. III-8. Infrared spectra of $K_4 \left[(ox)_2Co \underset{O}{\overset{O}{\underset{H}{\big\langle}}} Co(ox)_2 \right]$ (solid line) and its deuterated compound (broken line).

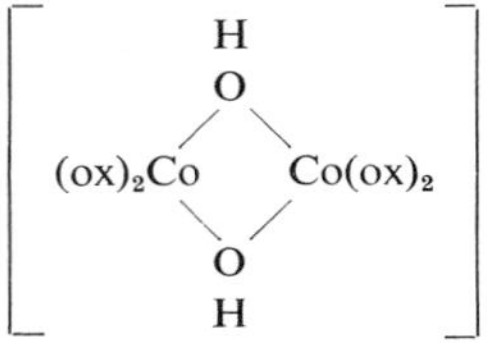

respectively. It should be emphasized that these frequencies are sensitive to the strength of the coordinate bond as well as to hydrogen bonds in the crystal. Therefore care must be taken in differentiating these two effects.

(3) Hydroxo (OH) Complexes

The infrared spectrum of the hydroxyl ion was discussed in Sec. II-1. The spectra of hydroxo complexes are expected to be similar to those of the metal hydroxides discussed previously. Although to date little has been reported about the infrared spectra of hydroxo complexes, Scargill[49] recently observed the O—H stretching bands at 3500–3200 cm^{-1} and the M—O—H bending bands at 1000–970 cm^{-1} in hydroxo complexes of ruthenium.

The OH group may also form a bridge between two metals. Figure III-8 shows the infrared spectrum of a Co(III) polynuclear complex having bridging OH groups.[49a] The bands near 1100 cm^{-1} may be due to the M—O—H bending mode in these compounds.

III-4. CARBONATO, NITRATO, SULFATO AND OTHER ACIDO COMPLEXES

As has been shown in Sec. III-1, the magnitude of the band shifts caused by coordination can be used as a measure of the strength of the coordinate bond. Where the symmetry of the ligand is lowered by coordination, marked changes in the spectrum are anticipated because of changes in the selection rule. A typical example of this effect is shown by the spectra of two complexes in which the same ligand coordinates to the metal as a unidentate and as a bidentate ligand.

(1) Carbonato (CO_3) Complexes

The carbonate ion coordinates to the metal in one of two ways:

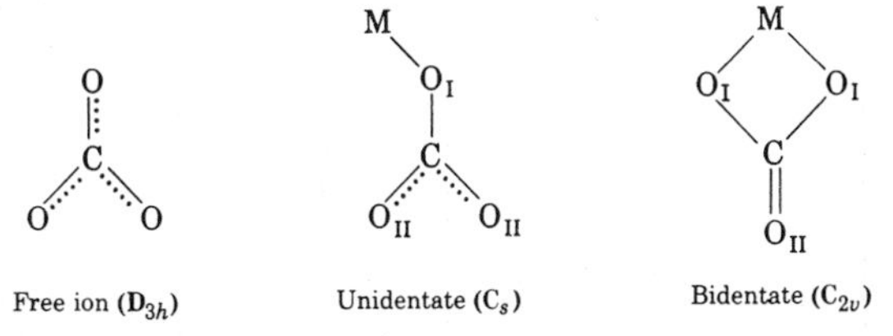

Free ion (D_{3h}) Unidentate (C_s) Bidentate (C_{2v})

The selection rule changes as shown in Table II-16. In $\mathbf{C}_{2v}$ and $\mathbf{C}_s$, the ν_1 vibration, which is forbidden in the free ion, becomes infrared active and each of the doubly degenerate vibrations, ν_3 and ν_4, splits into two

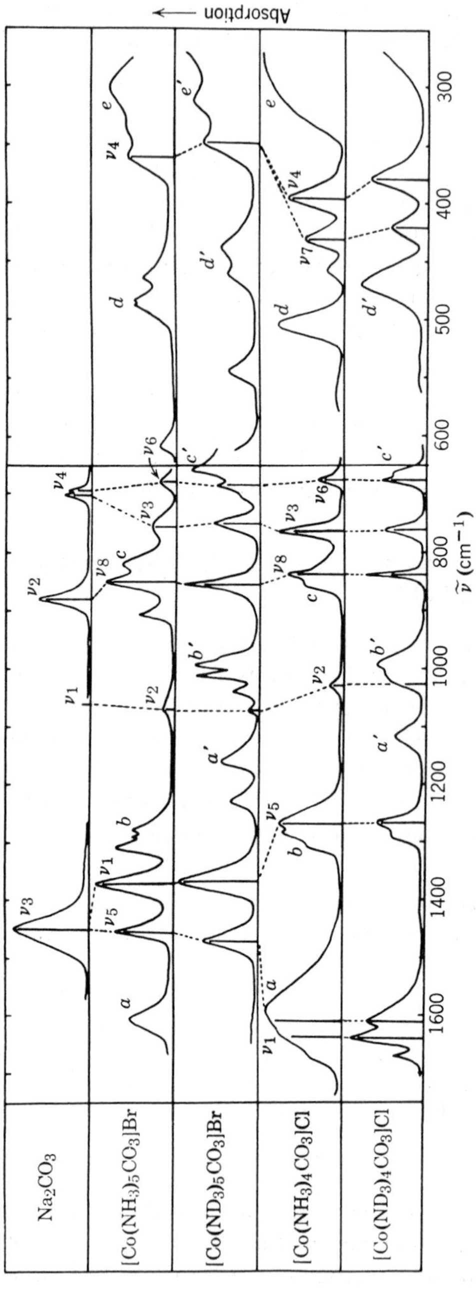

Fig. III-9. Infrared spectra of sodium carbonate, unidentate and bidentate Co(III) carbonato complexes: *a*, $\delta_d(NH_3)$; *b*, $\delta_s(NH_3)$; *c*, $\rho_r(NH_3)$; *d*, ν(Co—N); primes denote the corresponding vibrations for deuterated compounds.

bands. Nakamoto and colleagues[50] have demonstrated this effect experimentally (Fig. III-9). Although the number of infrared active fundamentals is the same for $\mathbf{C}_{2v}$ and $\mathbf{C}_s$, the splitting of the degenerate vibrations is larger in the bidentate than in the unidentate complex. This is also predicted quantitatively by the normal coordinate analysis carried out recently by Fujita et al.[51] for unidentate and bidentate carbonato complexes of Co(III). According to the results of these calculations, the CO stretching force constant, which is 5.46 for the free ion, becomes 6.0 for the CO_{II} bonds and 5.0 for the CO_I bond in the unidentate complex, whereas it becomes 8.5 for the CO_{II} bond and 4.1 for the CO_I bonds in the bidentate complex (all are UBF force constants in units of 10^5 dynes/cm). Thus the difference between the CO_{II} and CO_I stretching force constants is larger in the bidentate than in the unidentate complex. The observed and calculated frequencies and theoretical band assignments for these carbonato complexes are shown in Tables III-8*a* and III-8*b*.

In organic carbonates such as dimethyl carbonate, $(CH_3O_I)_2CO_{II}$, this effect is more striking because the CH_3—O_I bond is strongly covalent. In fact, the CO_{II} stretching band is observed at 1870 cm^{-1}, whereas the CO_I band is seen at 1260 cm^{-1}. Gatehouse and co-workers[52] have shown that the separation of the CO stretching bands increases along the series basic salt $<$ carbonato complex $<$ acid $<$ organic carbonate.

(2) Nitrato (NO_3) Complexes

The infrared spectra of the nitrato complexes are very similar to those of the carbonato complexes. Only unidentate nitrato complexes are known. Gatehouse and colleagues[53] have measured the infrared spectra of a number of unidentate nitrato complexes and interpreted the results for a model of $\mathbf{C}_{2v}$ symmetry. In terms of the notation in Table II-16, their results indicate that $\nu_1(A_1')$ of the free ion appears strongly at 1035–970 cm^{-1}, and $\nu_3(E')$ splits into two bands, one at 1530–1480 cm^{-1}, the other at 1290–1250 cm^{-1}. The out-of-plane bending mode (ν_2, A_2'') of the free ion appears at 830–815 cm^{-1}. For the in-plane bending mode (ν_4, E'), however, only one band is reported at 800–760 cm^{-1}. It is conceivable that the other band of this doubly degenerate mode may exist below 700 cm^{-1}.

The infrared spectra of bis-(triphenylphosphine oxide) dinitrato complexes of Co(II), Ni(II), Cu(II) and Zn(II) have been reported by Bannister and Cotton.[54]

(3) Sulfato (SO_4) Complexes

The free sulfate ion belongs to the high symmetry point group $\mathbf{T}_d$. Of the four fundamentals, only ν_3 and ν_4 are infrared active. If the ion

TABLE III-8a. CALCULATED AND OBSERVED FREQUENCIES OF UNIDENTATE Co(III) CARBONATO COMPLEXES (CM^{-1})

Species (C_{2v})	$\nu_1(A_1)$	$\nu_2(A_1)$	$\nu_3(A_1)$	$\nu_4(A_1)$	$\nu_5(B_2)$	$\nu_6(B_2)$	$\nu_7(B_2)$	$\nu_8(B_1)$
Calc. Freq.	1376	1069	772	303	1482	676	92	—
Assignment	$\nu(C—O_{II}) + \nu(C—O_I)$	$\nu(C—O_I) + \nu(C—O_{II})$	$\delta(O_{II}CO_{II})$	$\nu(Co—O_I)$	$\nu(C—O_{II})$	$\rho_r(O_{II}CO_{II})$	$\delta(CoO_IC)$	π
$[Co(NH_3)_5CO_3]Br$	1373	1070	756	362[a]	1453	678	—[b]	850
$[Co(ND_3)_5CO_3]Br$	1369	1072	751	351	1471	687	—	854
$[Co(NH_3)_5CO_3]I$	1366	1065	776	360	1449	679	—	850
$[Co(ND_3)_5CO_3]I$	1360	1063	742	341	1467	687	—	853
$[Co(NH_3)_5CO_3]NO_3\cdot\frac{1}{2}H_2O$	(1365)[c]	(1052)[c]	738	351	1482	690	—	856
$[Co(ND_3)_5CO_3]NO_3\cdot\frac{1}{2}D_2O$	(1370)[c]	(1053)[c]	745	344	1495	687	—	854
$[Co(NH_3)_5CO_3]ClO_4$	1370	—[d]	757	350	1455	681	—	852
$[Co(ND_3)_5CO_3]ClO_4$	1370	—[d]	760	338	1471	690	—	855

[a] Broad band due to overlapping with N—Co—N bending mode.
[b] Outside the CsBr region.
[c] Overlapped with $[NO_3]^-$ absorption.
[d] Hidden by strong $[ClO_4]^-$ absorption.

TABLE III-8*b*. CALCULATED AND OBSERVED FREQUENCIES OF BIDENTATE Co(III) CARBONATO COMPLEXES (CM^{-1})

Species (C_{2v})	$\nu_1(A_1)$	$\nu_2(A_1)$	$\nu_3(A_1)$	$\nu_4(A_1)$	$\nu_5(B_2)$	$\nu_6(B_2)$	$\nu_7(B_2)$	$\nu_8(B_1)$
Calc. Freq.	1595	1038	771	370	1282	669	429	—
Assignment	$\nu(C—O_{II})$	$\nu(C—O_I)$	Ring def. + $\nu(Co—O_I)$	$\nu(Co—O_I)$ + ring def.	$\nu(C—O_I)$ + $\delta(O_ICO_{II})$	$\delta(O_ICO_{II})$ + $\nu(C—O_I)$ + $\nu(Co—O_I)$	$\nu(Co—O_I)$	π
$[Co(NH_3)_4CO_3]Cl$	1593	1030	760	395	1265	673	430	834
$[Co(ND_3)_4CO_3]Cl$	1635, 1607	(1031)[a]	753	378	1268	672	418	832
$[Co(NH_3)_4CO_3]ClO_4$	1602	—[b]	762	392	1284	672	428	836
$[Co(ND_3)_4CO_3]ClO_4$	1603	—[b]	765	374	1292	676	415	835
$[Co(en)_2CO_3]Br$	1628, 1615	—[c]	759	353	1276	674	399	827
$[Co(enD)_2CO_3]Br$	1618	—[c]	768	348	1285	683	382	821
$[Co(en)_2CO_3]ClO_4$	1643	—[c]	757	372	1267, 1285	673	393	833
$[Co(enD)_2CO_3]ClO_4$	1615, 1603	—[c]	762	362	1275, 1288	680, 663	382	823
$K[Co(NH_3)_2(CO_3)_2]$	1623, 1597	1026	763, 744	366	1265	673	444, 411	839
$K[Co(ND_3)_2(CO_3)_2]$	1639, 1607	1026	762, 742	362	1260	673	438, 400	836
$[Co(NH_3)_6][Co(CO_3)_3]$	1590	1033	742	394, 351	1287	677	488, 465	831

[a] Overlapped with $\delta_s(ND_3)$. [b] Hidden by $[ClO_4]^-$ absorption. [c] Hidden by ethylenediamine bands.

is coordinated to a metal, the symmetry is lowered and splitting of the degenerate modes occurs together with the appearance of new bands in the infrared spectrum corresponding to Raman active bands in the free ion. The lowering of symmetry caused by coordination is different for the unidentate and the bidentate complexes, as shown by the accompanying structures. The change in the selection rules caused by the lowering of

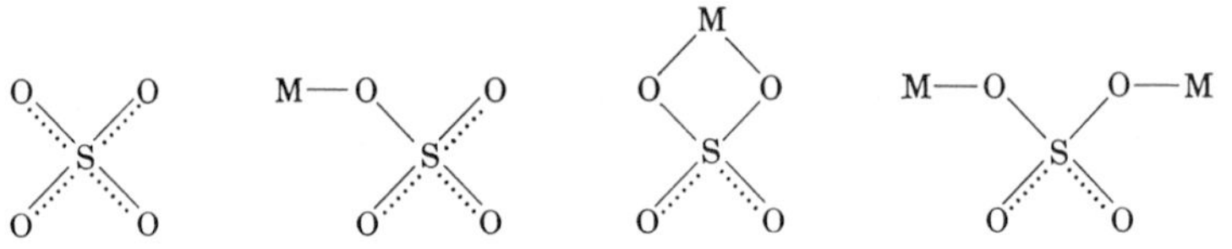

Free ion (T_d) | Unidentate complex (C_{3v}) | Bidentate complex (C_{2v}) | Bridged bidentate complex (C_{2v})

symmetry has already been indicated in Table II-26. Table III-9 and Fig. III-10 give the frequencies and the spectra obtained by Nakamoto et al.[50] for typical sulfato complexes. In $[Co(NH_3)_6]_2(SO_4)_3{\cdot}5H_2O$, ν_3 and ν_4 do not split, and ν_2 does not appear; although ν_1 is observed, it is very

TABLE III-9. VIBRATIONAL FREQUENCIES OF SULFATO COMPLEXES (CM^{-1})[50]

Compound	Symmetry	ν_1	ν_2	ν_3	ν_4
Free $[SO_4]^{2-}$ ion	$\mathbf{T}_d$	—	—	1104 (vs)[a]	613 (s)
$[Co(NH_3)_6]_2[SO_4]_3{\cdot}5H_2O$	$\mathbf{T}_d$	973 (vw)	—	1130–1140 (vs)	617 (s)
$[Co(NH_3)_5SO_4]Br$	$\mathbf{C}_{3v}$	970 (m)	438 (m)	1032–1044 (s) 1117–1143 (s)	645 (s) 604 (s)
$[(NH_3)_4Co(NH_2)(SO_4)Co(NH_3)_4][NO_3]_3$	$\mathbf{C}_{2v}$	995 (m)	462 (m)	1050–1060 (s) 1170 (s) 1105 (s)	641 (s) 610 (s) 571 (m)

[a] vs, very strong; s, strong; m, medium; w, weak; vw, very weak

weak. It is therefore concluded that $\mathbf{T}_d$ symmetry still holds, since the appearance of ν_1 may be attributed to a perturbation caused by the crystal field. In $[Co(NH_3)_5SO_4]Br$, however, both ν_1 and ν_2 appear with medium intensity; moreover, ν_3 and ν_4 each splits into two bands. Table II-26 suggests that this result can be explained by assuming lowering of the symmetry from $\mathbf{T}_d$ to $\mathbf{C}_{3v}$. In

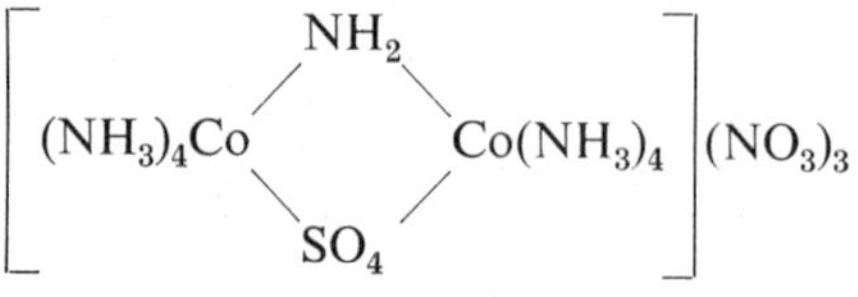

both ν_1 and ν_2 appear with medium intensity, and ν_3 and ν_4 each splits into three bands. These results suggest that the symmetry is once again lowered and probably reduced to $\mathbf{C}_{2v}$, as indicated in Table II-26. This conclusion was confirmed recently by Barraclough and Tobe,[54a] who obtained the infrared spectrum of a bidentate sulfato complex, $[Co(en)_2SO_4]Br$.

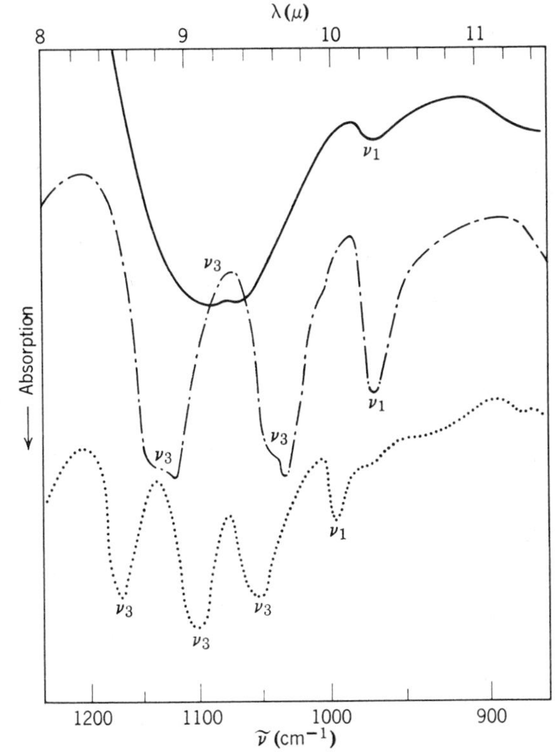

Fig. III-10. Infrared spectra of $[Co(NH_3)_6]_2(SO_4)_3 \cdot 5H_2O$ (solid line); $[Co(NH_3)_5SO_4]$ Br (dot-dash line); $\left[(NH_3)_4Co \begin{smallmatrix} NH_2 \\ SO_4 \end{smallmatrix} Co(NH_3)_4\right](NO_3)_3$ (dotted line).

(4) Other Acido Complexes

Similar considerations have been extended to complexes of other acido groups such as $[PO_4]^{3-}$,[55,55a] $[ClO_4]^-$,[56] and $[S_2O_3]^{2-}$.[56a] These studies have proved to be very useful in elucidating the structure of the complexes and the nature of the coordinate bond.

III-5. CYANO, RHODANATO AND AZIDO COMPLEXES

(1) Cyano (CN) Complexes

(a) C≡N Stretching Bands

Cyano complexes, just as simple inorganic cyanides, (Sec. II-1), exhibit sharp C≡N stretching bands at 2170–2040 cm^{-1}. Table III-10 gives

TABLE III-10. C≡N STRETCHING FREQUENCIES IN VARIOUS CYANO COMPLEXES IN THE SOLID STATE (CM^{-1})

Compound	Frequency[a] (cm^{-1})	References
$K_3[Cr(CN)_6]$	2135	57
$K_3[Mn(CN)_6]$	2125	57
$K_4[Mn(CN)_6]$	2060	57
$K_5[Mn(CN)_6]$	2048	57
$K_4[Fe(CN)_6]$	2094, 2073, 2062, 2044, 2031, 2026, 2006 2041 (aq.)	58, 59
$Na_3[Fe(CN)_5NH_3]\cdot 6H_2O$	2036	60
$Na_3[Fe(CN)_5H_2O]\cdot H_2O$	2043	60
$K_3[Fe(CN)_6]$	2125	60
$Na_2[Fe(CN)_5NH_3]\cdot H_2O$	2126	60
$Na_2[Fe(CN)_5H_2O]$	2120	60
$Na_2[Fe(CN)_5NO]\cdot 2H_2O$	2152	60, 60*a*
$K_6[Co_2(CN)_{10}]$	2133, 2090, 2079	61
$K_3[Co(CN)_5H_2O]$	2095	61
$K_3[Co(CN)_6]$	2143, 2129, 2126	61, 58
$K_2[Co(CN)_5H_2O]$	2140	61
$K_3[Co_2(CN)_8]$	2120, 2062	61
$K_2[Ni(CN)_4]\cdot H_2O$	2128	62
$K_4[Ni(CN)_4]$	1985	62, 63
$K_2[Ni(CN)_4]$	2135	64
$K_4[Ni_2(CN)_6]$	2128, 2079, 2055	64
$K_2[Ni(CN)_3NO]$	2133, 2118	61
$K_4[Ni(CN)_3CO]_2$	2135, 2055, 1983, 1905[b]	65
$K_3[Cu(CN)_4]$	2094, 2081, 2075	66, 67
$K_4[Mo(CN)_8]\cdot 2H_2O$	2119, 2096, 2049	68, 69
$K_4[Mo(CN)_8]$	2128, 2105	68
$K_3[Mo(CN)_8]\cdot 2H_2O$	2119, 2096, 2045	68
$K_3[Mo(CN)_8]$	2105, 2128	68
$K_3[Rh(CN)_6]$	2163	61
$K_3[Rh_2(CN)_8]$	2130, 2070	61
$K[Ag(CN)_2]$	2140	70
$K_2[Pd(CN)_4]\cdot 2H_2O$	2143	62
$K_3[W(CN)_8]\cdot 2H_2O$	2119, 2088, 2041	68
$K_4[W(CN)_8]$	2110	68
$K_3[W(CN)_8]$	2128, 2105	68
$K_3[Ir(CN)_6]$	2185	61
$K_2[Pt(CN)_4]3\cdot H_2O$	2150	71
$K[Au(CN)_2]$	2141	72
$K_2[Hg(CN)_4]$	2152	73
$K_2[Hg_2(CN)_6]$	2148, 2158	73

[a] More bands may be observed for some of these compounds under high resolution. For example, Bor[60a], using an LiF prism, observed four C≡N stretching bands for $[Fe(CN)_5NO]^{2-}$.

[b] CO stretching bands may be included.

the observed C≡N stretching frequencies for a number of cyano complexes. It demonstrates that some complexes exhibit band splitting under ordinary conditions or under high resolution in the crystalline state. Polynuclear cyano complexes show several C≡N stretching bands. Also, hydrates exhibit spectra different from those of the anhydrides.

That the C≡N stretching band of the free ion (K[CN], 2080 cm^{-1}) is shifted to a higher frequency by coordination is noteworthy since coordination usually weakens the ligand bond next to the coordinate bond, thus shifting the ligand stretching vibration to a lower frequency (see, for example, the N—H stretching band of ammine complexes, Sec. III-1) In terms of the accompanying resonance structures,[62] this result seems to

$$\text{Free ion:}\quad :\overset{-}{C}\equiv N: \;\leftrightarrow\; :C=\overset{\cdot\cdot\,-}{N}: \qquad \text{(IA)} \quad \text{(IIA)}$$

$$\text{Complex:}\quad M\text{—}C\equiv N: \;\leftrightarrow\; \overset{+}{M}=C=\overset{-}{\underset{\cdot\cdot}{N}}: \qquad \text{(IB)} \quad \text{(IIB)}$$

suggest that structure IIA contributes more to the total structure of the free ion than does structure IIB to the total structure of the complex.

According to El-Sayed and Sheline,[62] the C≡N stretching frequencies of the cyano complexes depend on several factors such as (1) the electronegativity, (2) the oxidation number and (3) the coordination number of the metal. The effect of electronegativity is seen in the frequency order of the C≡N stretching band which increases along the series $[Ni(CN)_4]^{2-}$ < $[Pd(CN)_4]^{2-}$ < $[Pt(CN)_4]^{2-}$. The electronegativity of Ni(II) is smallest and the contribution of structure IIB is largest. Therefore the C≡N stretching frequency of the Ni(II) complex is the lowest in this series. The effect of oxidation number is seen in the frequency order, which increases along the series $[Ni(CN)_4]^{4-}$ < $[Ni(CN)_4]^{2-}$. Here the larger negative charge of Ni(O) increases the contribution of structure IIB, resulting in a lower frequency shift in the Ni(O) complex. The effect of coordination number[74–76] is seen in the frequency order of the C≡N stretching band, which increases along the series $[Ag(CN)_4]^{3-}$ < $[Ag(CN)_3]^{2-}$ < $[Ag(CN)_2]^{-}$. Here an increase in the coordination number results in an increase in the negative charge on the metal which, in turn, increases the contribution of structure IIB, thus decreasing the frequency (Table III-11).

Jones and co-workers[74–76] have made an extensive infrared study of the equilibria of the cyano complexes of Ag(I), Cu(I), Ni(II) and Hg(II) in aqueous solutions. Figure III-11 shows the infrared spectra of aqueous silver cyano complexes obtained by changing the ratio of Ag^+ to $[CN]^-$ ions. Table III-11 lists frequencies and extinction coefficients from which

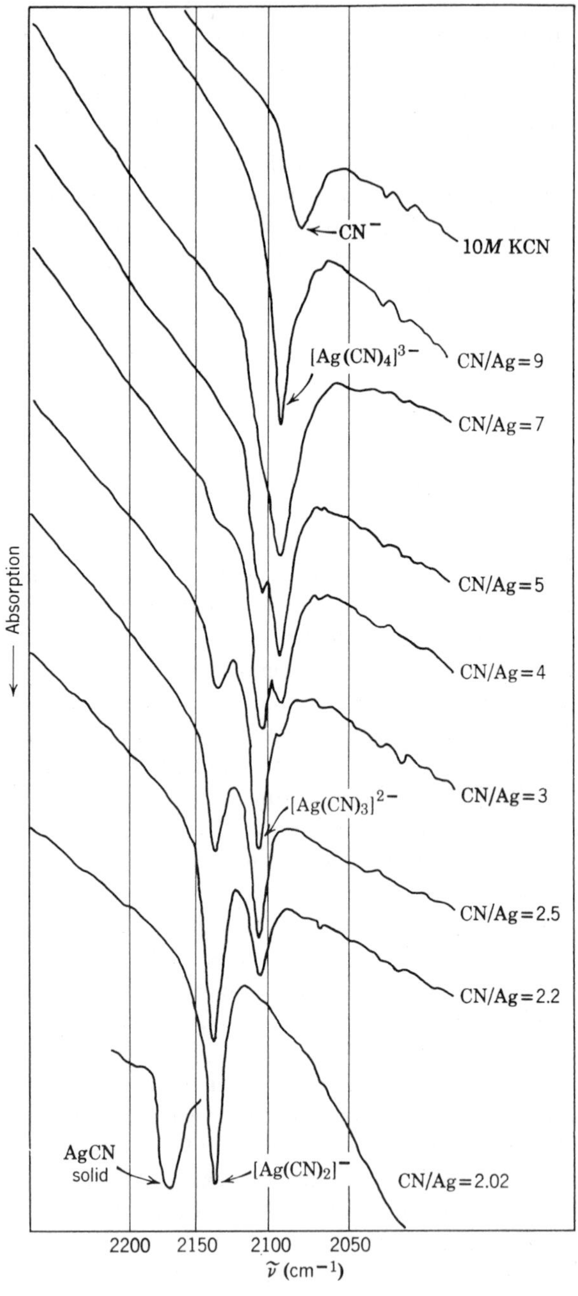

Fig. III-11. Infrared spectra of silver cyano complexes in aqueous solution.[74]

equilibrium constants can be calculated. Such investigations are highly important because the equilibrium constants of these very stable complexes are difficult to determine by the potentiometric method. Recently, Chantry and Plane[78] have studied the same equilibria using Raman spectra.

It is interesting to note that Prussian blue obtained by adding Fe^{3+} to $[Fe(CN)_6]^{4-}$ was shown to be identical with Turnbull's blue obtained by

TABLE III-11. FREQUENCIES AND MOLECULAR EXTINCTION COEFFICIENTS OF CYANO COMPLEXES IN AQUEOUS SOLUTIONS

Ion	Frequency (cm^{-1})	Mol. Extinction Coeff.	Reference
Free $[CN]^-$ ion	2080 ± 1	29 ± 1	74
$[Ag(CN)_2]^-$	2135 ± 1	264 ± 12	74
$[Ag(CN)_3]^{2-}$	2105 ± 1	379 ± 23	74
$[Ag(CN)_4]^{3-}$	2092 ± 1	556 ± 83	74
$[Cu(CN)_2]^-$	2125 ± 3	165 ± 25	75
$[Cu(CN)_3]^{2-}$	2094 ± 1	1090 ± 10	75
$[Cu(CN)_4]^{3-}$	2076 ± 1	1657 ± 15	75
$[Zn(CN)_4]^{2-}$	2149	113	76
$[Cd(CN)_4]^{2-}$	2140	75	76
$Hg(CN)_2$	2194	3	76
$[Hg(CN)_3]^-$	2161	26	76
$[Hg(CN)_4]^{2-}$	2143	113	76
$[Ni(CN)_4]^{2-}$	2124 ± 1	1068 ± 95	77
$[Ni(CN)_5]^{3-}$	2102 ± 2	1730 ± 230	77

adding Fe^{2+} to $[Fe(CN)_6]^{3-}$, as the two compounds exhibit the same single band at 2075 cm^{-1}.[79] The result confirms an old x-ray study made by Keggin and Miles.[80]

(b) Lower Frequency Bands

In addition to the C≡N stretching bands, the cyano complexes exhibit M—C stretching, M—C≡N and C—M—C bending bands in the lower frequency region. Figure III-12 shows the infrared spectra of $K_3[Co(CN)_6]$ and $K_2[Pt(CN)_4]\cdot 3H_2O$. In order to assign these low frequency bands, normal coordinate analyses have been done for cyano complexes of various structures. As Table III-12 shows, the results of these calculations indicate that the M—C stretching, M—C≡N bending and C—M—C bending vibrations appear at 500–350, 370–250 and about 100 cm^{-1}, respectively. The M—C stretching force constants used in these calculations are also given in the table. The M—C stretching frequencies of other

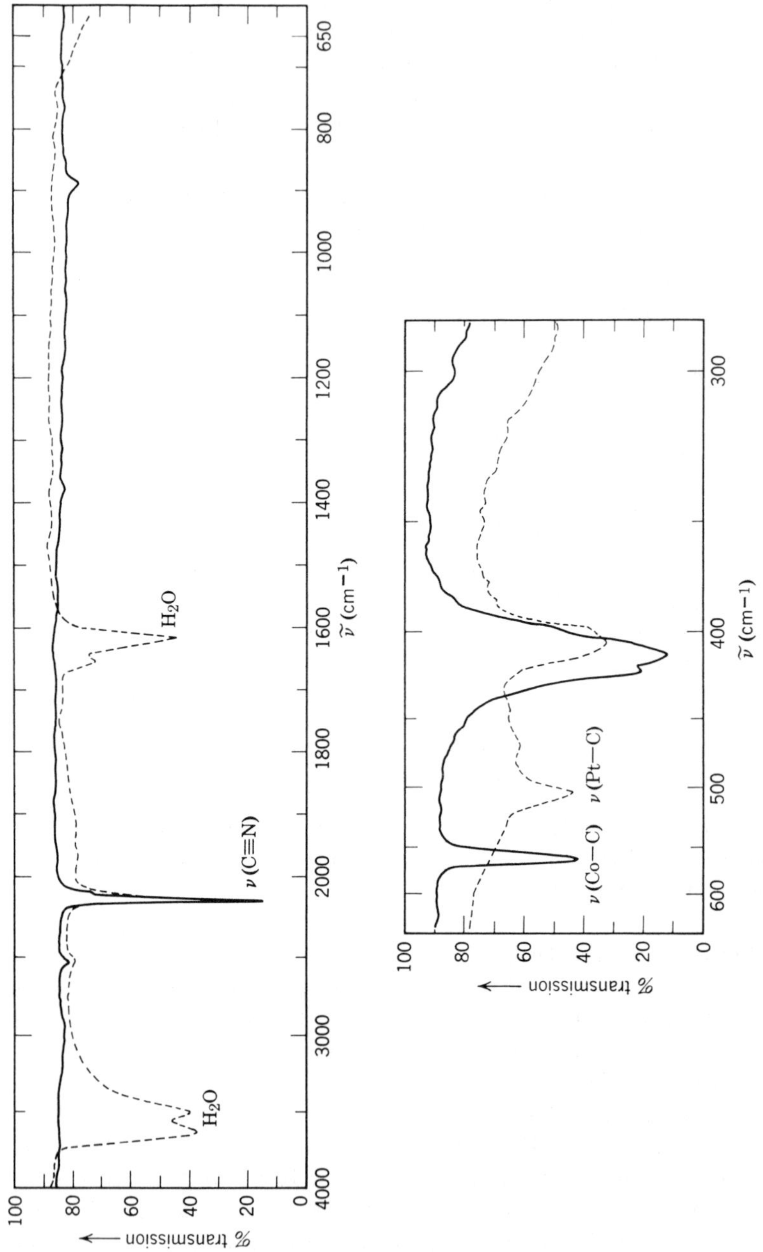

Fig. III-12. Infrared spectra of $K_3[Co(CN)_6]$ (solid line) and $K_2[Pt(CN)_4]\cdot 3H_2O$ (broken line).

cyano complexes are reported as $[Fe(CN)_6]^{3-}$, 505 cm^{-1}; $[Mn(CN)_6]^{3-}$, 514 cm^{-1}; $[Fe(CN)_6]^{4-}$, 584 cm^{-1}; $[Cr(CN)_6]^{3-}$, 462 cm^{-1};[83] and $[Co(CN)_6]^{3-}$, 564 cm^{-1}.[84] For recent normal coordinate analyses of octahedral cyano complexes, see Refs. 84*a* and 84*b*.

TABLE III-12. FREQUENCIES AND BAND ASSIGNMENTS OF THE LOWER FREQUENCY BANDS IN CYANO COMPLEXES (CM^{-1})

Compound	Symmetry	ν(M—C)	δ(M—C≡N)	δ(C—M—C)	ν(M—C) Force Constant [a]	References
$[Hg(CN)_2]$	$D_{\infty h}$	442 (IR) (415)	341 (IR) 276 (R)	(100)	2.607	81
$[Ag(CN)_2]^-$	$D_{\infty h}$	390 (IR) (360)	(310) 239 (R)	(107)	1.826	70
$[Au(CN)_2]^-$	$D_{\infty h}$	427 (IR) (452)	(368) 305 (R)	(100)	2.745	72
$[Cu(CN)_4]^{3-}$	T_d	364 (IR) 288 (R)	324 (R) 306 (IR)	(74) (63)	1.25–1.30	66, 67
$[Zn(CN)_4]^{2-}$	T_d	359 (IR)[b] 342 (R)	315 (IR)[b] 230 (R)	71 (R)	1.850	66*a*
$[Cd(CN)_4]^{2-}$	T_d	316 (IR)[b] 324 (R)	250 (R)[b] 194 (R)	61 (R)	1.654	66*a*
$[Hg(CN)_4]^{2-}$	T_d	330 (IR)[b] 335 (R)	235 (R)[b] 180 (R)	54 (R)	1.773	66*a*
$[Pt(CN)_4]^{2-}$	D_{4h}	505 (IR) 465 (R) 455 (R)	318 (R) 300 (IR)	95 (R)	3.425	71, 82
$[Ni(CN)_4]^{2-}$	D_{4h}	543 (IR) (419) (405)	433, 421 (IR) 488, (488) (325)	(54)	2.6	71*a*
$[Cr(CN)_6]^{3-}$	O_h	457 (IR) 374 (R) 336 (R)	694 (IR) 536 (R)	124 (IR) 106 (R)	1.9279	83

[a] Force constants (in units of 10^5 dynes/cm) were obtained by using the GVF field for all the ions except for $[Pt(CN)_4]^{2-}$, for which the UBF field was used.
[b] Coupled vibrations between ν(M—C) and δ(M—C≡N).

The Raman spectra of a large number of cyano complexes have been measured. Table III-13 lists the observed Raman frequencies. From the study of the infrared dichroism of single crystals, Jones has determined the orientation of linear cyano complex ions such as $[Ag(CN)_2]^-$ [70] and $[Au(CN)_2]^-$.[72] His results are in good agreement with those of x-ray analysis.

TABLE III-13. RAMAN FREQUENCIES OF CYANO COMPLEXES (CM^{-1})

Compound	Higher Frequency Bands	Lower Frequency Bands			Reference
K[CN]	(2160), 2077				20
$K_3[Cr(CN)_6]$	(2137)	782			20
$K_3[Fe(CN)_6]$	2136				20
$K_4[Fe(CN)_6]$	2090, 2056	505			20, 21, 85, 86
$K_3[Co(CN)_6]$	(2149), 2137	406		98	20, 21, 86
$Na_2[Ni(CN)_4]$	2159, 2147	439	294	94	20
$K_3[Cu(CN)_4]$	2096, 2074	502	360, 324		87
			304, 288		
$K_2[Zn(CN)_4]$	2143, (2055)		296		20, 21
$K_4[Mo(CN)_8]$	2135, 2121,	473	394	156	88
	2114	465	363		
		440	327		
$K_2[Cd(CN)_4]$	2134				20
$K_3[Rh(CN)_6]$	2166, 2147	445, 435		94	21
$K_3[Ir(CN)_6]$	2167, 2143	463, 450		95	21
$Na_2[Pt(CN)_4]$	2168, 2149	465, 455	320	95	21
$Na_2[Pd(CN)_4]$	2159, 2147	439	294	94	21
$Hg[CN]_2$	2189	412			89
$[Hg(CN)_4]^{2-}$	2148	342			89

(c) Bridged Cyano Complexes

As is seen in Table III-10, polynuclear cyano complexes absorb in two frequency ranges, one at 2130 and the other at 2090–2050 cm^{-1}. El-Sayed and Sheline[64] proposed the bridged structure I for $K_4[Ni_2(CN)_6]$, whereas Griffith and Wilkinson[61] prefer structure II, which has no bridging cyano

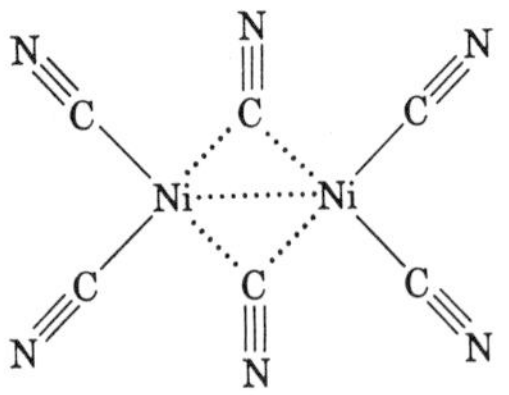

I

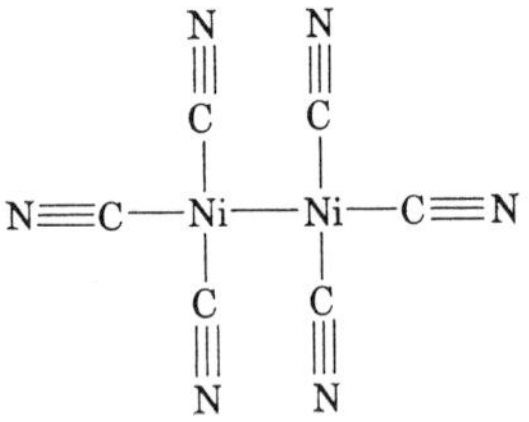

II

groups. Nast and co-workers[89a] also concluded from infrared spectra that two metal atoms in the $[Co_2(CN)_{10}]^{6-}$ ion are bonded directly to each other as in $Mn_2(CO)_{10}$ (see Sec. III-6). Bridged cyano complexes were prepared for the first time by Haim and Wilmarth.[89b] Dows, Haim and Wilmarth[89c] have found that the bridging cyano group absorbs at a higher frequency than does the terminal cyano group. For example, $[Na_2Co(CN)_5 \cdot H_2O]_x$ exhibits the bridging and terminal C≡N stretching bands at 2202 and 2130 cm^{-1}, respectively. This result is noteworthy since the bond order of the bridging group is usually lower than that of the terminal group.

(2) Thiocyanato(NCS) Complexes

The thiocyanato complexes exhibit C≡N and C—S stretching and N≡C—S bending vibrations at 2150–2080, 810–690, and 500–460 cm^{-1}, respectively. The infrared spectrum of a typical thiocyanato complex is shown in Fig. III-13. A comparison of the spectrum of the NCS group in a complex with that of the HNCS molecule has an interesting implication. The C≡N (1963 cm^{-1}) and C—S (963 cm^{-1}) stretching frequencies of the HNCS molecule[90] are lower and higher, respectively, than those of the thiocyanato complex. This indicates that the C≡N and C—S bond distances in HNCS should be longer and shorter, respectively, than those of the thiocyanato group in a complex. In fact, the structural data shown below for HNCS[91] and $NH_4[Cr(NH_3)_2(NCS)_4] \cdot H_2O$[92] agree with this prediction.

$$N=\!\!\!=\!\!\!=C=\!\!\!=\!\!\!=S \qquad Cr—N^+=\!\!\!=\!\!\!=C—\!\!\!\!—S^-$$
$$\overset{/}{} \quad \underset{1.22\ A \quad 1.56\ A}{} \qquad \underset{1.14\ A \quad 1.80\ A}{}$$
$$H$$

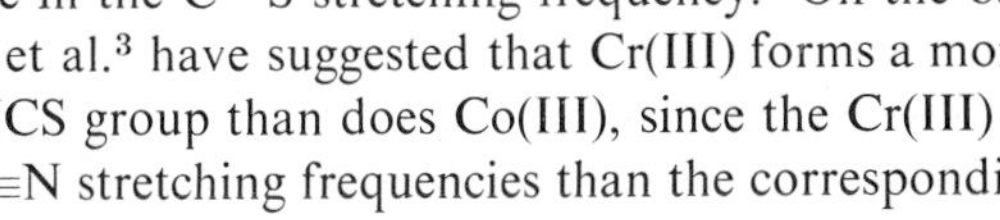

Thus it seems that an increase in the covalent character of the coordinate bond results in a decrease of the C≡N stretching frequency and a concomitant increase in the C—S stretching frequency. On the basis of this principle, Fujita et al.[3] have suggested that Cr(III) forms a more covalent bond with the NCS group than does Co(III), since the Cr(III) complexes exhibit lower C≡N stretching frequencies than the corresponding Co(III) complexes.

It has also been noted[3] that the C≡N stretching frequency of the complex is sensitive to the counter-ion. For example, $Hg[Cr(NH_3)_2(NCS)_4]_2$ exhibits two bands at 2160 and 2084 cm^{-1}, whereas

$$(CH_3)_3N(CH_2)_2OH[Cr(NH_3)_2(NCS)_4]$$

shows only one band at 2083 cm^{-1}. It has been suggested that the band at 2160 cm^{-1} may be due to an interaction which may be pictured as Cr—N$^+$≡C—S$^-$ ··· Hg^{2+}. In the other compound, such an interaction is negligibly small, for the positive charge of the cation is screened by the

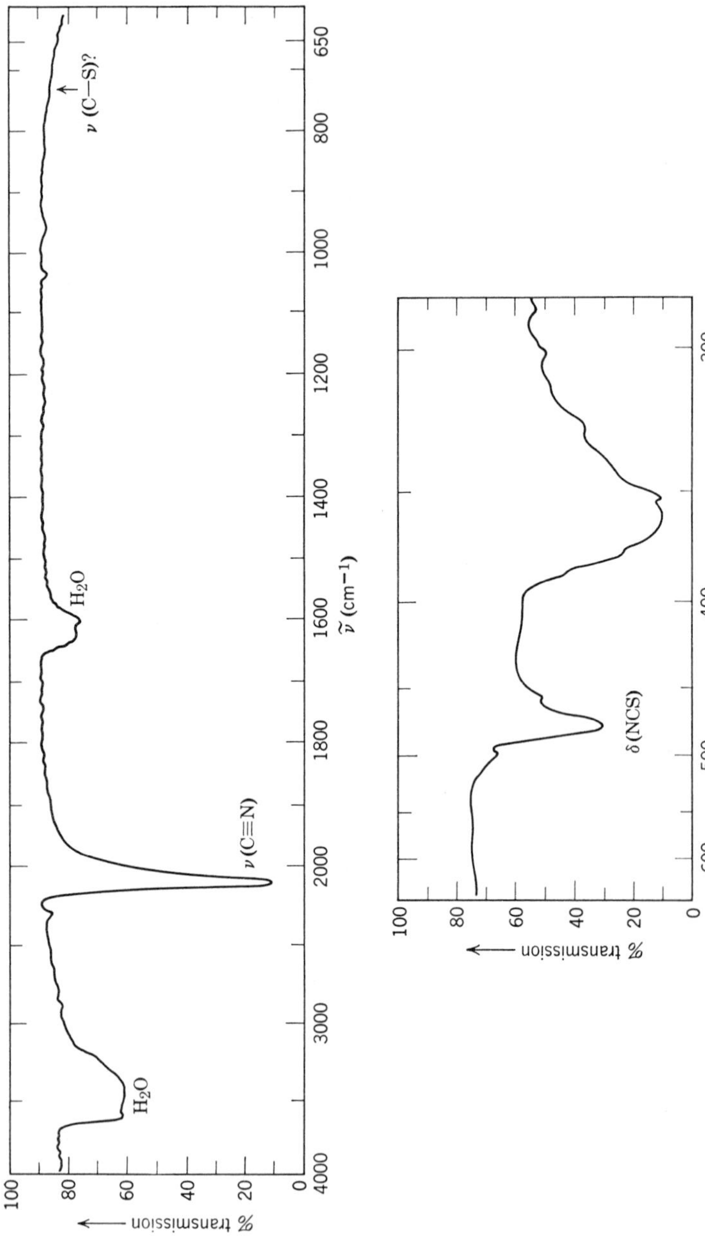

Fig. III-13. The infrared spectrum of $K_3[Cr(NCS)_6]\cdot 4H_2O$.

bulky aliphatic group. Thus a bridge formation such as mentioned above increases the C≡N stretching frequency.

The thiocyanato group may coordinate to the metal through nitrogen or sulfur. It is known from x-ray analysis that metals of the first transition series (e.g., V, Cr, Co, Ni, Cu, Zn) form M—N bonds, whereas those of the second half of the second and third transition series (e.g., Rh, Pd, Ag, Cd, Pt, Hg) form M—S bonds with the thiocyanato group. Mitchell and Williams[93] have suggested that the order of the C≡N stretching frequency is M—N=C=S ≤ M—S—C≡N < M · · · S^-—C≡N^+—M. Recently, Lewis and co-workers[93a] have found that the C—S stretching frequency is much higher in M—N=C=S (ca 820 cm^{-1}) than in M—S—C≡N (ca 700 cm^{-1}). Using this as a criterion together with x-ray and ultraviolet spectral studies, these workers have found that the bonding in the $[Mo(NCS)_6]^{3-}$ ion occurs through the nitrogen. Chamberlain and Bailar[94] and Baldwin[94a] using infrared spectra, have been able to differentiate *cis* and *trans* isomers of a number of Co(III) thiocyanato complexes.

As stated above, the thiocyanato group is able to form a bridge between two metal atoms. According to Chatt and Duncanson,[95] the bridging SCN group absorbs near 2182–2150 cm^{-1}, whereas the terminal SCN group absorbs at 2120–2100 cm^{-1}. For example, $[(P(n\text{-propyl})_3)_2Pt_2(SCN)_2Cl_2]$ (compound I), exhibits one bridging SCN band, whereas

$$[(P(n\text{-propyl})_3)_2Pt_2(SCN)_4],$$

(compound II), exhibits both bridging and terminal SCN bands. The infrared spectra of these compounds agree with the structures

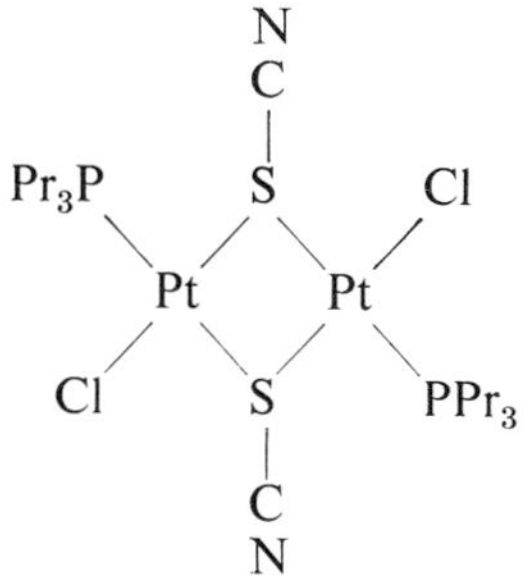

I

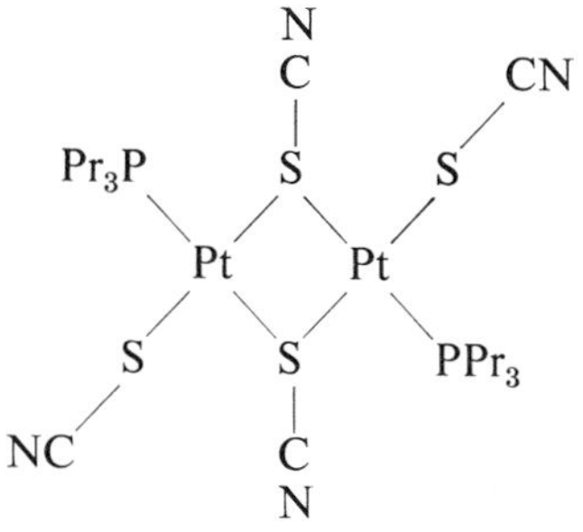

II

Compound I, however, exists as two isomers, α and β, which absorb at 2162 and 2169 cm^{-1}, respectively. Chatt and Duncanson[95] originally suggested a geometrical isomerism in which two SCN groups are in a *cis* or *trans* position with respect to the central ring. Later,[96–98] "bridge" isomerism such as shown below was demonstrated by x-ray analysis. A

$$Pr_3P \diagdown \underset{Pt}{\diagup} \diagup S—C\equiv N \diagdown \underset{Pt}{\diagup} \diagup Cl$$

Pr$_3$P   S—C≡N   Cl   Pr$_3$P   N≡C—S   Cl

　　Pt　　　　Pt　　　　　　　Pt　　　　Pt

Cl   N≡C—S   PPr$_3$ Cl   S—C≡N   PPr$_3$

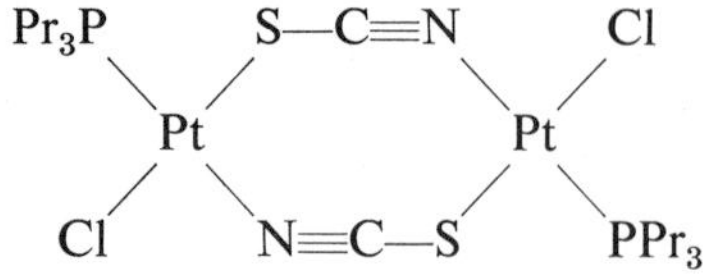

α   β

similar bridged structure for the thiocyanato group has been reported in [Cd(ethylenethiourea)$_2$(SCN)$_2$].[99]

(3) Azido (N$_3$) Complexes

The structure of the azido group is symmetrical in ionic crystals such as NH$_4$N$_3$, whereas it is asymmetrical in molecular crystals such as CH$_3$N$_3$ (Ref. I-35). The antisymmetric stretching (ν_3) frequency of NH$_4$N$_3$ is

$$NH_4^+[N_I \xrightarrow{1.15\,Å} N_{II} \xrightarrow{1.15\,Å} N_{III}]^- \qquad \underset{CH_3}{\overset{}{N_I}} \xrightarrow{1.24\,Å} N_{II} \xrightarrow{1.10\,Å} N_{III}$$

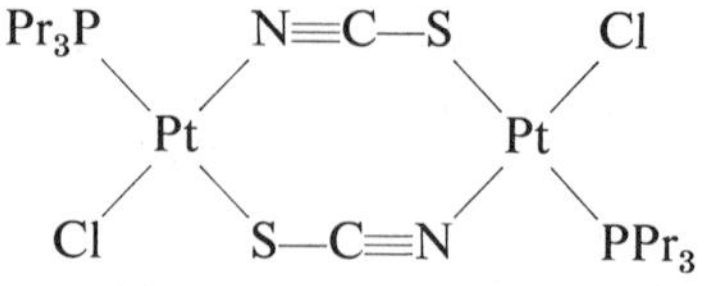

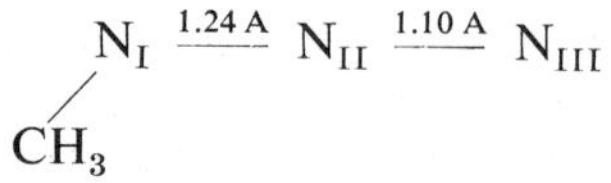

2030 cm^{-1} (Table II-5), whereas that of CH$_3$N$_3$ is 2143 cm^{-1}.[100] Thus, as the N$_I$—N$_{II}$ bond is weakened by coordination, the N$_{II}$—N$_{III}$ bond becomes stronger and ν_3 becomes higher. Fujita and colleagues[3] have found that ν_3 of [Cr(NH$_3$)$_5$N$_3$]I$_2$, 2094 cm^{-1}, is higher than that of [Co(NH$_3$)$_5$N$_3$]I$_2$, 2047 cm^{-1}. A similar trend is seen in [Cr(NH$_3$)$_3$(N$_3$)$_3$], 2072 cm^{-1}, and [Co(NH$_3$)$_3$(N$_3$)$_3$], 2017 cm^{-1}. These results may be interpreted as indicating that the M—N bond in the Co(III) complexes is more ionic than in the corresponding Cr(III) complexes. This result agrees with the observation that in aqueous solution the Co(III) azido complexes are more easily aquotized than the corresponding Cr(III) complexes.

III-6. CARBONYL AND NITROSYL COMPLEXES

(1) Carbonyl (CO) Complexes

Since metal carbonyls exhibit a variety of structures, their elucidation by means of vibrational spectra has been a subject of considerable interest. The method of determining molecular structure using group theory has already been explained in Secs. I-7–9. As stated at the end of Sec. I-9, however, care must be taken in applying this simple method to the observed spectra.

As a matter of convenience, metal carbonyls may be classified into the following four groups.

(a) Mononuclear Carbonyls

Since the structure of a mononuclear carbonyl is relatively simple, it can be determined from its vibrational spectrum without much difficulty. Normal coordinate analyses have been undertaken by a number of investigators, and complete band assignments are available for most of the compounds. Table III-14 lists the symmetry, the observed CO and M—C stretching frequencies and the M—C stretching force constants. For a

TABLE III-14. STRUCTURES AND VIBRATIONAL FREQUENCIES OF MONONUCLEAR METAL CARBONYLS (CM^{-1})

Compound	Symmetry	IR or R	Obs. ν(CO)	Obs. ν(MC)	K(M—C) (10^5 dynes/cm)	References
BH_3CO	C_{3v}	IR	2165	691	2.629 (GVF)	101–104
$Ni(CO)_4$	T_d	IR	2057	422	2.52 (GVF)	105–109
		R	2121, 2039	381, 422		110, 110*a*
$[Co(CO)_4]^-$	T_d	R	1918, 1883	532, 439	3.55 (GVF)	111–113
$[Fe(CO)_4]^{2-}$	T_d	R	1788	550, 464	4.06 (GVF)	111, 113
$Fe(CO)_5$	D_{3h}	IR	2028, 1994	472, 377	3.09–3.27 (GVF)	114
		R	2114, 2031	492, 414	2.47 (GVF)	115, 116
			1984	377		117–119
	C_{4v}	IR	2027, 2045	377, 364	1.625 (GVF)	120
$[Mn(CO)_5]^-$	D_{3h}	IR	1898, 1863			113
$Cr(CO)_6$	O_h	IR	2000	436	2.507 (GVF)	83, 121–123
					1.83 (UBF)	124
$Mo(CO)_6$	O_h	IR	2000	368	1.77 (UBF)	124, 121, 123
$W(CO)_6$	O_h	R	2121, 2015	432	— —	123

tetrahedral $M(CO)_4$ molecule, group theory predicts only one infrared active (F_2) and two Raman active CO stretching vibrations (A_1 and F_2). The same is true of the M—C stretching vibrations. As Table III-14 shows, the number of bands observed agrees with this prediction. The CO stretching frequency decreases remarkably in going from $Ni(CO)_4$ to $[Fe(CO)_4]^{2-}$. This may be due to an increase in the back donation of electrons from the metal to the CO group in the same order. As a result, the M—C stretching frequency and the corresponding force constant increase in the same order, as is seen in Table III-14.

Figure III-14 shows the structures of various metal carbonyls. If the $Fe(CO)_5$ molecule is trigonal bipyramidal (structure I), group theory predicts two infrared active (A_2'' and E') and three Raman active ($2A_1'$ and E') fundamentals for both the CO and Fe—C stretching vibrations.

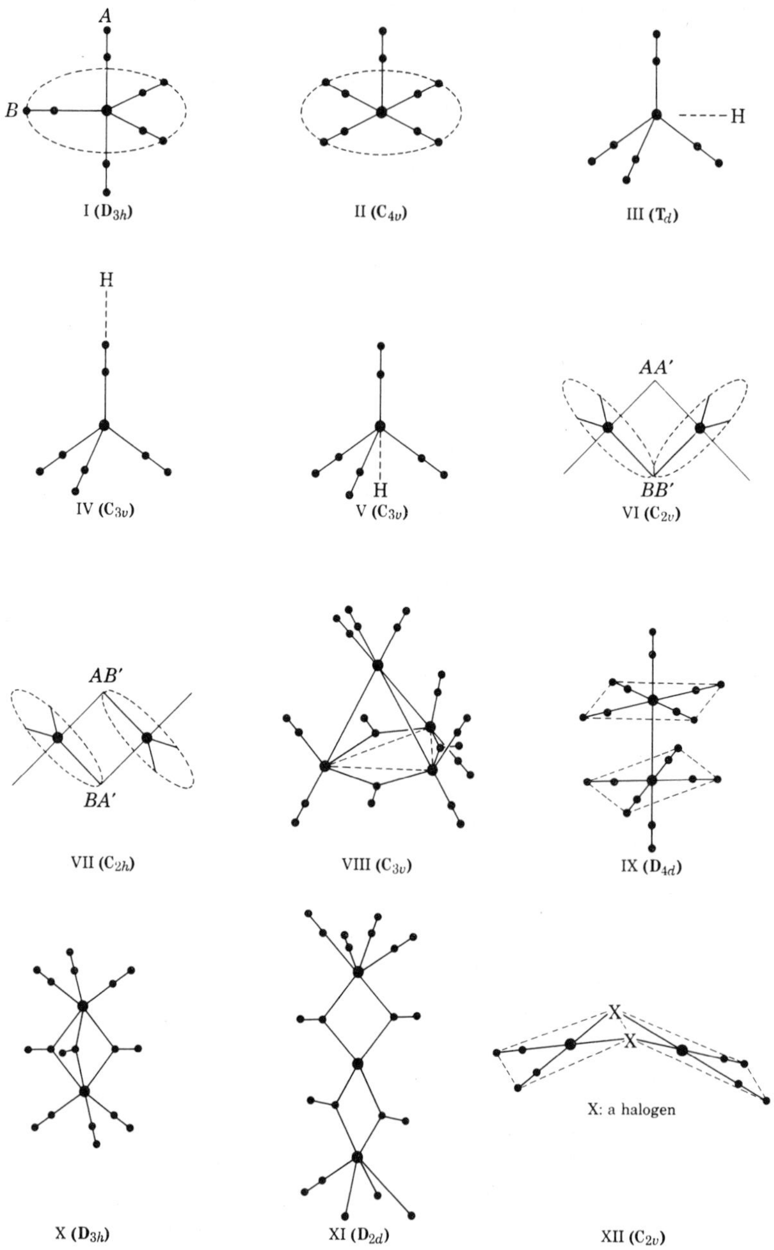

Fig. III-14. Structures of carbonyl compounds.

If the molecule is tetragonal pyramidal (structure II), it must exhibit three infrared active ($2A_1$ and E) and four Raman active ($2A_1$, B_1 and E) CO stretching bands. Although O'Dwyer[120] has proposed structure II, the infrared and Raman spectral data seem to fit structure I better.† Fateley and Lippincott[114] assigned the bands at 639 and 614 cm^{-1} to the Fe—C stretching modes, but these frequencies may be too high.[120]

For an octahedral $M(CO)_6$ molecule, the theory predicts one infrared active (F_{1u}) and two Raman active (A_{1g} and E_g) fundamentals both for the CO and for the M—C stretching modes. Since only these fundamentals are observed, $Cr(CO)_6$ and $Mo(CO)_6$ must be octahedral.

(b) Hydrocarbonyls

The location of the hydrogen atom in $HCo(CO)_4$ has been a subject of controversy. Friedel and colleagues[112,125] have concluded that the structure must be intermediate between III and IV (Fig. III-14). The infrared spectrum of $HCo(CO)_4$ exhibits one CO stretching band at 2049 cm^{-1} with a shoulder at 2066 cm^{-1}. This finding agrees with structure IV, but IV should exhibit one OH stretching band which, however, was not observed. Thus Friedel and co-workers concluded that the hydrogen may be close enough to one or more of the oxygens to produce two infrared active CO stretching modes, but not bound strongly enough to produce an observable OH stretching band. Edgell and colleagues[126] have proposed structure V, in which the hydrogen atom is on the three-fold axis and about 2 A away from the Co atom. Cotton[127] has shown, however, that the maximum overlap between the $1s$ orbital of hydrogen and the $2p\pi$ orbitals of carbon and oxygen occurs at a distance of about 1.2 A from the Co atom. Although the band at 704 cm^{-1} has been suggested as a Co—C stretching mode,[112] Edgell and co-workers concluded that this band is associated with a motion involving the hydrogen atom. This conclusion has been confirmed by Cotton and Wilkinson.[128] Recently, Edgell and Summitt[129] assigned the band at 1934 cm^{-1} to the Co—H stretching (corresponding GVF force constant, ca. 2.22×10^5 dynes/cm), and the band at 704 cm^{-1} to the Co—H bending mode. A similar structure may be expected for $[HFe(CO)_4]^-$, the Raman spectrum of which was obtained recently by Stammreich et al.[111] From nuclear magnetic resonance studies, Bishop et al.[130] have estimated the Fe—H distance in $H_2Fe(CO)_4$ to be about 1.1 A.

The infrared spectrum of $HMn(CO)_5$ has been studied by Wilson,[131] who concluded that a structure of $\mathbf{C}_{4v}$ symmetry, in which the $Mn(CO)_5$ group forms a square pyramid with the hydrogen atom on the four-fold axis, can be ruled out. Cotton and co-workers[132] reached the same conclusion, but none of these investigators could determine the structure. The infrared

† Recently, the $\mathbf{D}_{3h}$ structure of $Fe(CO)_5$ was proved by x-ray analysis (A. W. Hanson, *Acta Cryst.*, **15,** 930 (1962).

spectra of $HRe(CO)_5$ and $DRe(CO)_5$ have been obtained by Beck and co-workers,[132a] who assigned the bands at 1832 and 1318 cm^{-1} to the Re—H and Re—D stretching modes, respectively. However, no definite structures were deduced from their results.

(c) Polynuclear Carbonyls

In general, a terminal CO group absorbs at 2100–2000 cm^{-1}, whereas a bridging CO group absorbs at 1900–1800 cm^{-1}. Using an NaCl prism, Cable et al.[133] observed three terminal (2070, 2043 and 2025 cm^{-1}) and one bridging (1858 cm^{-1}) CO stretching bands for $Co_2(CO)_8$. Among several possible models for this compound, structures VI and VII of Fig. III-14 correspond best to predictions from group theory. They were constructed by joining two trigonal bipyramidal units (structure I) so that the axial-axial and the equatorial-equatorial CO groups are shared as shown in structure VI ($\mathbf{C}_{2v}$ symmetry), or two axial-equatorial CO groups are shared as shown in structure VII ($\mathbf{C}_{2h}$ symmetry). According to group theory, structure VI should show five terminal and two bridging CO stretching bands, and structure VII should show three terminal and one bridging CO stretching bands in the infrared spectrum. Since the spectrum obtained by Cable and co-workers[133] and Friedel et al.[112,134] agrees with the predictions based on structure VII, it was concluded that VII is more probable than VI. Recently, Cotton and Monchamp[135] and Bor and Markó,[135a] using a CaF_2 and an LiF prism, found five terminal (2075, 2064, 2047, 2035 and 2028 cm^{-1}) and two bridging (1867 and 1859 cm^{-1}) CO stretching bands, respectively (Fig. III-15). These results rather agree with structure VI. Recent x-ray analysis† indicates, however, that the structure of $Co_2(CO)_8$ is similar to that of $Fe_2(CO)_9$ (structure X), in which one bridging CO group is removed ($\mathbf{C}_{2v}$ symmetry).

The infrared spectrum of $Co_4(CO)_{12}$ was first obtained by Friedel et al.,[112] who found two terminal (2058 and 2030 cm^{-1}) and one bridging (1873 cm^{-1}) CO stretching bands. Using a CaF_2 prism, however, Cotton and Monchamp[135] have found four terminal (2070, 2062, 2045 and 2033 cm^{-1}) and one bridging (1869 cm^{-1}) CO stretching bands. The structure of this compound may be too complex to allow its determination from vibrational spectra alone. Recently, Corradini[136] deduced structure VIII (Fig. III-14) from x-ray analysis. According to group theory, this model should exhibit six terminal and two bridging CO stretching bands. The observed spectrum is, however, simpler than this prediction. Thus the infrared spectrum of $Co_4(CO)_{12}$ provides an example of a serious discrepancy between the theoretical prediction and the observed spectrum.[135]

The infrared spectra of $Mn_2(CO)_{10}$ and $Re_2(CO)_{10}$ were first reported

† G. G. Summer and H. P. Klug, *Abst. Nat. Am. Cryst. Assoc.*, Boulder, Colorado, July, 1960.

by Brimm et al.[137] Since no bridging CO stretching bands were found, they suggested that dimerization occurs through formation of an M—M bond. Cotton and co-workers[138] also studied the infrared spectra of these compounds and found three CO stretching bands between 2070 and 1985 cm^{-1}. They concluded that structures in which two $M(CO)_5$ pentagonal pyramids are joined by forming an M—M bond can be ruled out because they are expected to show only two infrared active CO stretching bands. Later, Dahl et al.,[139] using x-ray analysis, proved that the compound

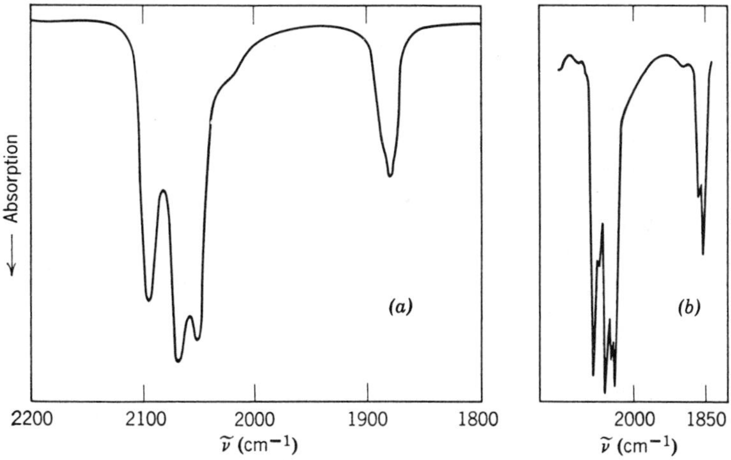

Fig. III-15. Infrared spectra of $Co_2(CO)_8$ in CO stretching region: (*a*) NaCl prism (hexane solution); (*b*) CaF_2 prism (pentane solution).

actually has structure IX. The discrepancy here, however, turned out to be due to an error in the infrared study (Ref. I-31).

The infrared spectrum of $Fe_2(CO)_9$ was first obtained by Sheline and Pitzer,[119] who found two terminal (2080 and 2034 cm^{-1}) and one bridging (1828 cm^{-1}) CO stretching bands. This result agrees with that predicted for structure X, obtained by x-ray analysis.[140] The infrared spectrum of $Fe_3(CO)_{12}$ was first reported by Sheline,[141] who observed two terminal (2043 and 2020 cm^{-1}) and one bridging (1833 cm^{-1}) CO stretching bands. On the basis of this result, Sheline proposed structure XI. Cotton and Wilkinson,[142] however, observed three terminal (2043, 2020 and 1997 cm^{-1}) and two bridging (1858 and 1826 cm^{-1}) CO stretching bands. Mills[143] rejected structure XI, which lacks a center of symmetry, from his x-ray study. Dahl and Rundle,[144,145] however, state that the symmetry argument fails owing to a disorder in the lattice; they present evidence that the three Fe atoms are located at the corners of an essentially equilateral triangle. Stammreich and co-workers[145a] found from Raman spectra that $M[Co(CO)_4]_2$ (M = Cd or Hg) has a linear OC—Co—M—Co—CO bond and takes a staggered conformation of $\mathbf{D}_{3d}$ symmetry.

(d) Substituted Metal Carbonyls

Irving and Magnusson[146] have reported the CO stretching frequencies of a number of Pt(II) carbonyl complexes such as $Pt(CO)_2X_2$, $Pt_2(CO)_2X_4$ and $[Pt(CO)X_3]^-$(X = Cl, Br or I). For all series of halogen compounds, it was found that the CO stretching frequency of the chloro complex had the highest value and that of the iodo complex the lowest, that of the bromo complex being intermediate. This result was interpreted as due predominantly to an inductive effect, since any mesomeric effect of the halogens should cause the reported order to be reversed. Brimm and co-workers[137] and Abel and Wilkinson[147] have reported the CO stretching frequencies of carbonyl halides of Mn and Re. McDowell and colleagues[147a] have done a normal coordinate analysis of $Co(CO)_3NO$. Abel and co-workers[148] have studied the infrared spectra of compounds of the type $M(CO)_3L_3$ (M = Cr, Mo or W; L = pyridine, $(C_6H_5)_3P$, $(C_6H_5)_3As$, $(C_6H_5)_3Sb$, PCl_3, $AsCl_3$ or $SbCl_3$, etc.), and noted that the CO stretching frequency has a rather wide range (2100–1700 cm^{-1}), although all the compounds studied are mononuclear. Infrared data have been accumulated for a number of metal carbonyls substituted with a variety of organic ligands: ditertiary arsines (Cr, Mo, W, Fe),[149] phosphines (Fe, Ni),[150,150a] isocyanides (Fe, Cr, Mo),[150,151] substituted benzenes (Cr).[152] Recently Orgel[152a] offered a general theoretical discussion of the infrared spectra of substituted metal carbonyls of the type $M(CO)_{6-n}L_n$, where M is a d^6 atom or ion and L is a substituent. Winkhaus and Wilkinson[153] have obtained the infrared spectra of binuclear olefin-substituted Co carbonyl compounds of the type $Co_2(CO)_6L$ and $Co_2(CO)_4L_2$, where L represents a diene. Appearance of bridging CO stretching bands suggests that the two bridging CO groups originally present in $Co_2(CO)_8$ are retained in these compounds. Hieber and Beck[153a] obtained the infrared spectra of compounds of the type $Fe_2(CO)_6X_2$, where X represents S, Se, SC_2H_5 or SeC_2H_5. Apparently the two Fe atoms are bridged by two S or Se atoms in these compounds. Garland and Wilt[153b] showed that the infrared spectra of $Rh_2(CO)_4X_2$ (X = Cl or Br) can be interpreted on the basis of structure XII, which was found from x-ray analysis by Dahl et al.[153c]

(2) Nitrosyl (NO) Complexes

As stated in Sec. II-1, the nitrosonium ion ($[NO]^+$) absorbs at about 2220 cm^{-1}, whereas nitric oxide (NO) absorbs at 1876 cm^{-1}. The NO group in metal nitrosyl complexes may be cationic ($[NO]^+$), anionic ($[NO]^-$) or nearly neutral (NO), depending on the nature and valence state of the metal, and on the ligands present in the same complex. From infrared data on a wide range of nitrosyl complexes, Lewis et al.[154] have shown that the cationic $[NO]^+$ stretching frequency falls in the range between 1940 and 1575 cm^{-1} whereas the anionic $[NO]^-$ stretching band is observed in the range between 1200 and 1040 cm^{-1}.

Using these criteria, they concluded that the previously reported structure, $Na_2[Co(NO_2)_4(H_2O)(NO)]$, must be $Na_2[Co(NO_2)_4(OH)(NO^+)]$ since this compound exhibits a cationic $[NO]^+$ stretching band at 1720 cm^{-1}. They also studied the infrared spectra of $[Co(NH_3)_5NO]X_2$, where two isomers exist: the black series (X = Cl$^-$, $[NO_3]^-$ or $[IO_3]^-$) and the red series (X = Br$^-$, I$^-$ or $[SO_4]^{2-}$). The black series exhibits the NO stretching band at 1170 cm^{-1} and, therefore, does not have a cationic $[NO]^+$ group. From other evidence, a dimeric structure having an N—N bond was

$$\left[\begin{array}{c} (NH_3)_5Co \qquad O^- \\ \diagdown \quad \diagup \\ N \\ | \\ N^+ \\ \diagup\!\diagup \quad \diagdown \\ O \qquad Co(NH_3)_5 \end{array}\right]^{4+}$$

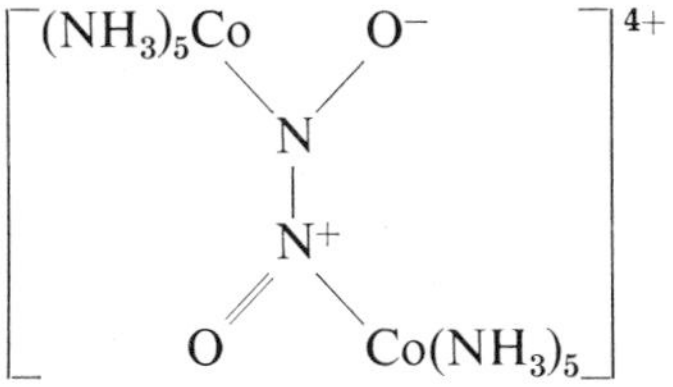

proposed. The red series, on the other hand, is monomeric and exhibits an NO stretching band between 1195 and 1045 cm^{-1}. Therefore the structure must be $[Co(NH_3)_5(NO^-)]X_2$. Infrared spectroscopy has also been applied to the structural determination of a number of nitrosyl complexes of other transition metals. Table III-15 lists the chemical

TABLE III-15.   THE $[NO]^+$ STRETCHING FREQUENCIES OF NITROSYL COMPLEXES (CM^{-1})[155]

Structure	$\nu(NO^+)$
$K_3[Cr^I(CN)_5NO]\cdot H_2O$	1645
$K_4[Mo^{II}(OH)_2(CN)_5NO]$	1595
$Ni(NO)[O(C_2H_5)_2]OH$	1820
$[Rh(NO)_2Cl]_2$	1703, 1605
$K[Co^I(CN)(CO)_2NO]$	1720
$[Pt(NO)(en)_2Cl]Cl_2$	1750
$K_2[Pd(NO)(NO_2)_4NO_3]$	1720
$K_5[V(CN)_5NO]$	1575

formulas and the $[NO]^+$ stretching frequencies of some nitrosyl complexes as obtained by Griffith et al.[155]

Bertin and co-workers[156] also studied the infrared spectra of the black and red salts, $[Co(NH_3)_5NO]X_2$, and attributed the band at 1620 cm^{-1} to

NO stretching and the band at about 1100 cm^{-1} to NH vibrations of ammonia coordinated to the metal. Recently, Griffith et al.[155] confirmed their own band assignments by studying the isotope effect on the infrared spectra of $[Co(NH_3)_5NO](NO_3)_2$ using N^{15}. Jahn[157] measured the infrared spectra of a number of nitrosyl halides of Fe, Co and Ni. The NO frequencies of these compounds are between 1860 and 1760 cm^{-1}, and they must therefore contain a cationic or neutral NO group. For $[Co_2(NO)_4X_2]$ (X = Cl, Br or I), he proposed a structure of V_h symmetry such as

$$
\begin{array}{ccccc}
\text{ON} & & \text{Cl} & & \text{NO} \\
& \diagdown \; \diagup & & \diagdown \; \diagup & \\
& \text{Co} & & \text{Co} & \\
& \diagup \; \diagdown & & \diagup \; \diagdown & \\
\text{ON} & & \text{Cl} & & \text{NO}
\end{array}
$$

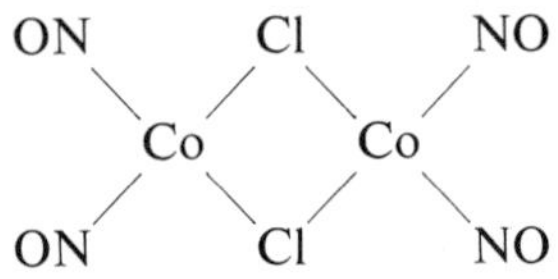

Waddington and Klanberg[158] measured the NO stretching frequencies of nitrosyl compounds such as $NOBF_3Cl$ (2335 cm^{-1}), $NOSbF_5Cl$ (2300 cm^{-1}), $NOSbCl_4$ (1900 cm^{-1}) and $NOAsCl_4$ (1860 cm^{-1}). The first two frequencies represent the free $[NO]^+$ ion, whereas the latter two frequencies are near those of coordinated neutral and cationic $[NO]^+$.

III-7. COMPLEXES OF UREA, SULFOXIDES AND RELATED COMPOUNDS

(1) Complexes of Urea and Related Compounds

Penland and co-workers[159] studied the infrared spectra of *urea complexes* to determine whether coordination occurs through nitrogen or oxygen. The electronic structure of urea may be represented by a resonance hybrid of structures I, II and III, with each contributing roughly an equal amount.

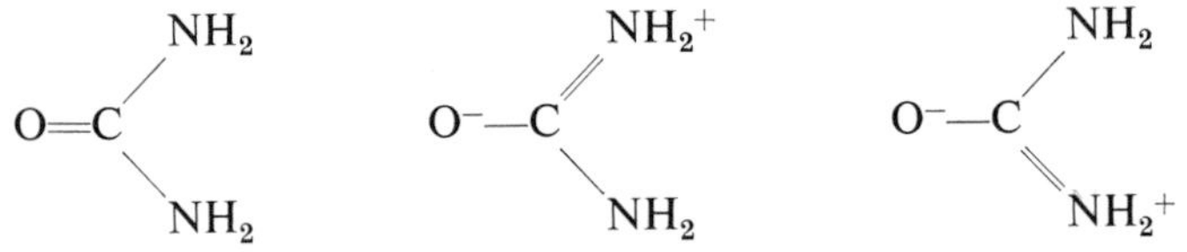

$$
\underset{\text{I}}{
\begin{array}{c}
\diagup \text{NH}_2 \\
\text{O=C} \\
\diagdown \text{NH}_2
\end{array}}
\qquad
\underset{\text{II}}{
\begin{array}{c}
\diagup\!\!\diagup \text{NH}_2^+ \\
\text{O}^-\!\!-\!\text{C} \\
\diagdown \text{NH}_2
\end{array}}
\qquad
\underset{\text{III}}{
\begin{array}{c}
\diagup \text{NH}_2 \\
\text{O}^-\!\!-\!\text{C} \\
\diagdown\!\!\diagdown \text{NH}_2^+
\end{array}}
$$

If coordination occurs through nitrogen, contributions of structures II and III will decrease. This results in an increase of the CO stretching frequency with a decrease of the CN stretching frequency. The NH stretching frequency in this case may fall in the same range as those of the amido complexes (Sec. III-1). If coordination occurs through oxygen, the contribution of structure I will decrease. This may result in a decrease of the CO stretching frequency but no appreciable change in the NH stretching frequency. Since the spectrum of urea itself has been analyzed completely,[160] band shifts caused by coordination can be checked immediately. The results shown in Table III-16 indicate that coordination occurs through nitrogen in the Pt(II) complex, and through oxygen in the Cr(III) complex. It was also found that Pd(II) coordinates to the nitrogen whereas Fe(III), Zn(II) and Cu(II) coordinate to the oxygen of urea.

Lane and colleagues[161] studied the infrared spectra of *methylthiourea complexes* and concluded that methylthiourea forms M—S bonds with

TABLE III-16. SOME VIBRATIONAL FREQUENCIES OF UREA AND ITS METAL COMPLEXES (CM^{-1})[159]

$[Pt(urea)_2Cl_2]$	Urea	$[Cr(urea)_6]Cl_3$	Predominant Mode
3390	3450	3440	$\nu(NH_2)$, free
3290	3350	3330	
3130, 3030		3190	$\nu(NH_2)$, bonded
1725	1683	1505[a]	ν(C—O)
1395	1471	1505[a]	ν(C—N)

[a] ν(C—O) and ν(C—N) couple in the Cr complex.

Zn(II) and Cd(II), and M—N bonds with Pd(II), Pt(II) and Cu(II). From infrared studies on *thiourea* ($(NH_2)_2CS$) *complexes*, Yamaguchi et al.[162] found that all the metals studied (Pt, Pd, Zn and Ni) form M—S bonds since, as for the M—O bonds in urea complexes, the CN stretching frequency increases and the CS stretching frequency decreases upon coordination without appreciable change of the NH stretching frequency. Lane and co-workers[163] obtained the spectrum of the *tetrakis*-(ethylenethiocarbamido)-Cu(II) complex.

(2) Complexes of Sulfoxides and Related Compounds

Cotton and colleagues[164] studied the infrared spectra of *sulfoxide complexes* to see whether coordination occurs through oxygen or sulfur. The electronic structure of sulfoxides may be represented by a resonance hybrid of the structures

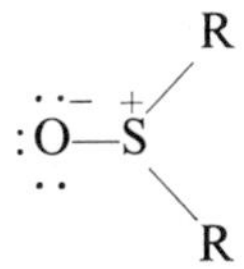

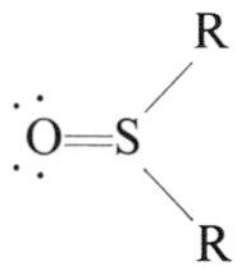

II

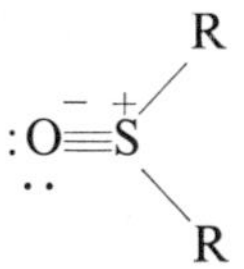

III

If coordination occurs through oxygen, contributions of structures II and III will decrease and will result in a decrease of the SO stretching frequency. If coordination occurs through sulfur, the contribution of structure I will decrease and may result in an increase of the SO stretching frequency. It has been concluded that coordination occurs through oxygen in the $[Co(DMSO)_6]^{2+}$ ion since the SO stretching frequencies of this ion (950 cm^{-1}) are lower than that of free dimethylsulfoxide (DMSO) which absorbs at 1100–1055 cm^{-1}. On the other hand, coordination may occur through sulfur in $PdCl_2 \cdot 2DMSO$ and $PtCl_2 \cdot 2DMSO$ since the SO stretching frequencies of these compounds (1157–1116 cm^{-1}) are higher than that of the free ligand. Using the same arguments, Francis and Cotton[165] concluded that coordination occurs through oxygen for Co(II), Ni(II) and Cu(II), and through sulfur for Pd(II) and Pt(II) in *complexes of tetrahydrothiophene oxide*. Recently, Drago and Meek[166] studied the infrared spectra of DMSO complexes. They claim that the bands at about 950 cm^{-1} (previously assigned to the SO stretching mode) and 1000 cm^{-1} are due to the methyl rocking and the SO stretching modes, respectively. If so, the SO stretching frequency is not very sensitive to the nature of the metal. This finding may be attributed to the coupling between the two modes mentioned above. Selbin and co-workers[166a] have also compared the SO and CS stretching frequencies of DMSO complexes of various metals.

Cotton and colleagues[167] have also investigated the infrared spectra of *complexes of phosphine oxides and arsine oxides*. They found that the PO stretching frequency of trimethyl- or triphenylphosphine oxide (1200–1170 cm^{-1}) decreases by 70–20 cm^{-1} upon complex formation. On the other hand, the AsO stretching frequency of triphenyl arsine oxide (880 cm^{-1}) decreases by 40 cm^{-1} in some complexes and increases by 30–20 cm^{-1} in others.

III-8. COMPLEXES OF ETHYLENEDIAMINE AND RELATED COMPOUNDS

As Fig. III-16 illustrates, the infrared spectra of ethylenediamine (en) complexes are very complicated. Although no theoretical band assignments are available for these complexes, studies of the vibrational spectra afford valuable information about the conformation of the chelate ring.

As shown in Fig. III-17, ethylenediamine may exist in the *cis*, *trans* or *gauche* form, depending on the angle of internal rotation. The *trans* form is not suitable for coordination because the two nitrogen atoms are far apart. Thus ethylenediamine in a chelate ring must be *cis* or *gauche*. Using optical rotatory dispersion, Kobayashi[168] concluded that the chelate

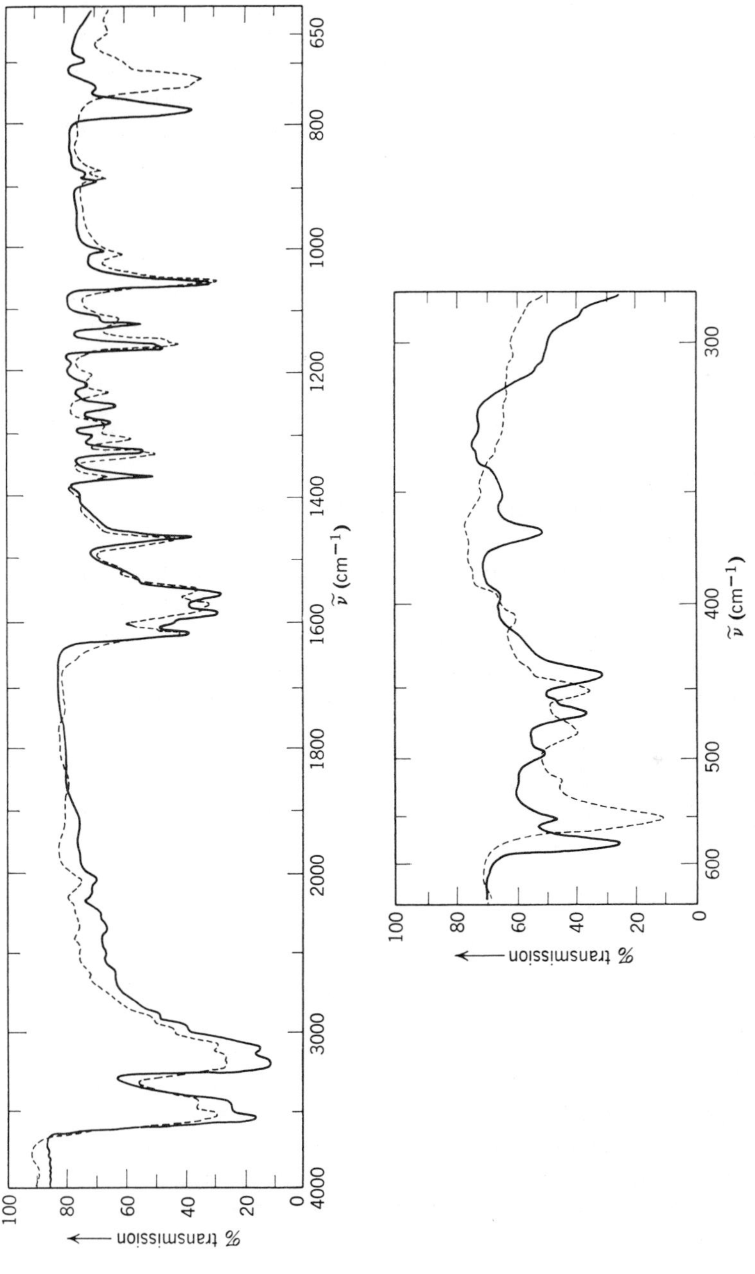

Fig. III-16. Infrared spectra of $[Co(en)_3]Br_3$ (solid line) and $[Cr(en)_3]Cl_3$ (broken line).

ring in *d*-$[Co(en)_3]Br_3$ is not planar. Later, Nakahara et al.[4] found from x-ray analysis that the chelate ring in $[Co(en)_2Cl_2]Cl{\cdot}HCl{\cdot}H_2O$ is not planar and that the ethylenediamine molecules are in the *gauche* form.

In another approach, Mizushima and co-workers (Ref. I-27) made an extensive study of the internal rotation of 1,2-substituted ethane derivatives and concluded that these molecules exist as a mixture of *trans* and

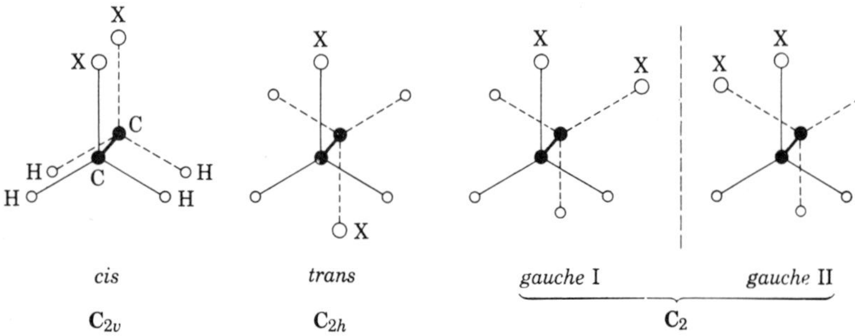

Fig. III-17. Rotational isomers of 1,2-substituted ethane.

gauche forms in the gaseous and liquid state and in solution, but that only the *trans* form occurs in the crystalline state. In an extension of this work, Mizushima et al.[169] determined the conformation of the chelate rings in metal complexes of 1,2-dithiocyanatoethane and 1,2-dimethylmercaptoethane. Through a comparison of the spectrum of the complex with that

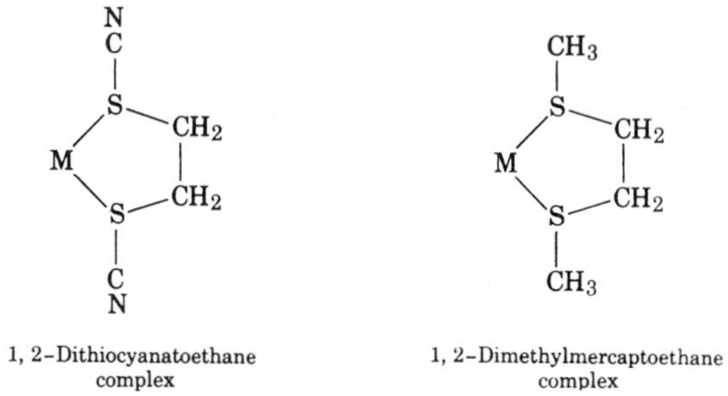

of the free ligand in solution (*trans* plus *gauche*) and in the crystalline state (*trans*), the conformation of the chelate ring in both of these ligands was found to be *gauche*.

Powell and Sheppard[170] compared the infrared spectra of a number of ethylenediamine complexes and found two types of spectra: *A*-type spectra, which are seen in octahedral Co(III), Cr(III) and Rh(III) and square-planar Pt(II) and Pd(II) complexes; and *B*-type spectra, which are seen in octahedral Ni(II) and square-planar Cu(II) complexes. In general, the *B*-type spectrum is slightly simpler than the *A*-type spectrum. These workers concluded that this difference can be attributed only to a difference of conformation of the chelate ring. Since the Co(III) complex is definitely *gauche*,[4] the *A*-type spectrum must result from the *gauche* conformation. Although Powell and Sheppard attributed the *B*-type spectrum to the *cis* conformation, the chelate rings in the $[Cu(en)_2]^{2-}$ [171] and $[Ni(en)_3]^{2-}$ [172] ions have been proved, by x-ray analysis, to be *gauche*. They have, accordingly, abandoned their earlier hypothesis.[173] At the present time, the origin of the difference between the two types of spectra is still unknown. Powell and Sheppard[173] have found that the NH_2 rocking and M—N stretching frequencies in a series of ethylenediamine complexes of various metals can be correlated with stability constants, irrespective of the spectral type mentioned above.

Powell and Sheppard[174] have also studied the infrared spectrum of $(C_2H_4)Cl_2Pt(en)PtCl_2(C_2H_4)$, in which the ethylenediamine molecule is likely to be *trans*. Since the symmetry of the *trans* form is higher than that of the *cis* and *gauche* forms, the spectrum of the *trans* form must be simpler than those obtained previously for the *gauche* and *cis* forms. This was found to be true. Brodersen[175] concluded, on the basis of his infrared and x-ray studies on $[Hg(en)Cl_2]_\infty$, that *trans*-ethylenediamine coordinates to the mercury atom in this manner:

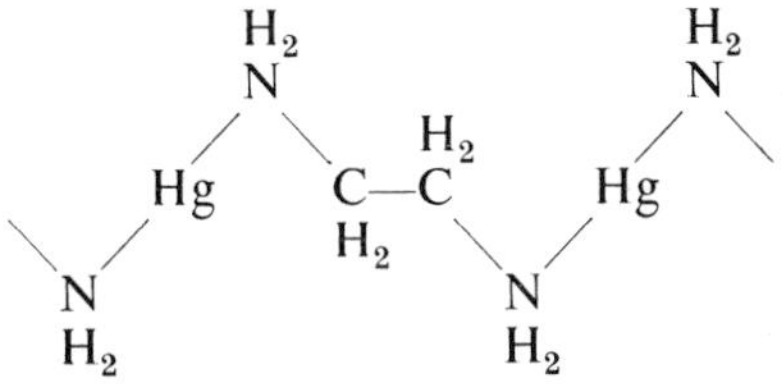

Similar structures have been suggested by Newman and Powell[175a] for complexes like $[M(en)Cl_2]_\infty$ (M = Zn or Cd). For the spectra of other ethylenediamine complexes, see Refs. 8, 32, 94, 94*a* and 176.

III-9. COMPLEXES OF α-DIIMINES AND RELATED COMPOUNDS

The structures of the metal chelate compounds of α-diimines and related compounds are shown in Fig. III-18. The relatively high stability of these compounds is usually attributed to resonance forms such as[177]

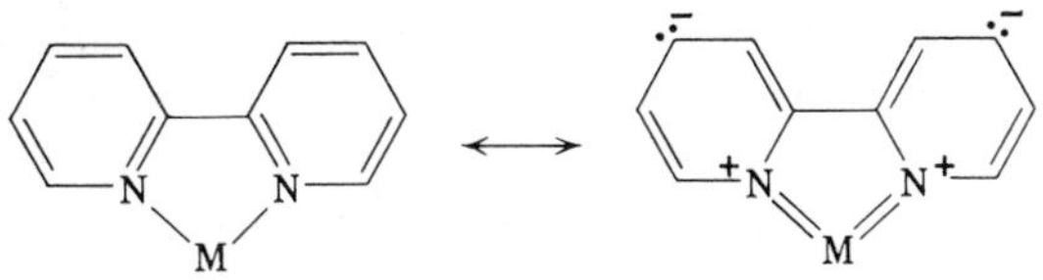

If this is correct, the M—N bond in these compounds must have partial

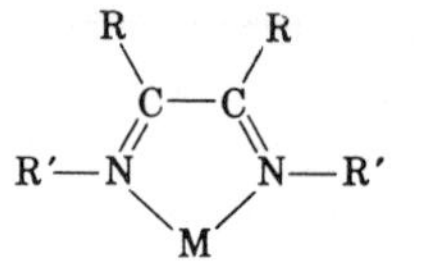

I_a R = H, R′ = CH_3, glyoxal-bis-methylimine (GMI)

I_b R = R′ = CH_3, biacetyl-bis-methylimine (BMI)

I_c R = CH_3, R′ = NH_2, biacetyldihydrazone (BDH)

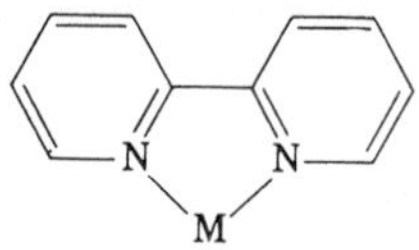

II 2, 2′-Bipyridine (BIPY)

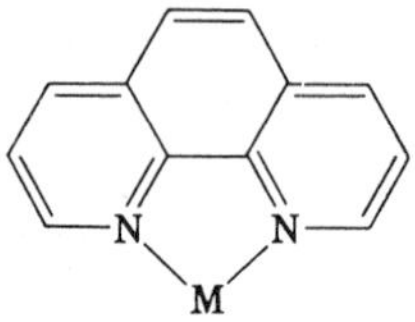

III 1, 10-Phenanthroline (PHEN)

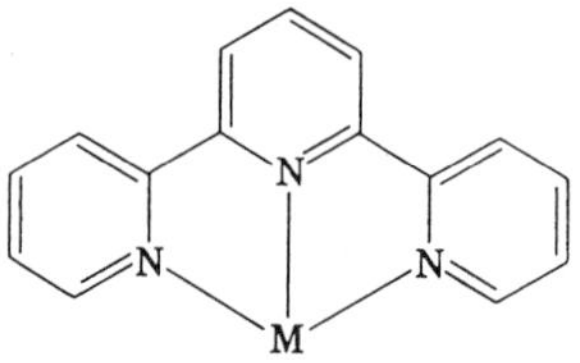

IV 2, 2′, 2″-Terpyridine (TRPY)

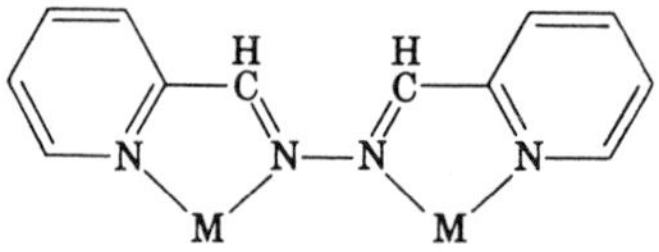

V 2-Pyridinaldazine (PAA)

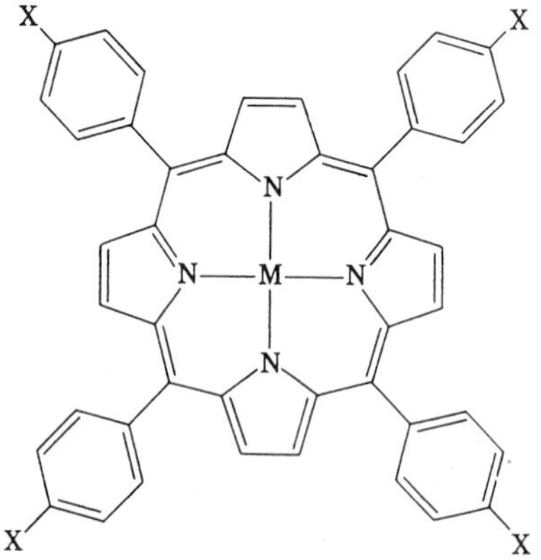

X = H, Cl, OCH_3

VI *p*-Substituted tetraphenylporphine (TPP)

Fig. III-18. Structures of metal chelate compounds of α-diimines and related compounds.

double bond character, and the corresponding force constant must be large compared with those of other coordinate bonds. The M—N stretching force constant obtained from normal coordinate analysis would provide direct evidence for this resonance in the chelate ring. The complex of GMI (structure I*a*) is most suitable for theoretical analysis because its structure is the simplest of those shown in Fig. III-18.

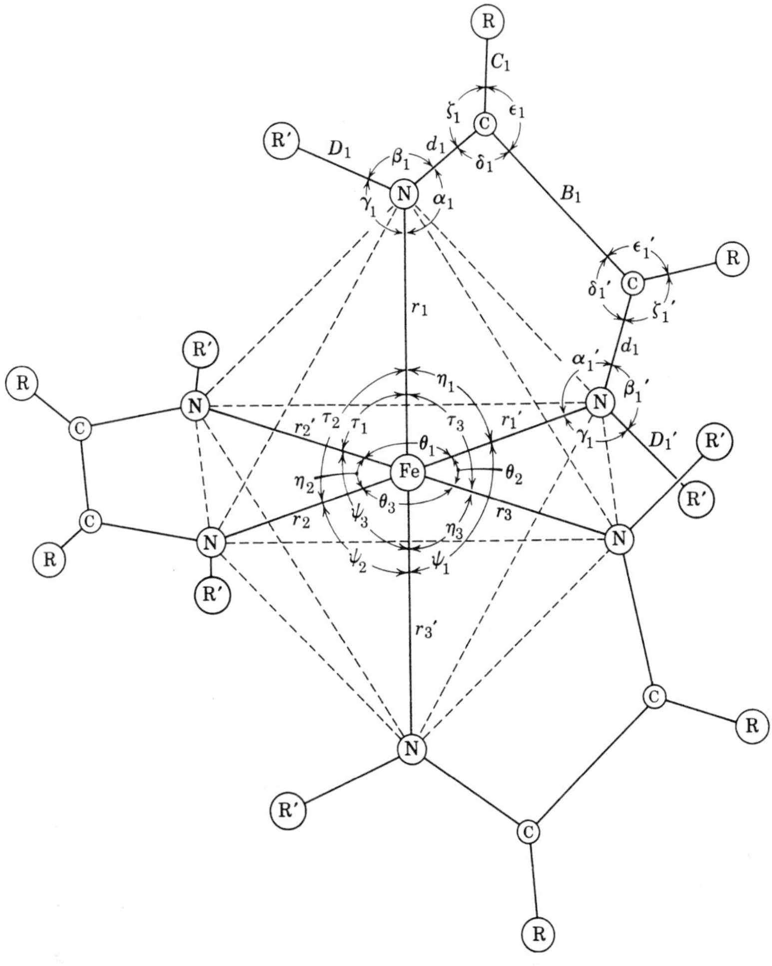

Fig. III-19. Molecular model and internal coordinates of the 1:3 complex. (Internal coordinates are shown only for one chelate ring.)

In doing a normal coordinate analysis, however, it is better to employ a 1:3 (metal/ligand) model of the GMI complex, since strong interaction between ligands may introduce a large error in the estimation of the force constants.† Although this necessitates the construction of high order G and F matrices, the calculation can be done without any fundamental difficulty. Figure III-19 shows the 1:3 complex model and the internal

† If a simple 1:1 model for the complex is used for the calculation of the 1:3 complex, the metal-ligand stretching force constant is overestimated by roughly 10–15% (see Ref. 242).

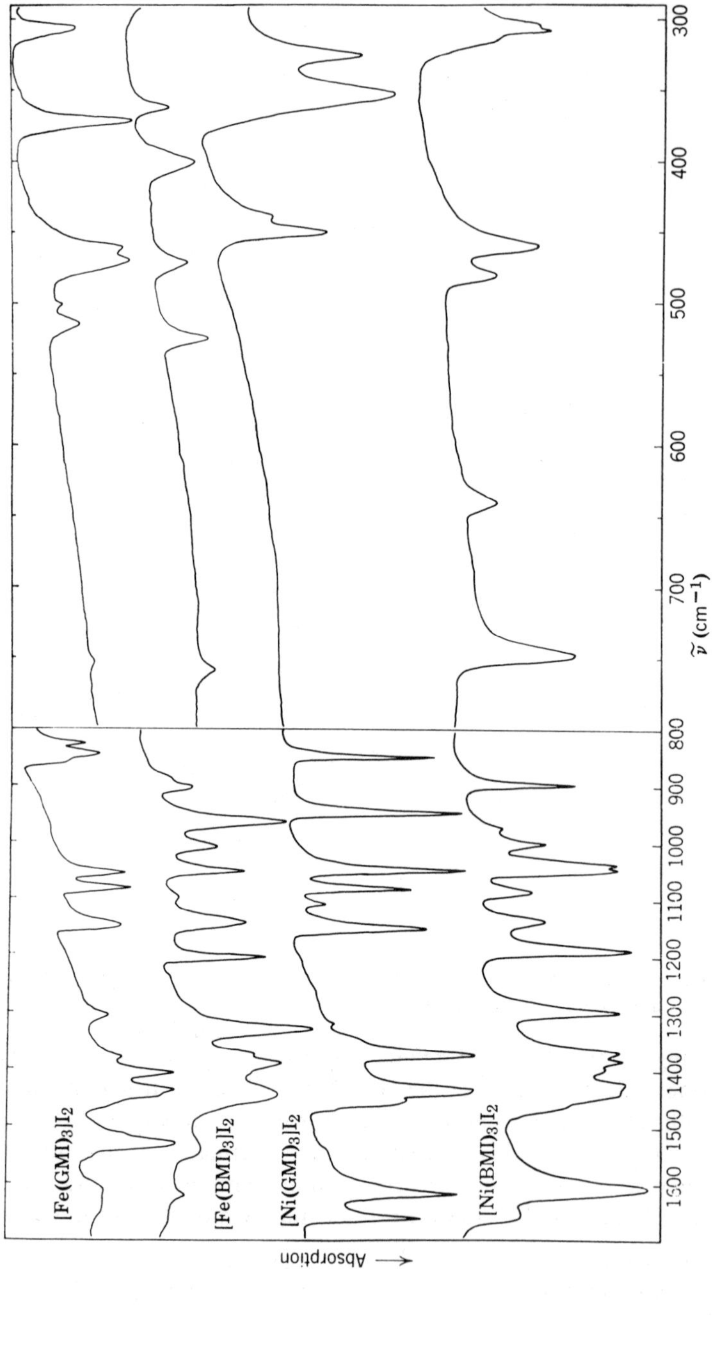

Fig. III-20. Infrared spectra of α-diimine chelate compounds with Fe(II) and Ni(II).

coordinates. Using these 75 internal coordinates, Nakamoto[178] has undertaken a normal coordinate analysis of the $Fe(GMI)_3$ ion, which is known to be the most stable of the GMI complexes. Figure III-20 shows the infrared spectra of Fe(II) and Ni(II) complexes of GMI and BMI. Table III-17 gives a comparison of observed and calculated frequencies together with the theoretical band assignments. The Fe—N stretching force constant (UBF) used here is 4.7×10^5 dynes/cm. This value is much larger

TABLE III-17. COMPARISON OF CALCULATED AND OBSERVED FREQUENCIES OF $[Fe(GMI)_3]I_2$ (CM^{-1})[178]

Obs.	Calc.	Predominant Mode
1530	1549 (A_1), 1547 (E)	ν(C⋯N) + ν(C⋯C)
	1530 (A_2), 1525 (E)	ν(C⋯N) + δ(C—H)
1438	—	$\delta_d(CH_3)$
1407	—	$\delta_s(CH_3)$
1305	1323 (A_1), 1335 (E)	δ(C—H) + ν(C⋯N)
	1290 (A_2), 1261 (E)	δ(C—H) + ν(C⋯N)
1149	1123 (A_2), 1142 (E)	$\nu(N—CH_3)$ + ν(Fe⋯N)
1084	1104 (A_1), 1087 (E)	$\nu(N—CH_3)$ + ν(Fe⋯N)
1057	1057 (A_1), 1071 (E)	ν(C⋯C)
847, 829	—	π(C—H)
745	756 (A_2), 742 (E)	ν(Fe—N) + $\nu(N—CH_3$
515, 501	631 (A_1), 655 (E)	ν(Fe—N) + $\nu(N—CH_3)$
470, 461	482 (A_2), 448 (E)	ring def. + $\delta(N—CH_3)$
372	352 (A_2), 325 (E)	ring def. + $\delta(N—CH_3)$
306	303 (A_1), 260 (E)	$\delta(N—CH_3)$ + ring def.
—	188 (A_1), 218 (E)	$\delta(N—CH_3)$ + ring def.
—	142 (A_2), 174 (E)	δ(N—Fe—N)
—	192 (A_1), 130 (E)	δ(N—Fe—N)

than the Pt—C stretching force constant in the $[Pt(CN)_4]^{2-}$ ion, 3.43×10^5 dynes/cm,[71] which is the largest value so far obtained for a coordinate bond. On the other hand, the C⋯N stretching force constant is only 6.5×10^5 dynes/cm, which is much smaller than that of the usual C=N double bond. The calculations also indicate the presence of strong coupling between various vibrational modes. Therefore empirical band assignments based on the idea of group frequency are not applicable in a chelate ring having such strong resonance. It should be noted that the Fe—N stretching mode couples strongly with the $N—CH_3$ stretching mode. Therefore no pure Fe—N stretching vibration exists in this compound. As Fig. III-20 indicates, the spectrum of the $[Ni(GMI)_3]^{2+}$ ion is very different from that of the $[Fe(GMI)_3]^{2+}$ ion.[179] This contrast is also seen between the Fe(II) and Ni(II) complexes of BMI. Although calculations have not yet been made for the $[Ni(GMI)_3]^{2+}$ ion, the appearance of strong bands near 1600 cm^{-1} (probably due to a coupling of the C$\cdots$N and C$\cdots$C stretching modes) may indicate that the Ni—N bond is much weaker than the Fe—N bond in α-diimine complexes.

Schilt and Taylor[180] recently reported the infrared spectra of a number of metal chelate compounds of BIPY and PHEN. The spectra of these compounds are too complicated to allow any band assignments. Schilt[181] prepared *mixed ligand complexes* such as $[Ni(PHEN)(CN)_2(H_2O)]$ and $[Ni(PHEN)(CN)_2(H_2O)_{0.5}]$ and compared their infrared spectra with that of $[Ni(PHEN)_3][Ni(CN)_4]\cdot 4H_2O$. Stoufer and Busch[182] have obtained the infrared spectra of some metal chelate compounds of BDH and have noted that the C$\cdots$N stretching frequency of the Fe(II) complex is lower than that of any other metal–BDH complex. Stratton and Busch[183] obtained the infrared spectra of PAA complexes. The infrared spectra of metal complexes of 2-pyridinaldoxime and pyridinal-methylamines have also been reported by Busch and co-workers.[183a] Thomas and Martell[184] have reported the infrared spectra of some metal chelate compounds of TPP and its para-substituted derivatives. It was found from the relative band shifts that the strength of the M—N bond follows the series Pt(II) > Pd(II) > Ni(II) > Co(II) ≈ Cu(II) and X = H > Cl > OCH_3. Ueno and Martell[185] have studied the infrared spectra of the vanadyl complexes of the same ligands. Goldstein and co-workers[186] have reported the spectra of *p*-chloro-TPP complexes.

III-10. COMPLEXES OF DIMETHYLGLYOXIME

Infrared studies on the complexes of dimethylglyoxime are highly interesting in connection with hydrogen bonding. In 1952, Rundle and Parasol[187] made the very interesting observation that the OH stretching bands usually observed near 3100 cm^{-1} in glyoximes are shifted to considerably lower frequencies in the Ni(II) complexes. Figure III-21 compares the infrared spectra of dimethylglyoxime and its Ni(II) complex. A weak band at 1775 cm^{-1} in $Ni(DMG)_2$ (DMG: dimethylglyoximate anion) disappears upon deuteration and is therefore assigned to the OH stretching mode. This extraordinarily low OH stretching frequency was attributed to strong intramolecular hydrogen bonding, since Rundle and Parasol observed that, as the OH ··· O distance decreases, the OH stretching frequency becomes lower in a series of compounds in which the OH ··· O distance varies progressively. This correlation of *frequency vs. distance* was elaborated later by Nakamoto et al.[188]

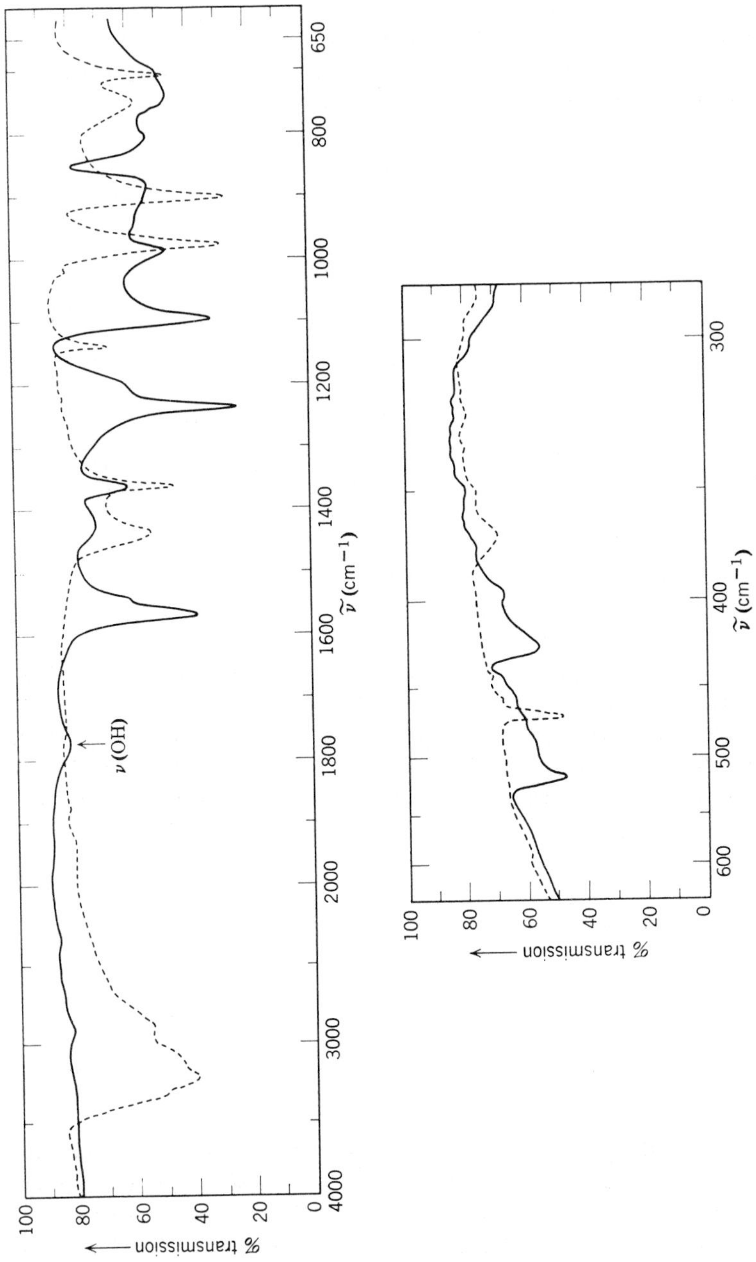

Fig. III-21. Infrared spectra of $Ni(DMG)_2$ (solid line) and HDMG (broken line).

Godycki and Rundle[189] carried out an x-ray analysis of $Ni(DMG)_2$ and demonstrated the existence of an extremely short OH ··· O hydrogen bond (2.44 A), as shown in Fig. III-22. They also suggested that such an extremely short hydrogen bond may be symmetrical, the hydrogen atom being equidistant from the two oxygen atoms.

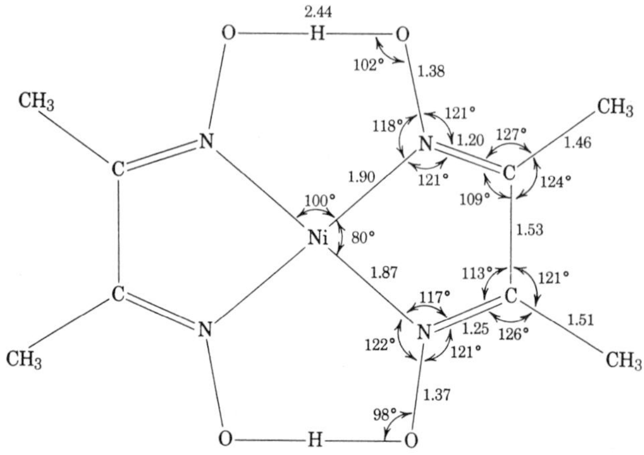

Fig. III-22. The structure of $Ni(DMG)_2$.[189]

Fujita and co-workers[190] found weak OH stretching bands at 1770–1680 cm^{-1} in $[Co(DMG)_2XY]$ (X,Y = Cl^-, Br^-, $[NO_2]^-$ or OH_2). Since the presence of a weak OH stretching band in this frequency range is an indication of an OH ··· O hydrogen bond similar to that of $Ni(DMG)_2$, it was concluded that the structure must be I. (The broken line denotes

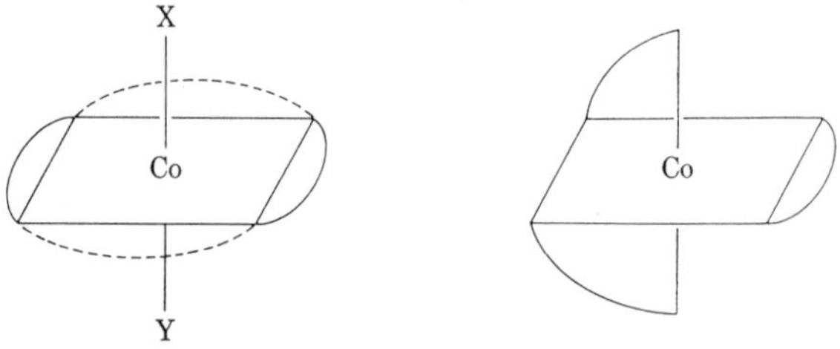

I II

hydrogen bonding, similar to that in $Ni(DMG)_2$.) Nakahara and colleagues[191] have shown that the structure of $Co(DMG)_3$ must be II, since it has no band between 1770 and 1680 cm^{-1}. Frasson and co-workers[192] made an x-ray analysis of $Pt(DMG)_2$ and obtained an OH ··· O distance of 3.03 A. The observed OH stretching frequency, 3450 cm^{-1}, of this compound gives an OH ··· O distance of 2.9 A from the *frequency vs. distance* diagram constructed by Nakamoto et al. This is in good agreement with the result of x-ray analysis.

Recently, Blinc and Hadži[193] have reinvestigated the infrared spectra of the DMG complexes of various metals; they claim that a newly found band at 2350 cm^{-1} in $Ni(DMG)_2$ is the OH stretching band, and that the band at 1780 cm^{-1} found by Rundle and Parasol is the OH bending mode. If this is so, the OH ··· O distance, as calculated from the "frequency vs distance" diagram, would be 2.56 A. Blinc and Hadži, accordingly, suggested that the OH ··· O bond is bent, and probably not symmetric. Table III-18 indicates the OH frequencies and band assignments obtained by these authors.

TABLE III-18. OH STRETCHING AND BENDING FREQUENCIES IN DIMETHYLGLYOXIME COMPLEXES (CM^{-1})[193]

Compound	ν(OH)	ν(OD)	δ(OH)	δ(OD)
$Ni(DMG)_2$	2350	—	1780	—
d-$Ni(DMG)_2$	—	1810, 1910	—	1265
$Pd(DMG)_2$	2340	—	1710	—
d-$Pd(DMG)_2$	—	1830, 1970	—	1210
Na(DMG)	3020	—	1650	—
d-Na(DMG)	—	2340	—	1237
K(DMG)	3030	—	1650	—

III-11. COMPLEXES OF CARBOXYLIC ACIDS, OXY-ACIDS AND ALCOHOLS

The infrared spectra of complexes of carboxylic acids have been studied extensively.[194,195] Since the antisymmetric COO stretching frequency is most sensitive to a change in the metal, the relationship between this frequency and some physical property of the metal has been discussed by several investigators. For example, Theimer and Theimer[196] claimed that the radius of the metal atom is the main factor in determining the COO stretching frequency, whereas Kagarise[197] found that the electronegativity of the metal is important. Recently, Ellis and Pyszora[198] suggested that the COO stretching frequency in complexes of carboxylic acids may be a complicated function of the mass, radius and electronegativity of the metal.

In examining the effect of coordination on the COO stretching frequency, it is important to interpret the results on the basis of structure of these complexes as determined by x-ray analysis. For example, the acetate anion ([ac]$^-$) coordinates with a metal in one of these ways:

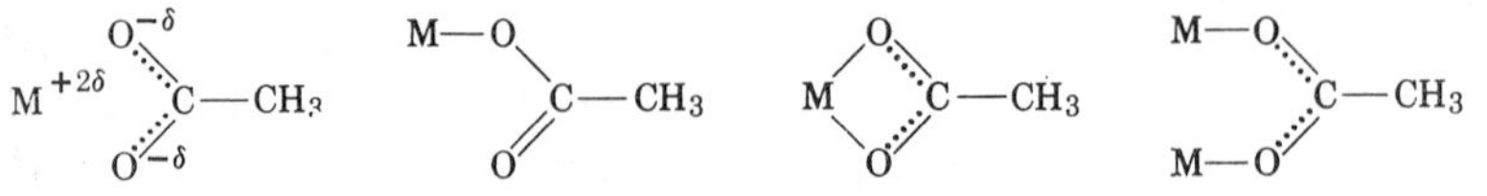

I II III IV

According to the results of x-ray analysis, the structure of sodium formate[199] is I, the two CO bond lengths being equal (1.27 A). On the other hand, Li(ac)·$2H_2O$[200] has structure II, the two CO bond lengths being different (1.33 and 1.22 A). Structure II occurs frequently among the salts of metals of higher valency. The bidentate structure III is reported for $Zn(ac)_2 \cdot 2H_2O$[201] and $Na[UO_2(ac)_3]$.[202] Although this structure is less common than II, many anhydrous salts, such as $Cr(ac)_3$ and $Mn(ac)_3$, may have structure III. With this structure, maximum coordination number of the metal is satisfied. The unusual bridged structure IV was found in $Cr_2(ac)_4 \cdot 2H_2O$,[203] $Cu_2(ac)_4 \cdot 2H_2O$,[204] $Be_4O(ac)_6$[205] and $Zn_4O(ac)_6$.[206]

The vibrational spectrum of the acetate ion has been studied by Jones and McLaren,[207] Wilmshurst,[208] Itoh and Bernstein[209] and Nakamura.[210] Table III-19 indicates the infrared frequencies and band assignments for the acetate and formate ions obtained by Itoh and Bernstein. On the basis of these band assignments, it is highly interesting to compare the spectra of the four types of metal acetate structures mentioned above. Since the symmetry of the free ion (C_{2v}) is low, no marked differences in the spectrum would be expected for the various structures. The effect on the frequency of changing the metal, however, should be different for each structural type. For example, in a series of salts having structure II, the antisymmetric COO stretching frequency will increase, and the symmetric COO stretching frequency will decrease, as the M—O bond becomes stronger. This will be shown later for the complexes of amino acids (Sec. III-12). Such a trend is not seen, however, for a series of compounds having structure IV. Nakamoto and co-workers[211] have found that, in the symmetrical bridged structure IV, both the COO stretching bands are shifted in the same direction upon changing the metal. Figure III-23 compares the infrared spectra of $Cu_2(ac)_4 \cdot 2H_2O$ and $Cr_2(ac)_4 \cdot 2H_2O$. The infrared spectra of $Cr_2(ac)_4 \cdot 2H_2O$ and $UO_2(ac)_2$ are also given in Refs. 212 and II-68, respectively.

The infrared spectra of metal salts of oxyacids such as lactic, tartaric and citric acids have been studied by several investigators. Goulden[213] has found that the OH in-plane bending band of the hydroxyl group in the lactate ion (1275 cm^{-1}) is shifted to 1390 cm^{-1} upon chelation to zinc.

TABLE III-19. INFRARED FREQUENCIES AND BAND ASSIGNMENTS FOR THE FORMATE AND ACETATE IONS (CM^{-1})[209]

$[HCOO]^-$		$[CH_3COO]^-$			
Na Salt	Aq. Sol'n	Na Salt	Aq. Sol'n	C_{2v}	Band Assignment
2841	2803	2936	2935	A_1	$\nu(CH)$
—	—	—	1344		$\delta(CH_3)$
1366	1351	1414	1413		$\nu(COO)$
—	—	924	926		$\nu(CC)$
772	760	646	650		$\delta(OCO)$
—	—	—	—	A_2	$\rho_t(CH_3)$
—	—	2989	3010 or 2981	B_1	$\nu(CH)$
1567	1585	1578	1556		$\nu(COO)$
—	—	1430	1429		$\delta(CH_3)$
—	—	1009	1020		$\rho_r(CH_3)$
1377	1383	460	471		$\rho_r(COO)$ or $\delta(CH)$
—	—	2989	2981 or 3010	B_2	$\nu(CH)$
—	—	1443	1456		$\delta(CH_3)$
—	—	1042	1052		$\rho_r(CH_3)$
1073	1069	615	621		$\pi(COO)$ or $\pi(CH)$

Girard and Lecomte[214] have studied the infrared spectra of potassium salts of bismuth and antimony tartrates and have proposed the structure

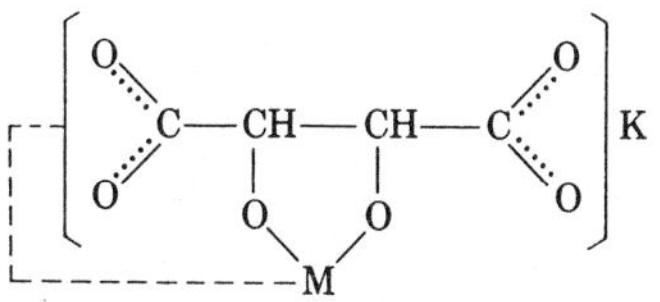

M = Bi(III) or Sb(III)

Recently, Kirschner and Kiesling[215] concluded from the infrared spectrum that the structure of copper tartrate is

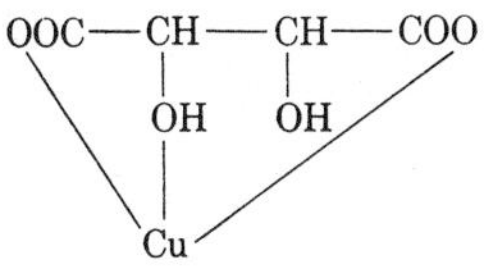

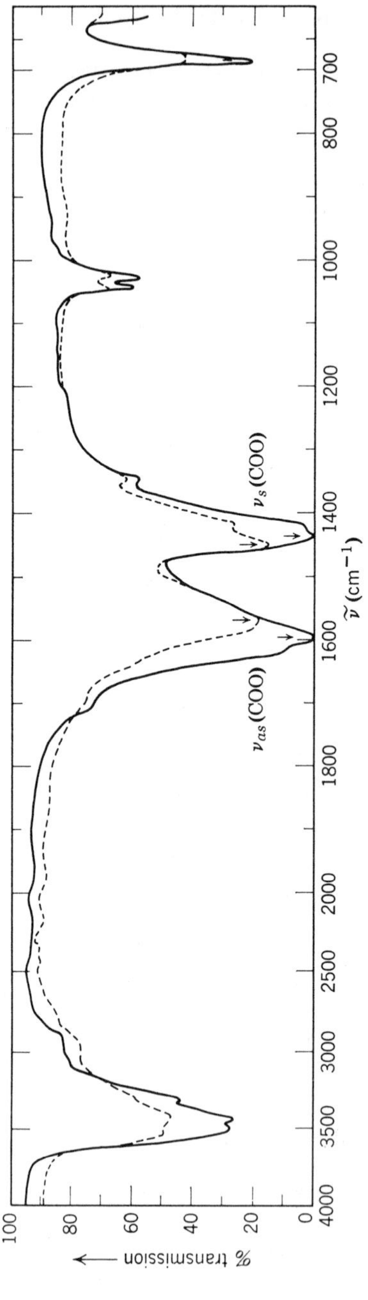

Fig. III-23. Infrared spectra of $Cu_2(ac)_4 \cdot 2H_2O$ (solid line) and $Cr_2(ac)_4 \cdot 2H_2O$ (broken line).

since it shows a single band at 1634 cm^{-1} (coordinated COO group) and C—O stretching bands at 1080 and 1063 cm^{-1}, the latter being due to the coordinated C—OH group. Kuroda and Kubo[216] studied the infrared spectra of the copper salts of a series of dicarboxylic acids of the type $[(CH_2)_{n-2}(COO)_2]Cu$ ($n = 2$–10) and concluded that variation of the antisymmetric COO stretching frequency is closely related to variation of the magnetic moment in this series.

Although a large amount of infrared data is available on metal alkoxides, there is little available on metal complexes of organic alcohols. Miyake,[217] however, studied the infrared spectra of metal complexes of ethyleneglycol and its derivatives, and found two types of spectra which depend on the water content of the salts used for preparation of the complexes. The A-type spectra are obtained when the water content of the salts is greater than 15%, and the B-type spectra are obtained when it is less than 15%. Miyake concluded that the structures of the complexes giving rise to the A- and B-type spectra are

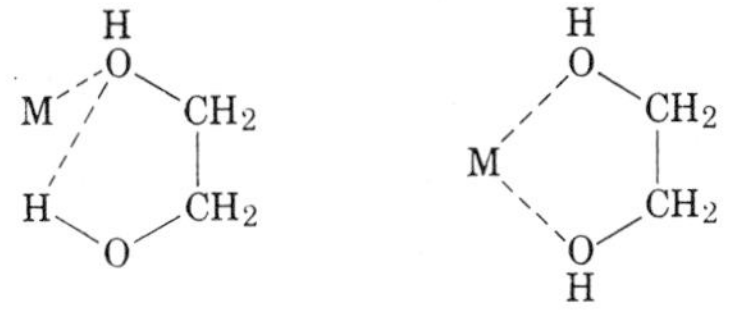

A B

He also concluded that conformation of ethyleneglycol is *gauche* for both types.

III-12. COMPLEXES OF AMINO ACIDS

It is well known that amino acids exist as dipolar (zwitter) ions in the crystalline state. Empirical band assignments have been made for the dipolar ions of glycine,[218] α-alanine[219] and α-aminoisobutyric acid.[220] Table III-20 indicates the frequencies and band assignments for glycine and α-alanine. The infrared spectra of crystalline amino acids have been measured by Klotz and Gruen[221] and Thompson et al.[222] Edsall and co-workers[223] have made extensive Raman spectral measurements on a great number of amino acids in aqueous solution. Krishnan and Balasubramanian[224] have also studied the Raman spectra of amino acids in the crystalline state.

An example of the infrared spectrum of a metal complex of an amino acid has already been shown in Fig. III-7. X-ray analysis indicates that, in $[Ni(gly)_2]\cdot 2H_2O$,[225] $[Zn(gly)_2]\cdot H_2O$ and $[Cd(gly)_2]\cdot H_2O$,[226] two glycinate ions (gly) coordinate to the metal by forming a *trans* square-planar

TABLE III-20. INFRARED FREQUENCIES AND BAND ASSIGNMENTS OF GLYCINE AND α-ALANINE IN THE CRYSTALLINE STATE (CM^{-1})[218,219]

Glycine	α-Alanine	Band Assignment
1610	1597	$\nu_{as}(COO^-)$
1585	1623	$\delta_d(NH_3^+)$
1492	1534	$\delta_s(NH_3^+)$
—	1455	$\delta_d(CH_3)$
1445	—	$\delta(CH_2)$
1413	1412	$\nu_s(COO^-)$
—	1355	$\delta_s(CH_3)$
1333	—	$\rho_w(CH_2)$
—	1308	$\delta(CH)$
1240(R)	—	$\delta_t(CH_2)$
1131, 1110	1237, 1113	$\rho_r(NH_3^+)$
1033	1148	$\nu_{as}(CCN)$
—	1026, 1015	$\rho_r(CH_3)$
910	—	$\rho_r(CH_2)$
893	918[a], 852[a]	$\nu_s(CCN)$
694	648	$\rho_w(COO^-)$
607	771	$\delta(COO^-)$
516	492	$\rho_t(NH_3^+)$
504	540	$\rho_r(COO^-)$

[a] Both of these bands are coupled vibrations between $\nu_s(CCN)$ and $\nu(C—CH_3)$.

structure like that in Fig. III-24. Furthermore, it has been shown that the oxygens of the carboxyl groups which are not coordinated to the metal are hydrogen-bonded either to the amino group of the neighboring molecule or to water of crystallization, or are bonded weakly to the metal of the neighboring complex. Thus the COO stretching frequencies of complexes of amino acids are affected by coordination as well as by intermolecular interaction. Similar effects have been observed in ammine complexes (Sec. III-1). Therefore the infrared spectra of amino acid complexes obtained in the crystalline state must be interpreted with caution.

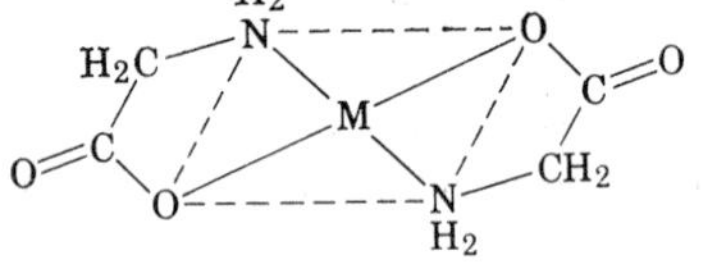

Fig. III-24.

Of the various vibrational modes of the amino acids given in Table III-20, the COO stretching bands can be assigned empirically without difficulty, and they are most sensitive to the effects of coordination and intermolecular interaction. In general, the antisymmetric COO stretching frequency is much more sensitive to these influences than is the symmetric one. Thus the former alone often gives a sufficient measure of these influences. It should be noted that, in some metal complexes, partial overlapping of the NH_3^+ or NH_2 deformation band with the antisymmetric COO stretching band makes it difficult to identify the latter. This obstacle can be avoided by measuring the spectrum of the deuterated compound. Care must also be taken in assigning the symmetric COO stretching band, since it is located near the CH_3 degenerate deformation band.

In order to examine the effect of coordination and hydrogen bonding, Nakamoto et al.[211] have made extensive measurements of the COO stretching frequencies of various metal complexes of amino acids in different physical states. Table III-21 indicates the observed frequencies in D_2O solution, in the hydrated crystalline state, and in the anhydrous crystalline state. In the anhydrous crystalline state only the CO···HN or CO···DN hydrogen bonds are possible. In D_2O solutions, only the CO···DO bonds are probable, whereas both types may coexist in the hydrated crystalline state. It is hardly possible, however, to compare the strength of hydrogen bonds in various physical states without detailed crystal structural data. Nevertheless, the effect of hydrogen bonding is strikingly demonstrated in Table III-21, which indicates that the frequencies may change by 10 to 30 cm^{-1} upon change of physical state. For any one physical state, however, the same frequency order for a series of metals is always found, regardless of the nature of the ligand. In other words, antisymmetric frequencies increase, the symmetric frequencies decrease, and the separation between the two frequencies increases in the following series of metals:

$$\text{Ni(II)} < \text{Zn(II)} < \text{Cu(II)} < \text{Co(II)} < \text{Pd(II)} \approx \text{Pt(II)} < \text{Cr(III)}$$

An exception is seen in the glycino and α-alanino complexes of Ni(II), Zn(II) and Cu(II) in the hydrated solid state. In general, however, these results indicate that the effect of coordination is still the major factor in determining the frequency order in a given physical state.

The frequency order above can best be explained if it is assumed that the covalent character of the M—O bond increases along the series, since an increase of covalent character leads to a more asymmetrical carboxyl group and results in an increase in the frequency separation of the two COO stretching bands (Sec. III-11). A similar conclusion was reached

TABLE III-21. ANTISYMMETRIC AND SYMMETRIC COO STRETCHING FREQUENCIES AND THEIR SEPARATION IN THE METAL CHELATE COMPOUNDS OF VARIOUS AMINO ACIDS (CM^{-1})[211]

Compound[a]	Antisymmetric COO Stretching			Symmetric COO Stretching			Separation		
	D_2O Solution	Hydrated Crystal	Anhydrous Solid	D_2O Solution	Hydrated Crystal	Anhydrous Solid	D_2O Solution	Hydrated Crystal	Anhydrous Solid
Glycine	1615	—	1595	1411	—	1399	204	—	196
Ni[NH_2·CH_2·COO]$_2$·2H_2O	1589	1609	1583	1413	1408	1400	176	201	183
Zn[NH_2·CH_2·COO]$_2$·H_2O	1594	1598	1603	1407	1400	1384	187	198	219
Cu[NH_2·CH_2·COO]$_2$·H_2O	1604	1593	1607	—	1387	1366	—	206	241
α-Co[NH_2·CH_2·COO]$_3$·2H_2O	1624	1625	—	1366	1364	—	258	261	—
β-Co[NH_2·CH_2·COO]$_3$·H_2O	—	1636[b]	—	—	—	—	—	—	—
tr.-Pd[NH_2·CH_2·COO]$_2$	—	—	1642[b]	—	—	1373[b]	—	—	269[b]
tr.-Pt[NH_2·CH_2·COO]$_2$	—	—	1643[b]	—	—	1374[b]	—	—	269[b]
Cr[NH_2·CH_2·COO]$_3$·H_2O	—	1659, 1639 } 1649[b]	1658, 1643 } 1651[b]	—	1381, 1365 } 1373[b]	1372[b]	—	276[b]	279[b]
α-Alanine	1612	—	1595	1413	—	1406	199	—	189
Ni[NH_2·CH(CH_3)·COO]$_2$·4H_2O	1581	1591	1589	1412	1414	1420	169	177	169
Zn[NH_2·CH(CH_3)COO]$_2$·H_2O	1592	1602	1605	1410	1392	1393	182	210	212
Cu[NH_2·CH(CH_3)COO]$_2$·H_2O	1601	1606	1620	—	1386	1386	—	220	234
Co[NH_2·CH(CH_3)COO]$_3$·H_2O	1612	1632[b]	—	—	1383[b]	—	—	249[b]	—
tr.-Pt[NH_2·CH(CH_3)COO]$_2$	—	—	1641, 1653 } 1647[b]	—	—	1382[b]	—	—	265[b]
Cr[NH_2·CH(CH_3)COO]$_3$·H_2O	—	1656[b]	—	—	1381, 1347 } 1364[b]	—	—	292[b]	—
β-Alanine	1578	—	1570	1405	—	1399	173	—	171
Ni(NH_2·CH_2·CH_2·COO]$_2$·2H_2O	—	1607[b]	1560[a]	—	1413[b]	1402[b]	—	194[b]	158
Cu[NH_2·CH_2·CH_2·COO]$_2$·6H_2O	1561	1562	1587	1406	1401	1412	155	161	175
dl-Valine	1610	—	1585	1410	—	1416	200	—	169
Ni[(CH_3)$_2$·CH_2·CH_2·NH_2·COO]$_2$·2H_2O	—	1587[b]	1596[b]	—	1408[b]	—	—	179[b]	—
Cu[(CH_3)$_2$·CH_2·CH_2·NH_2·COO]$_2$	—	—	1619[b]	—	—	1387[b]	—	—	232[b]
dl-iso-Leucine	1613	—	1585	1408	—	1417	205	—	168
Ni[CH_3·CH_2·CH(CH_3)CH_2·NH_2·COO]$_2$·2H_2O	—	1591	—	—	1411[b]	—	—	180[b]	—
Cu[CH_3·CH_2·CH(CH_3)CH_2·NH_2·COO]$_2$·H_2O	—	1623[b]	—	—	1391, 1385 } 1388[b]	—	—	235[b]	—
N-Methylglycine	1616	—	1614	1408	—	1413	208	—	201
Ni[(CH_3)NH·CH_2·COO]$_2$·2H_2O	1590	1607	1600	1408	1398	1418	182	209	182
Cu[(CH_3)NH·CH_2·COO]$_2$·2H_2O	1606	1635	1624	1390	1369	1386	216	266	238
N-Phenylglycine	—	—	1563[b]	—	—	1380[b]	—	—	183[b]
Ni[C_6H_5)NH·CH_2·COO]$_2$·3H_2O	—	1599[b]	—	—	1389[b]	—	—	210[b]	—
Co[(C_6H_5)NH·CH_2·COO]$_2$·2H_2O	—	1602[b]	—	—	1388[b]	—	—	214[b]	—
Cu[(C_6H_5)NH·CH_2·COO]$_2$	—	—	1616[b]	—	—	1385, 1360 } 1373[b]	—	—	243[b]
N,N-Dimethylglycine	1623	—	1631	1402	—	1396	221	—	235
Ni[(CH_3)$_2$N·CH_2·COO]$_2$·2H_2O	1606, 1590 } 1598	1599[b]	1606[b]	1410	1405[b]	1430[b]	188	194[b]	176[b]
Cu[(CH_3)$_2$N·CH_2·COO]$_2$·3H_2O	1613	1614[b]	1630[b]	1387	1376[b]	1384, 1358 } 1371[b]	226	238[b]	259[b]

[a] The formulas are for non-deuterated forms.

[b] Frequencies obtained from non-deuterated crystals.

by Rosenberg,[227] who measured the infrared spectra of metal glycinates at liquid air temperatures. He suggested that the covalent character of the M—O bond increases along the series Ni(II) < Cu(II) < Pt(II). On the other hand, Quagliano and co-workers[228] concluded (1) that the M—O bonds in Cu(II), Ni(II) and Zn(II) glycinates are essentially ionic because their frequencies are almost the same as those of potassium glycinate and sodium acetate; (2) that these metals use *sp* hybrid orbitals in forming linear bonds with the nitrogens of the ligands; (3) that the two oxygens of the carboxyl group are symmetrically arranged with respect to the metal. Duval and Lecomte[229] have reported the infrared spectra of a number of metal complexes of various amino acids. Nakamura[230] has made empirical band assignments for glycino and alanino complexes of Cu(II), Ni(II) and Co(II). He attributed the bands between 600 and 570 cm^{-1} to the M—N stretching modes in these complexes.

III-13. COMPLEXES OF EDTA AND RELATED COMPOUNDS

Figure III-25 shows the structures of several polydentate ligands.

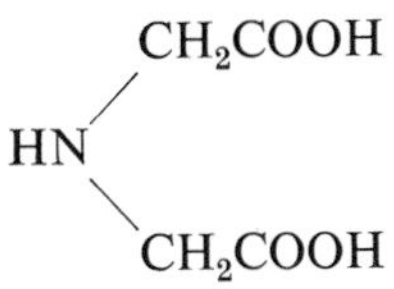

Iminodiacetic acid (IMDA)

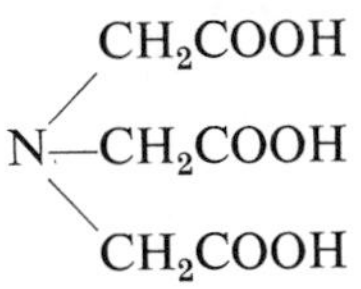

Nitrilotriacetic acid (NTA)

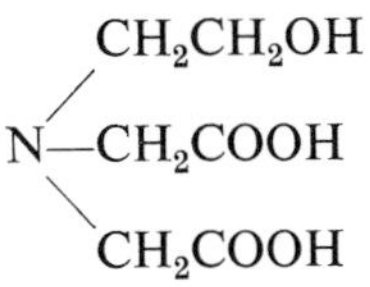

N-Hydroxyethyliminodiacetic acid (HIMDA)

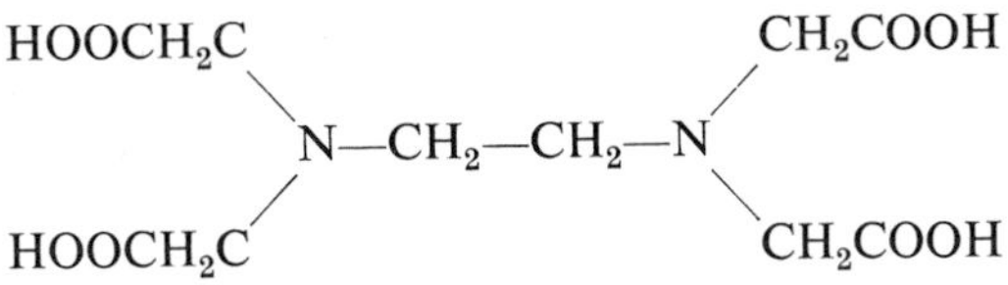

Ethylenediaminetetraacetic acid (EDTA)

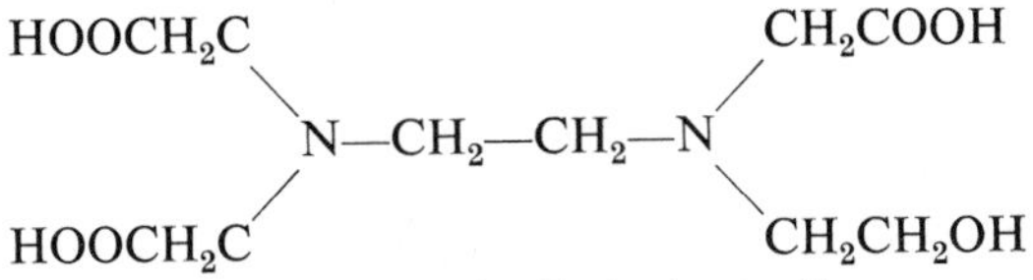

N-Hydroxyethylethylenediaminetriacetic acid (HEDTA)

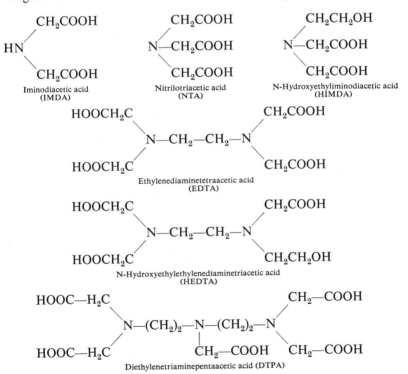

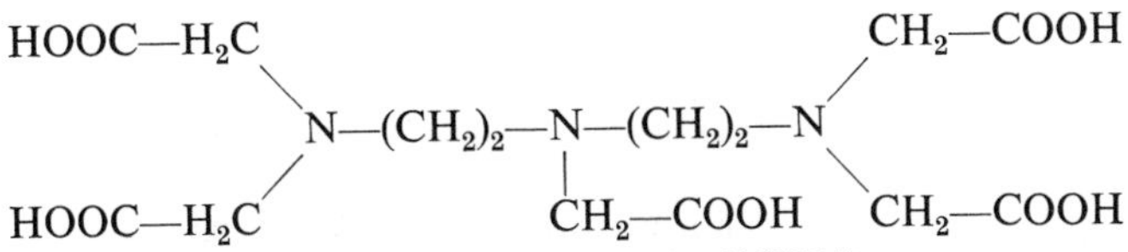

Diethylenetriaminepentaacetic acid (DTPA)

Fig III-25. Structures of some EDTA derivatives.

Although the structures of metal chelate compounds of these ligands are too complex to allow any theoretical approach, infrared studies are still useful for distinguishing the un-ionized, the coordinated and the free ionized COO groups in these compounds. The method is based on the simple rule that the un-ionized and uncoordinated COO stretching band occurs at 1750–1700 cm^{-1}, whereas the coordinated COO stretching band is at 1650–1590 cm^{-1}; the exact frequency depends on the nature of the metal. As has been shown in Sec. III-11, the COO group, when coordinated to metals such as Cr(III) and Co(III), absorbs at 1650–1620 cm^{-1}, whereas with Cu(II) and Zn(II) it absorbs at 1610–1590 cm^{-1}. On the other hand, the free ionized COO stretching band usually appears near 1630–1575 cm^{-1}. Therefore, it is also possible to distinguish the coordinated and free COO stretching bands, if a metal such as Co(III) is selected for complex formation.

Busch and co-workers[231] have determined from infrared spectra the coordination number of the metals in various metal chelate compounds of EDTA and its derivatives. Table III-22 indicates some of their results.

TABLE III-22. ANTISYMMETRIC COO STRETCHING FREQUENCIES AND NUMBER OF FUNCTIONAL GROUPS USED FOR COORDINATION IN EDTA COMPLEXES (CM^{-1})[231]

Compound	Un-ionized COOH	Coordinated $COO^- \cdots M$	Free COO^-	Number of Coordinated Groups
$H_4[Y]$	1697	—	—	*a*
$Na_2[H_2Y]$	1668	—	1637	*a*
$Na_4[Y]$	—	—	1597	*a*
$Ba[Co(Y)]_2 \cdot 4H_2O$	—	1638	—	6
$Na_2[Co(Y)Cl]$	—	1648	1600	5
$Na_2[Co(Y)NO_2]$	—	1650	1604	5
$Na[Co(HY)Cl] \cdot \frac{1}{2}H_2O$	1750	1650	—	5
$Na[Co(HY)NO_2] \cdot H_2O$	1745	1650	—	5
$Ba[Co(HY)Br] \cdot 9H_2O$	1723	1628	—	5
$Na[Co(YOH)Cl] \cdot \frac{3}{2}H_2O$	—	1658	—	5
$Na[Co(YOH)Br] \cdot H_2O$	—	1654	—	5
$Na[Co(YOH)NO_2]$	—	1652	—	5
$[Pd(H_2Y)] \cdot 3H_2O$	1740	1625	—	4
$[Pt(H_2Y)] \cdot 3H_2O$	1730	1635	—	4
$[Pd(H_4Y)Cl_2] \cdot 5H_2O$	1707, 1730	—	—	2
$[Pt(H_4Y)Cl_2] \cdot 5H_2O$	1715, 1730	—	—	2

[Y], tetranegative ion; [HY], trinegative ion; $[H_2Y]$, dinegative ion; $[H_4Y]$, neutral species of EDTA; [YOH], trinegative ion of HEDTA.

[a] Ref. 231*a*.

Moeller and colleagues[232] have studied the infrared spectra of EDTA complexes of some rare earth metals and have concluded that the structures of $H[MY]\cdot xH_2O$ and $Na[MY]\cdot yH_2O$ must be $[M(OH_2)(HY)]\cdot(x-1)H_2O$ and $Na[M(OH_2)(HY)]\cdot(y-1)H_2O$, respectively, since they exhibit the un-ionized COO stretching bands. The infrared spectra of EDTA complexes with divalent, trivalent and tetravalent metals have been studied extensively by Sawyer and Paulsen.[233] They concluded that the coordinated COO stretching frequency of these complexes is shifted to higher frequency as the M—O bond becomes more covalent. The same conclusion has been reached for metal complexes of amino acids (Sec. III-12).

However, the effects of intermolecular interactions such as hydrogen bonding often complicate the spectra obtained in the crystalline state. In this respect, infrared spectra obtained in aqueous solutions should be of special significance because the complexes are then in a uniform environment. Thus the effects of intermolecular interaction which are characteristic of the different crystal lattices can be avoided, if the spectra of the aqueous solutions are compared. Studies of infrared spectra of aqueous solutions also provide a valuable tool for elucidating the equilibria in solution. As mentioned in Sec. III-5, Jones and co-workers have studied the equilibria of a number of cyano complexes by measuring the infrared spectra of their aqueous solutions. Nakamoto et al.[234] have studied the equilibria of IMDA, NTA, EDTA and related compounds in D_2O solutions.† Only the results obtained for IMDA are briefly described.

Figure III-26 shows the structures of six possible species which may be present in aqueous solutions of IMDA. In order to distinguish between these species and to follow their interconversion, the infrared spectra of IMDA in D_2O solutions have been measured as a function of pH (or pD).‡ Figure III-27 shows the infrared spectra obtained between 1850 and 1500 cm^{-1}. As stated before, the un-ionized COO group absorbs at 1750–1700 cm^{-1}, whereas the ionized COO group absorbs at 1630–1575 cm^{-1}. Using this as a criterion together with the results of potentiometric

† In order to measure the infrared spectrum of an aqueous solution, it is necessary to use a special absorption cell; the window material must be CaF_2, BaF_2, AgCl or some other salt which is insoluble in water, and a thin spacer (0.02–0.01 mm thick) must be used. Even with a thin spacer, it is not possible to measure the spectrum of the solute in the regions at between 3700 and 2800, 1750 and 1600 cm^{-1} and below 1000 cm^{-1}, where water absorbs strongly. The C≡N stretching band (2200–2000 cm^{-1}) can be measured in aqueous solution since it is outside of these regions. However, the COO stretching band (1750–1550 cm^{-1}) must be studied in D_2O solution, which absorbs at ca. 2800–2100, 1350–1050 cm^{-1} and below 600 cm^{-1}.

‡ Differences between pH and pD values are within the tolerances required for meaningful interpretation of the results and for comparison with the potentiometric data.

titration ($pK_2 = 2.54$, $pK_3 = 9.12$),[235] it may be concluded that the predominant species changes from I to II*a* to III*a* to IV as the pH (or pD) increases. A marked shift of the ionized COO band is observed in going from III*a* to IV. This is due to the greater inductive effect of a formal

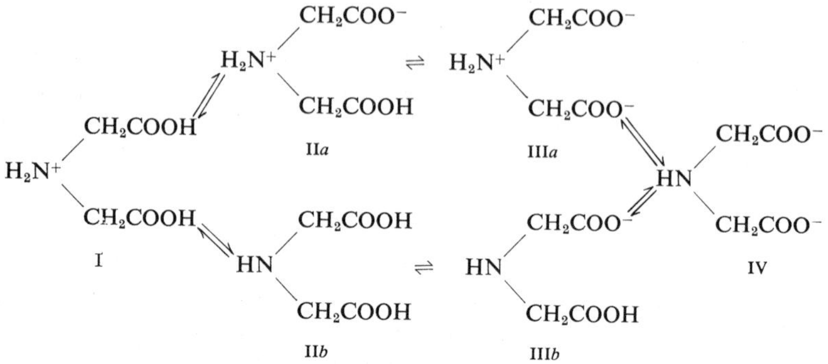

Fig III-26. The solution equilibria of imminodiacetic acid.

positive charge on the nitrogen atom and the consequent increase in the bond order of the CO bond in III*a*. Thus it is possible to distinguish two types of ionized COO groups:

$$\overset{+}{\mathrm{NH}}\text{—}CH_2\text{—}COO^- \ (1630\text{–}1620\ \mathrm{cm}^{-1})$$

and

$$\mathrm{N}\text{—}CH_2\text{—}COO^- \ (1585\text{–}1575\ \mathrm{cm}^{-1})$$

In general, the intensity per group of these two ionized COO^- bands is approximately equivalent, and about three times that of the un-ionized COO group.

If a Cu(II) salt is added to III*a* in a 1:2 ratio, two bands are observed at

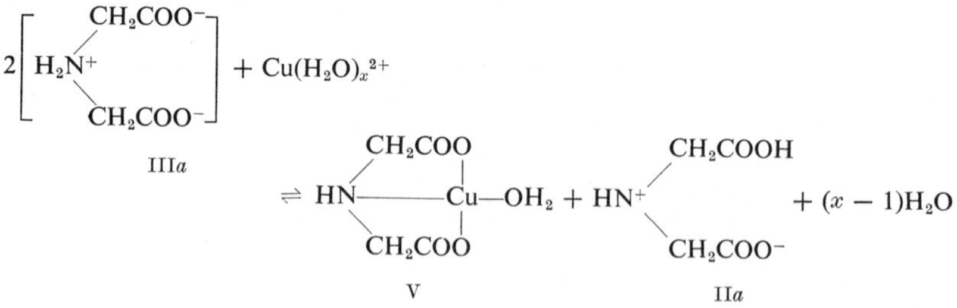

1610 and 1724 cm^{-1}. If a reaction such as that shown above is assumed, the strong band at 1610 cm^{-1} may be interpreted as a superposition of

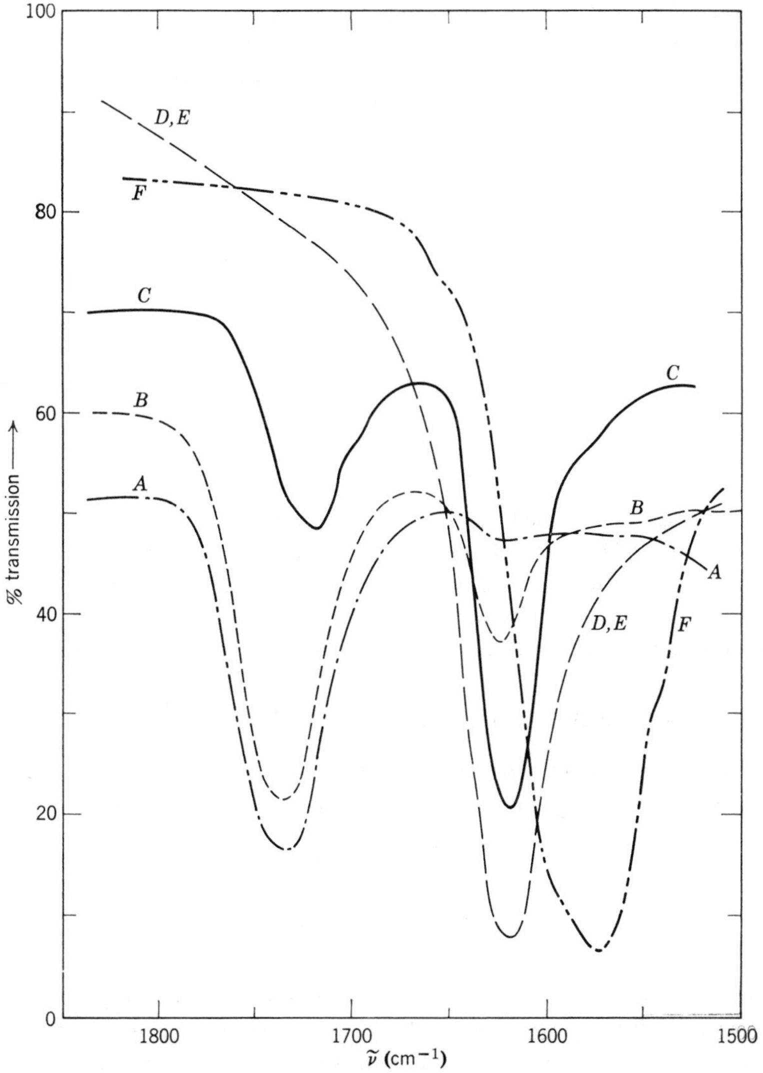

Fig. III-27. Infrared spectra of IMDA in D_2O solutions. [pH = 0.4 (*A*), 1.1 (*B*), 2.2 (*C*), 4.1 (*D*), 7.5 (*E*), 10.9 (*F*).]

absorption from the coordinated COO groups of V and the ionized COO groups of II*a* and III*a*. As stated before, the coordinated and free COO group absorption cannot be distinguished if Cu(II) is used for complex formation. The weak band at 1724 cm^{-1} is ascribed to the un-ionized COO group of II*a*. The composition of the crystals obtained from this solution is $[Cu\{HN(CH_2COO)_2\}H_2O]\cdot H_2O$, corresponding to V. These crystals, however, have a COO absorption band at 1575 cm^{-1}, which is much lower than that found in aqueous solution.

If a Cu(II) salt is added to IV in a 1:2 ratio, only one band is observed at 1596 cm^{-1}. This is compatible with the reaction

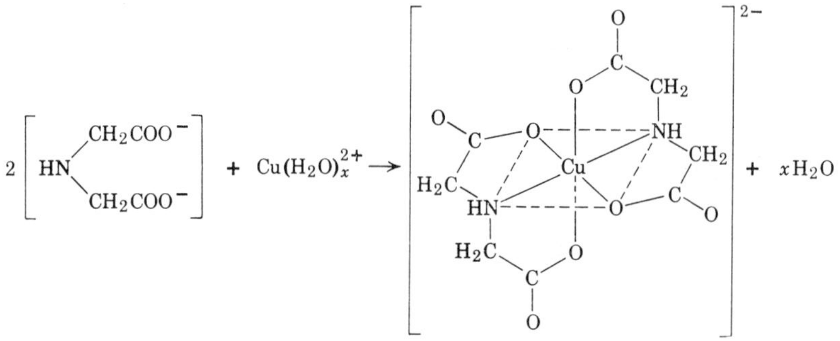

IV VI

The crystals obtained from this solution have a composition, $Na_2[Cu\{HN(CH_2COO)_2\}_2]$, corresponding to VI. However, they exhibit two bands at 1632 and 1590 cm^{-1}. Either the usual distortion of the octahedral configuration in Cu(II) complexes or intermolecular interactions may be responsible for the band splitting in the crystalline state.

III-14. COMPLEXES OF OXALIC ACID AND RELATED COMPOUNDS

The infrared spectra of oxalato ($[ox]^{2-}$) complexes have been studied extensively. Douvillé and co-workers[236] measured the infrared spectra of

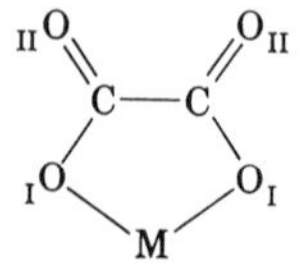

a number of metal oxalates and made empirical band assignments by comparing these spectra with that of N_2O_4. Empirical band assignments were also made by using the results of normal coordinate analysis of the free oxalate ion.[237–241] Figures III-28*a* and 28*b* show the infrared spectra of oxalato complexes of various metals.

These earlier investigations were concerned, however, only with the ligand vibrations, and no direct information is available on the metal-oxygen vibrations in oxalato complexes. As stated in Sec. III-9, empirical band assignments based on the concept of group frequencies are not applicable to chelate ring systems, since coupling between various vibrational modes is anticipated as a result of resonance in the ring. In order to

Table III-23. Frequencies and Band Assignments in Various Oxalato Complexes (cm^{-1})[242]

$K_2[Zn(ox)_2]\cdot 2H_2O$	$K_2[Cu(ox)_2]\cdot 2H_2O$	$K_2[Pd(ox)_2]\cdot 2H_2O$	$K_2[Pt(ox)_2]\cdot 3H_2O$	$K_3[Fe(ox)_3]\cdot 3H_2O$	$K_3[V(ox)_3]\cdot 3H_2O$	$K_3[Cr(ox)_3]\cdot 3H_2O$	$K_3[Co(ox)_3]\cdot 3H_2O$	$K_3[Al(ox)_3]\cdot 3H_2O$	$[Cr(NH_3)_4(ox)]\cdot Cl$	Assignment	
1632	(1720) 1672	1698	1709	1712	1708	1708	1707	1722	1704	$\nu_{as}(C{=}O)$	ν_7
—	1645	1675, 1657	1674	1677, 1649	1675, 1642	1684, 1660	1670	1700, 1683	1668	$\nu_{as}(C{=}O)$	ν_1
1433	1411	1394	1388	1390	1390	1387	1398	1405	1393	$\nu_s(C{-}O) + \nu(C{-}C)$	ν_2
1302	1277	1245 (1228)	1236	1270, 1255	1261	1253	1254	1292, 1269	1258	$\nu_s(C{-}O) + \delta(O{-}C{=}O)$	ν_8
890	886	893	900	885	893	893	900	904	914, 890	$\nu_s(C{-}O) + \delta(O{-}C{=}O)$	ν_3
785	795	818	825	797, 785	807, 797	810, 798	822, 803	820, 803	804	$\delta(O{-}C{=}O) + \nu(M{-}O)$	ν_9
622	593	610	—	580	581	595	—	—	—	crystal water?	
519	541	556	575, 559	528	531	543	565	587	545	$\nu(M{-}O) + \nu(C{-}C)$	ν_4
519	481	469	469	498	497	485	472	436	486, 469	ring def. $+ \delta(O{-}C{=}O)$	ν_{10}
428, 419	420	417	405	366	368	415	446	485	366	$\nu(M{-}O)$ + ring def.	ν_{11}
377, 364	382, 370	368	370	340	336	358	364	364	347	$\delta(O{-}C{=}O)$	ν_5
291	339	350	328	—	—	313	332	—	328	π	

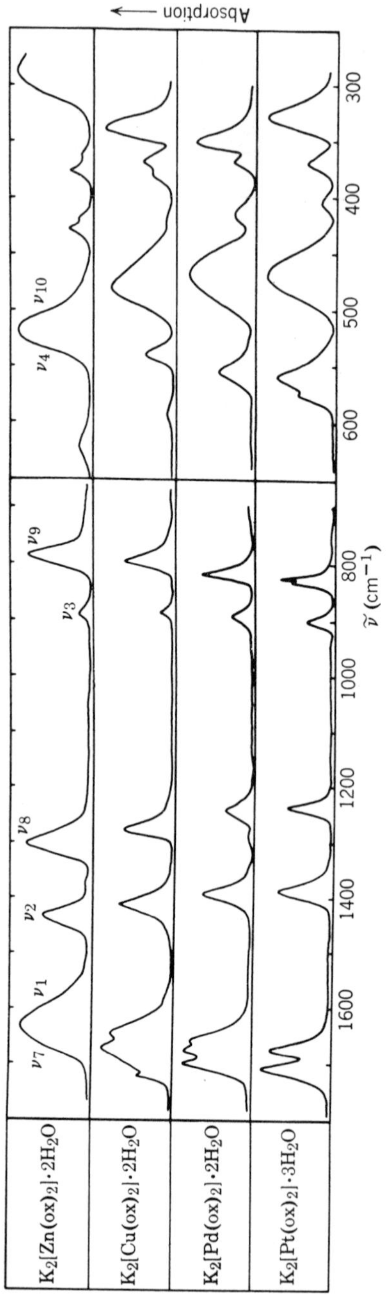

Fig. III-28*a*. Infrared spectra of oxalato complexes of divalent metals.

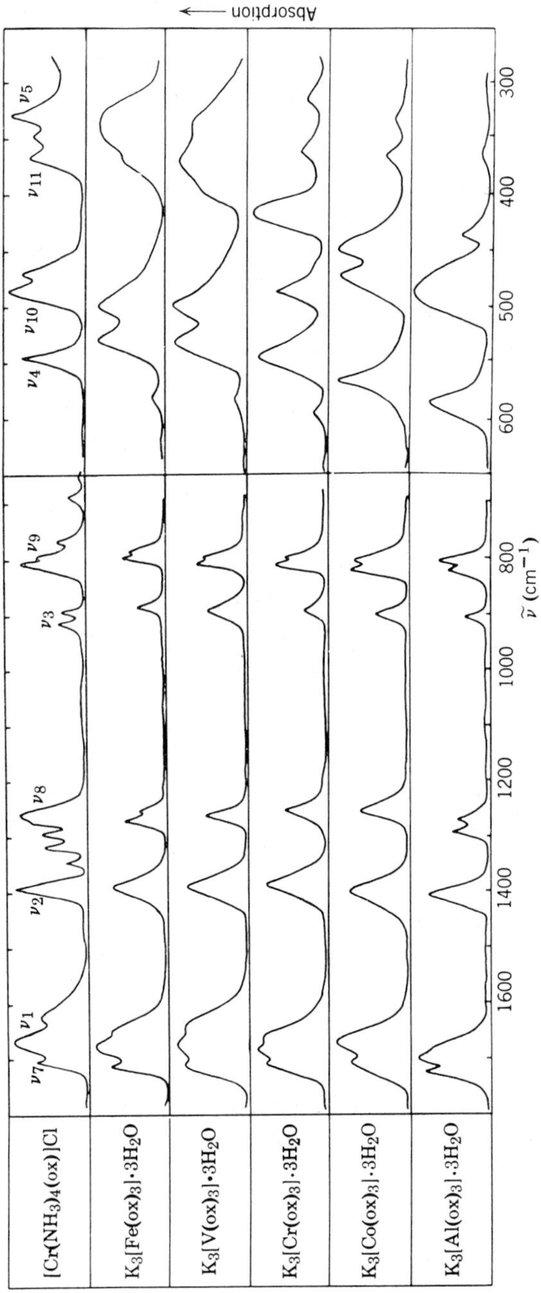

Fig. III-28*b*. Infrared spectra of oxalato complexes of trivalent metals.

make theoretical band assignments, as well as to locate the metal-oxygen vibrations, Fujita et al.[242] carried out a normal coordinate analysis. Table III-23 gives the observed frequencies and band assignments obtained. The values of the C—O_{II}, C—O_I and C—C stretching force constants (UBF) used in the calculations, when compared with those of the free ion,[239] have interesting implications. X-ray analysis[243] indicates that the four C$\cdots$O bonds in the free ion are equivalent, the bond length being 1.27 A. The C$\cdots$O stretching force constant in this ion is 7.20×10^5 dynes/cm. In the Cr(III) complex, however, x-ray analysis[244] indicates that the two C—O_I bonds coordinated to the metal are lengthened (1.39 A) and the two C—O_{II} bonds are shortened (1.17 A). Accordingly, the C—O_I stretching force constant is 5.30, whereas the C—O_{II} stretching force constant is 9.40×10^5 dynes/cm. A similar correspondence between the force constant and the bond distance is also seen in the C—C bond. The C—C distance in the free ion is 1.56 A (2.5×10^5 dynes/cm) and that in the complex is 1.25 A (3.60×10^5 dynes/cm).

These results seem to suggest that, as the M—O bond becomes stronger, the C—O_I bond order decreases and the C—O_{II} and C—C bond orders increase. Comparison of the infrared spectra of oxalato complexes of various metals may be useful in examining this trend, because a shift of the M—O stretching band to a higher frequency is expected to accompany a shift of the C—O_I stretching band to a lower frequency, together with a shift of the C—O_{II} stretching band to a higher frequency. As Table III-23 shows, however, there are no pure C—O_I or M—O stretching modes in the oxalato complexes. Nevertheless, linear relationships exist between ν_4 (predominantly M—O stretching) and the average of ν_1 and ν_7 (both are C—O_{II} stretching), and between ν_4 and either ν_2 or ν_8 (both are predominantly C—O_I stretching). These correlations are illustrated in Fig. III-29 for the oxalato complexes of divalent metals.

In oxalato complexes of trivalent metals, strict linear relationships between the frequencies do not exist. It is found, however, that ν_4 and ν_{11} (both are predominantly M—O stretching modes) increase along the series Fe $<$ V $<$ Cr $<$ Co $<$ Al, which is the same order as that observed in a series of acetylacetonato complexes (Sec. III-15).

Nakamoto and Fujita[245] have made a normal coordinate analysis of the chelate ring of the dithiooxalato Pt(II) complex. The results of their calculations indicate that the Pt—S stretching bands appear at 440–420

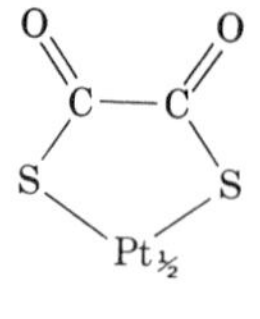

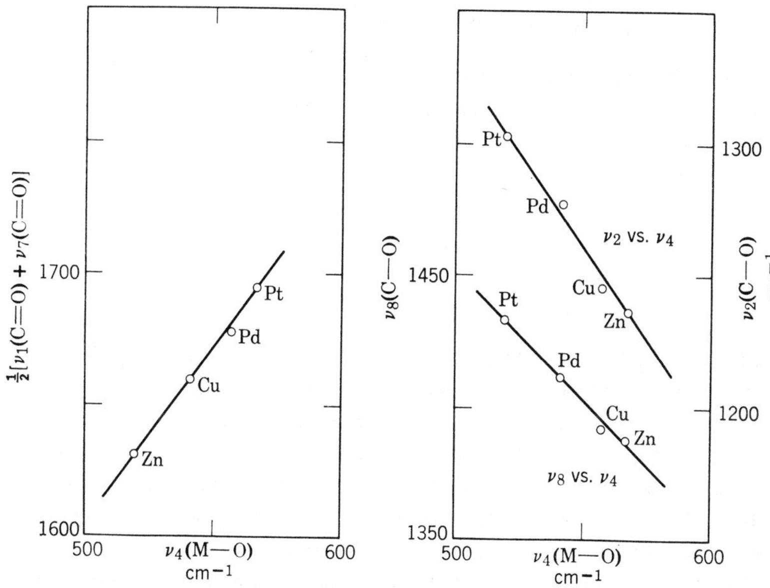

Fig. III-29. M—O stretching frequency vs. C═O and C—O stretching frequencies in oxalato complexes of divalent metals.

and 320 cm^{-1}, and that the Pt—S stretching force constant (2.30×10^5 dynes/cm) is smaller than the Pt—O stretching force constant (2.70×10^5 dynes/cm) of the corresponding oxalato complex.

From an infrared study of *metal rubeanates* Barceló[246] has proposed the structure

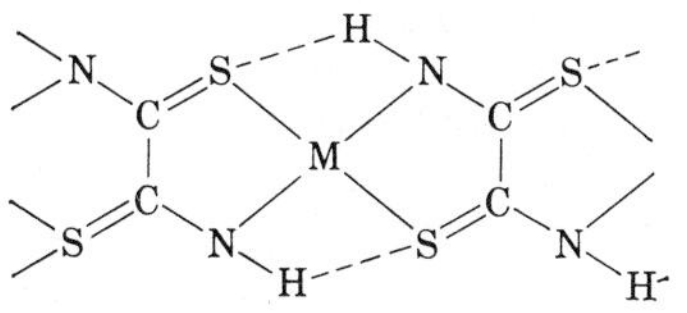

(M = Co, Ni or Cu)

Recently, Kuroda et al.[246a] have interpreted the infrared spectra of *metal oxamides* on the basis of the structure (V_h symmetry)

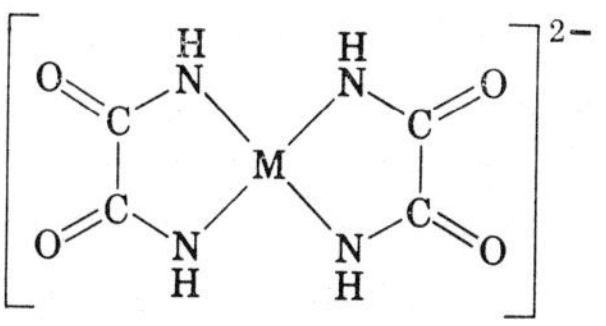

(M = Ni or Cu)

III-15. COMPLEXES OF β-DIKETONES

(1) Complexes of Acetylacetone

There are a number of β-diketones which form metal chelate compounds of the type

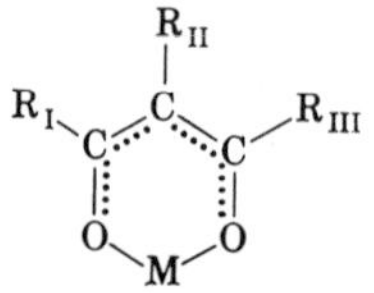

Among them, the acetylacetonate anion ($R_I = R_{III} = CH_3$, $R_{II} = H$, abbreviated acac) has the simplest structure. According to the result of an x-ray analysis of $Fe(acac)_3$,[247] the chelate ring is planar and symmetrical (C_{2v}), and the two C⋯O are equivalent, as are the two C⋯C bonds in the ring. This result provides strong evidence for the existence of resonance in the chelate ring. Calvin and Wilson[248] have suggested that the M—O bond is also involved in the resonance system.

The infrared spectra of metal acetylacetonates have been studied extensively by many investigators. For example, Lecomte et al.[249] have assigned the bands by assuming the spectra to be derived from the coupled vibrations of two acetone molecules bound together by a chemical linkage. Mecke and Funck[250] have made very complete empirical band assignments for the keto and enol forms of acetylacetone and its monovalent metal chelate compounds. All these spectra, however, were obtained only in the NaCl region, and all band assignments were empirical.

A normal coordinate analysis of the chelate ring of $Cu(acac)_2$ was first made by Nakamoto and Martell,[251] with 1:1 complex model. A detailed procedure of calculation is given in Appendix III. The vibrational frequencies of acetylacetonates of other metals were then calculated by the perturbation method.[252] Table III-24 lists the observed frequencies and the calculated force constants for each metal. Figures III-30*a* and III-30*b* show the infrared spectra of acetylacetonates of trivalent and divalent metals in both the NaCl and KBr regions.

Theoretical band assignments obtained from these calculations have allowed three conclusions to be drawn: (1) The highest frequency band (ν_8) in the carbonyl region is a C⋯C stretching and not a C⋯O stretching band, as previously suggested. (2) The ν_4 and ν_{12} bands, found between 700 and 590 cm^{-1}, are sensitive to changes in the metal. Although Lecomte and co-workers[249] have suggested that they may be due to M—O stretching vibrations, these calculations show that ν_4 is due to coupled M—O and ring deformation, while ν_{12} is due to coupled M—O and

C—CH_3 bending vibrations. (3) The newly found bands at 500–400 cm^{-1} are M—O stretching vibrations coupled slightly with the C—CH_3 stretching vibration.

The relation between infrared spectra and the stability of the acetylacetonates is of considerable interest. For example, Bellamy and Branch[253] concluded that no simple relation exists between the C⋯O stretching frequency and stability in a series of acetylacetonates, although a linear

TABLE III-24. OBSERVED FREQUENCIES AND CALCULATED UBF FORCE CONSTANTS IN METAL ACETYLACETONATES (CM^{-1})[252]

Co(III)	Cr(III)	Fe(III)	Al(III)	Pd(II)	Cu(II)	Ni(II)	Co(II)	Zn(II)	Be(II)	Predominant Modes or Force Constant
1578	1575	1572	1590	1570	1580	1598	1601	1592	1571	ν(C⋯C), ν_8
1527 —	1524 —	1526 —	1545 1530	1547 1523	1554 1534	1598 —	1601 —	1592 —	1530 —	ν(C⋯O), ν_1
1430 —	1427 —	1425 —	1466 —	1430 —	1464 —	1514 1453	1513 1461	1523 1464	1455 —	ν(C⋯O) + δ(C—H), ν_9
1390	1385	1390	1387	1395	1415	1398	1398	1394	1387	$\delta_d(CH_3)$
1372	1370	1365	1387	1358	1356	1367	1366	1361	1387	$\delta_s(CH_3)$
1284	1281	1276	1288	1273	1274	1261	1261	1264	1298	ν(C⋯C) + ν(C—CH_3), ν_2
1195	1195	1190	1191	1199	1190	1198	1199	1197	1185	δ(C—H), ν_{10}
1022	1025	1022	1028	1022	1020	1020	1020	1019	1015	$\rho_r(CH_3)$
934	934	930	935	936	937	929	931	927	930	ν(C—CH_3) + ν(C⋯O), ν_3, ν_{11}
780 771 764	788 772	800 770	773 —	781 —	781 —	764 —	767 —	769 —	780 —	π(C—H)
691	677	663	685	697	684	666	672	666	1040	Ring def. + ν(M—O), ν_4
671 662	658	654	658	676	654	—	659	651	824	δ(C—CH_3) + ν(M—O), ν_{12}
633 —	609 594	559 549	594 577	659 —	614 —	579 563	580 566	559 —	720 659	π
466	459	434	490	464	455	452	422	422	500	ν(M—O), ν_5
432	416	411	425 416	442	427	427	—	—	423 415	π
6.70	6.70	6.70	6.80	6.75	6.90	7.65	7.70	7.55	6.70	K(C⋯O), 10^5 dynes/cm
2.40	2.30	1.65	2.60	2.65	2.20	2.05	1.50	1.50	2.25	K(M—O), 10^5 dynes/cm

The spectrum of the Be(II) complex is markedly different from those of other metals. For the infrared spectra of acetylacetonates of other metals, see Refs. 252*a*–252*c*.

relation between the two was found in *metal salicylaldehydes*. On the other hand, Holtzclaw and Collman[254] and West and Riley[255] claim that the order of the carbonyl stretching frequencies is the same as the stability order, if the highest frequency band near 1600 cm^{-1} (ν_8) is selected as the C⋯O stretching band. Calculations show, however, that ν_8 is the C⋯C stretching band. The frequency order of ν_8 is

$$\begin{array}{lccccc} & \text{Pd} & < \text{Cu} & < \text{Zn} & < \text{Ni} & < \text{Co} \\ \nu_8\ (\text{cm}^{-1}) & 1570 & 1580 & 1592 & 1598 & 1601 \end{array}$$

On the other hand, the order of the stability constants, obtained from potentiometric titration,[256] is

$$\begin{array}{lccccc} & \text{Pd} & > \text{Cu} & > \text{Ni} & > \text{Co} & > \text{Zn} \\ \log k_1k_2 & 27.1 & 14.93 & 10.38 & 9.51 & 8.81 \end{array}$$

Thus, with the exception of Zn, the ν_8 frequency decreases as the stability constant increases. In general, however, the spectra in the carbonyl region

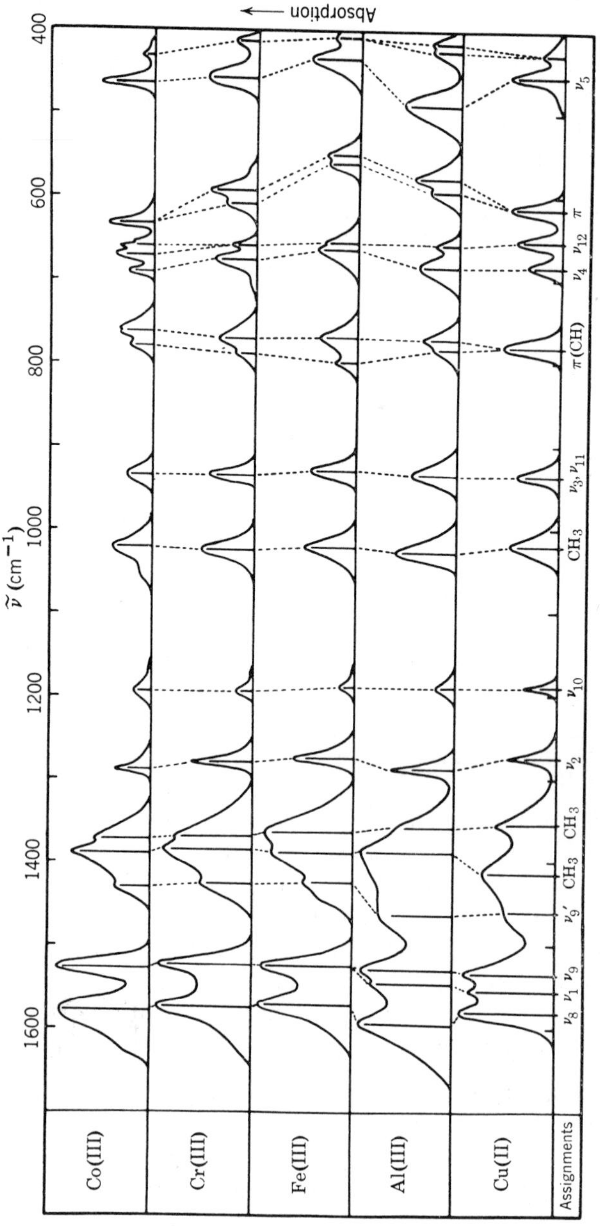

Fig. III-30*a*. Infrared spectra of acetylacetonates of Cu(II) and several trivalent metals.

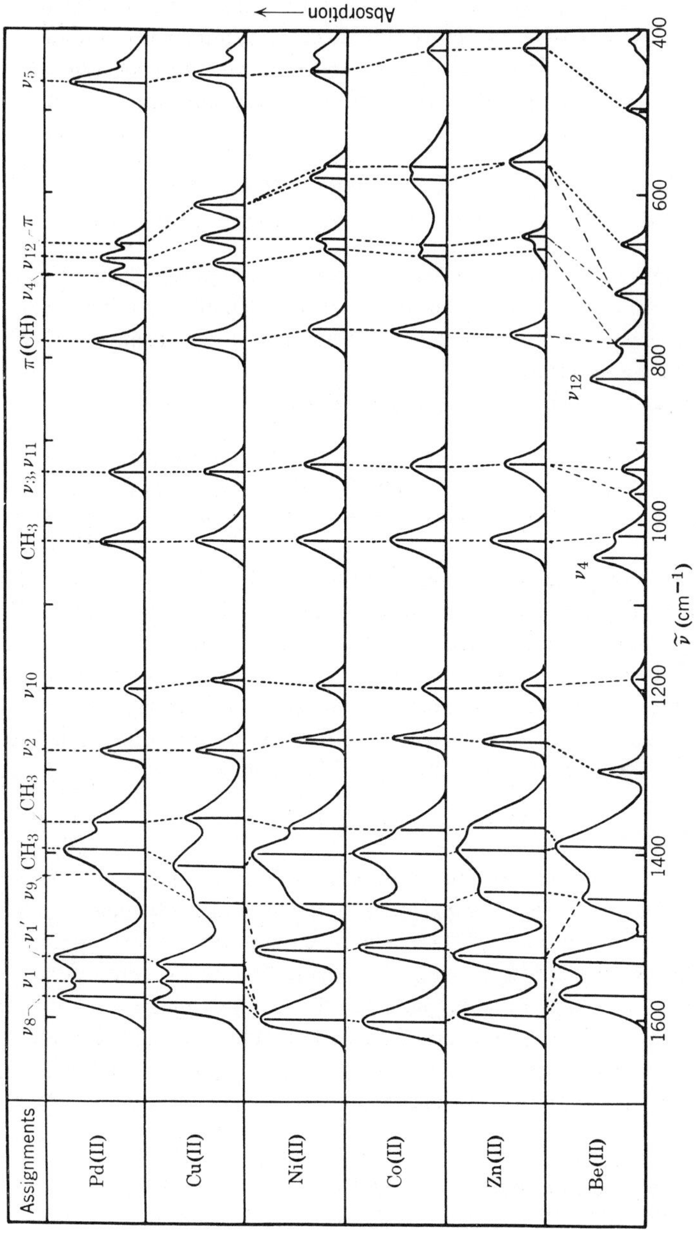

Fig. III-30*b*. Infrared spectra of acetylacetonates of divalent metals.

are more complicated than in the lower frequency region where the M—O stretching band (ν_5) appears. It seems more reasonable to compare the M—O stretching frequencies or the force constants with stability constants. In a series of trivalent metals, the order with respect to the M—O stretching frequency and the corresponding force constant is

	Al >	Co >	Cr >	Fe
ν_5 (cm^{-1})	490	466	459	434
K(M—O) (10^5 dynes/cm)	2.60	2.40	2.30	1.65

The same order is obtained for the oxalato complexes of these metals (Sec. III-15). Although no stability data are available for these trivalent metals, this may be interpreted as an indication of decreasing M—O bond order along this series.

For a series of divalent metals the order is

	Pd >	Cu >	Ni >	Zn ≈	Co
ν_5 (cm^{-1})	464	455	452	422	422
K(M—O) (10^5 dynes/cm)	2.65	2.20	2.05	1.50	1.50

Thus the order of the ν_5 frequencies or the M—O stretching force constants is the same as the order of the stability constants shown previously. Since the magnitude of the frequency shifts, however, does not match that of the differences in stability constants, there is no obvious quantitative agreement. A quantitative relation between the spectral and thermodynamic data can be obtained if the M—O stretching force constant is compared with the enthalpy, ΔH_{ML}, of the reaction

$$[M^{2+}]_g + 2[L]_{aq.} \rightleftharpoons [M^{2+}L_2]_{aq.}$$

The M—O stretching force constant is considered a unique spectroscopic quantity for this purpose, since it is not a function of mass and bond distance as is the frequency. The heat of reaction for the formation of the M—O bond from the free metal ion and the free ligand anion is the best quantity with which to compare the M—O stretching force constant. Using known values of the stability constant, the heat of hydration, and the entropy of the reaction, the heat of reaction, ΔH_{ML}, relative to that of the Mn(II) complex, is calculated as

	Ni ≈	Cu ≫	Zn ≈	Co
ΔH_{ML} (Kcal/mole)	68.7	66.7	48.3	45.5
K(M—O) (10^5 dynes/cm)	2.20	2.05	1.50	1.50

These two sequences are quantitatively in good agreement.

(2) Addition Complexes between Metal Acetylacetonates and Bases

It is well known that some metal acetylacetonates form addition complexes with water, pyridine and other bases. If there is bonding in these compounds between the basic atom of the donor molecule and the central metal ion, a marked shift of the M—O stretching band (ν_5) is anticipated. Figure III-31 compares the infrared spectrum of $VO(acac)_2$ with those of the pyridine and methylamine addition complexes.[257] In vanadyl acetylacetone, the strong band at 995 cm^{-1} is due to the V=O stretching vibration of the oxo group. The coordinated V—O′ (oxygen of acetylacetone) stretching band (ν_5) is seen at 480 cm^{-1}. When these compounds form addition complexes with pyridine and methylamine, these bands shift markedly to lower frequencies, as shown in Table III-25. The force constants calculated by the perturbation method are also given in the table. These results definitely indicate that the nitrogen atoms of pyridine and methylamine are strongly bound to the vanadium atom, since simple association of donor molecules with metal acetylacetonates cannot cause such marked changes in the spectra. It is conceivable that a change of electronic configuration of the vanadium atom from tetragonal pyramidal (e.g., dsp^3) to octahedral (d^2sp^3) hybridization could be responsible for such a marked change. Similar studies have also been made on the addition complexes of $Ni(acac)_2$ and $UO_2(acac)_2$ with weak bases.[257]

TABLE III-25. THE VO STRETCHING FREQUENCIES AND FORCE CONSTANTS IN $VO(acac)_2$ AND ITS ADDITION COMPLEXES (CM^{-1})[257]

Compound	ν(V=O)	ν(V—O)
$VO(acac)_2$	995	480
	(9.04)[a]	(2.85)
$VO(acac)_2$·pyridine	964	464
	(8.49)	(2.40)
$VO(acac)_2$·methylamine	964	452
	(8.49)	(2.05)

[a] Numbers in parentheses indicate the UBF force constant in units of 10^5 dynes/cm.

Sacconi and co-workers[258] have studied the infrared spectra of a number of addition complexes of uranyl β-diketones and have concluded that, in H_2O and NH_3 addition complexes, the oxygen or nitrogen of each molecule coordinates to the uranium atom, since the OH or NH stretching frequency of the addition complex is shifted to a lower frequency. Comyns

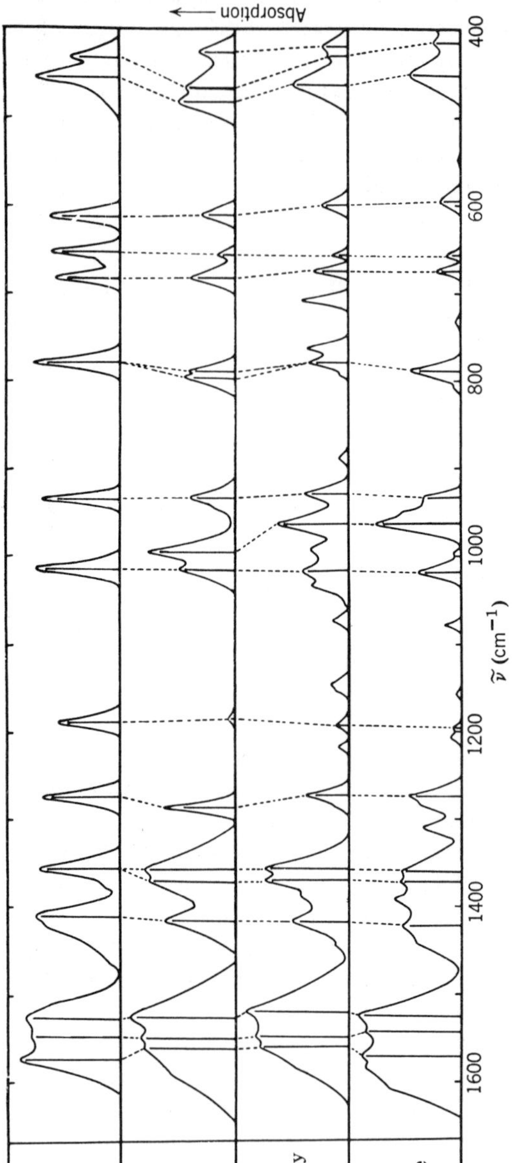

Fig. III-31. Infrared spectra of bis-acetylacetonato-oxovanadium(IV), its addition compounds, and bis-acetylacetonato-Cu(II).

and colleagues[259] studied the infrared spectra of three modifications of uranyl acetylacetonate monohydrate. Sartori and Costa[260] have concluded from infrared studies that, in the 1:3 addition complex of $Cr(acac)_3$ and triphenylaluminum, the aluminum atom coordinates to the oxygens of acetylacetone.

(3) Complexes of Other β-Diketones

The infrared spectra of metal chelate compounds of other β-diketones have been studied extensively. Belford and co-workers[261] have studied the effect of substitution of CF_3, OC_2H_5 and $N(C_2H_5)_2$ for the CH_3 group of $Cu(acac)_2$. Holtzclaw and Collman[254] and Dryden and Winston[262] have extensively investigated the Cu(II) complexes of various β-diketones, and have discussed the relation between the CO stretching frequency and the electronic effect of the substituent. Charette and Teyssié[263] also have studied the infrared spectra of metal complexes of *polymethacroylacetone* and its low molecular weight analogs. Bryant and colleagues[264] have listed the CO stretching frequencies of a number of metal chelate compounds of *substituted cycloheptatrienones*.

Interesting results have been obtained concerning the electronic effect of various substituents on the infrared spectra of metal acetylacetonates. Nakamoto and co-workers[265] have found that substitution of CF_3 for CH_3 causes marked shifts of the C⩦C (ν_8) and C⩦O (ν_1) stretching bands to higher frequencies and of the M—O (ν_5) stretching band to a lower frequency. This is seen in Fig. III-32. According to electronic theory, the strong positive inductive effect of the CF_3 group should strengthen both the C⩦C and the C⩦O bonds and weaken the M—O bond. As Table III-26 shows, the force constants obtained from the perturbation calculations support this deduction.

As Fig. III-32 demonstrates, however, substitution of phenyl for CH_3 shifts the C⩦C and M—O stretching bands to slightly higher frequencies without an appreciable shift of the C⩦O stretching frequency. If the resonating structure is approximated by

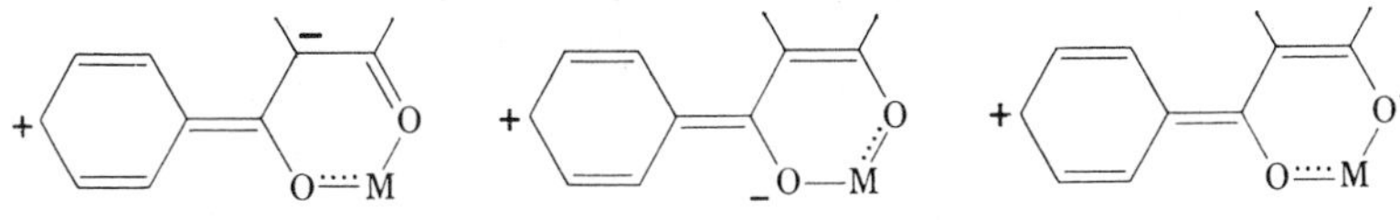

A B C

it may be deduced that the effect of the mesomeric electron-release by the phenyl group should be a general strengthening of the M—O bonds by an increase of negative charge on the oxygen atoms. Superimposed on this effect, there would be an increased tendency toward π bonding in

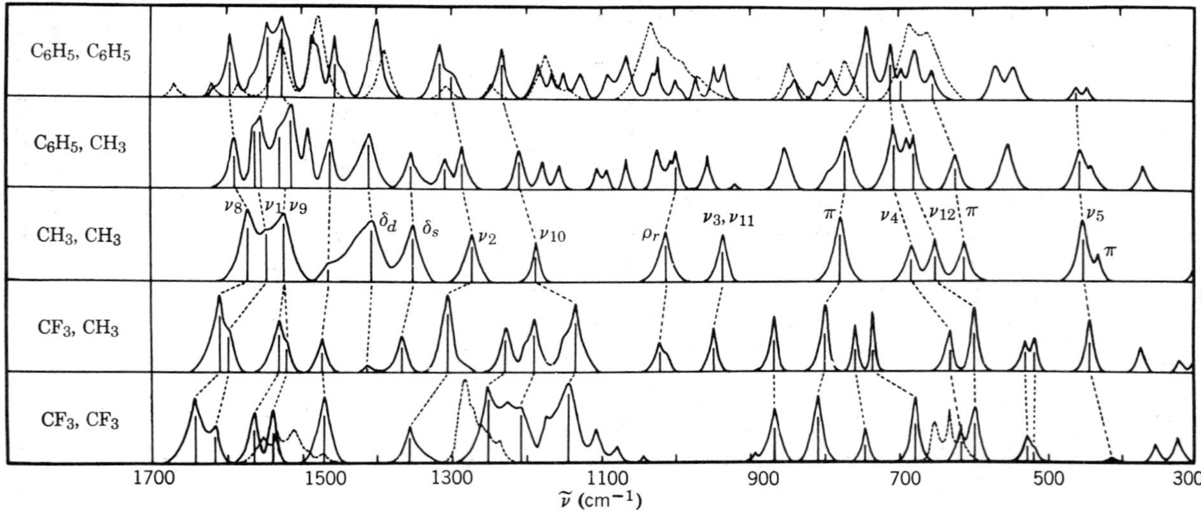

Fig. III-32. Infrared spectra of Cu(II) complexes of various β-diketones. (Dotted curves for dibenzoylmethane and hexafluoroacetylacetone complexes indicate the infrared spectra of benzene and tetrafluoromethane, respectively; δ_d, δ_s and ρ_r denote vibrations of the methyl groups.)

TABLE III-26. FREQUENCIES, STABILITY, AND UBF FORCE CONSTANTS IN Cu(II) AND Ni(II) COMPLEXES OF VARIOUS β-DIKETONES (CM^{-1})[265]

Metal	Cu(II)			Ni(II)		
R, R′	CF_3,CF_3	CH_3,CH_3	C_6H_5,C_6H_5	CF_3,CF_3	CH_3,CH_3	C_6H_5,C_6H_5
ν_8(C⋯C)	1644	1580	1593	1643	1598	1595
ν_1(C⋯O)	1614	1548 1524	1544	1613	1598	1595
ν_5(M—O)	415	455	462	397	452	458
Stability constant[a]	—	23.66	24.94	—	17.08	20.72
K(C⋯O)	7.90	6.90	6.82	7.72	7.65	7.55
K(C⋯C)	5.81	5.35	5.49	5.88	5.35	5.36
K(M—O)	1.75	2.20	2.31	1.35	2.05	2.25

[a] $\log k_1k_2$ (Ref. 265*a*).

the M—O linkages. It can be seen that both of these effects would strengthen the M—O and C—C bonds more than the C—O bonds of the chelate ring. These ideas agree well with the observations depicted in Fig. III-32 and Table III-26. It was suggested previously[254] that phenyl substitution weakens the M—O bond since the neighboring C—O bonds are weakened by conjugation with the phenyl rings. It appears, however, that phenyl substitution slightly strengthens the coordinate bond.

III-16. COMPLEXES OF OTHER LIGANDS

Studies of vibrational spectra have been made for a number of coordination compounds which are not included in the previous sections. Some interesting results obtained from these investigations are described briefly here.

Woodward and Hall[266] have made band assignments for the Raman spectrum of the *trifluorophosphine complex*, $Ni(PF_3)_4$, based on $\mathbf{T}_d$ symmetry. They found that the stretching force constant of the Ni—P bond (2.71×10^5 dynes/cm) is very close to that of the Ni—C bond in $Ni(CO)_4$. Miller and Carlson[267] have obtained the infrared and Raman spectra of the *isocyanato complexes*, $Si(NCO)_4$ and $Ge(NCO)_4$, and have concluded that the symmetry of the former is $\mathbf{T}_d$ (the Si—N═C═O bond is linear), whereas the latter deviates to some unknown degree from $\mathbf{T}_d$ symmetry. The M—N stretching frequencies of these compounds are found at 730–670 cm^{-1} (F_2) and at 495–490 cm^{-1} (A_1). Cotton and Zingales[268] have studied the NC stretching modes of *isonitrile complexes* of the types

$M(NCR)_6$ and $M(NCR)_4$ ($M = Ni^0$, Cr^0, Mn^+ or Mn^{2+}; $R = CH_3$, C_6H_5, etc.). They postulate that back donation of electrons from metal to ligand causes significant bending of the NCR chains. When isonitriles are bonded to positive metal ions, however, little or no back donation occurs, and the NC stretching frequency actually increases as a result of the inductive effect of the electrophilic metal ion. Matsubara[269] has made band assignments for infrared spectra of *aliphatic dinitrile complexes* of Cu(I) such as

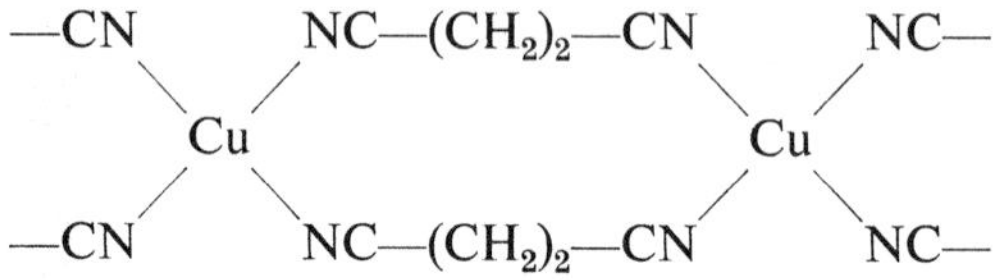

Succinonitrilo complex

on the basis of the results of normal coordinate analyses of the free ligands.

Chatt and co-workers[270] have investigated the infrared spectra of *dithiocarbamato complexes*, the structure of which may be represented by a hybrid of the structures

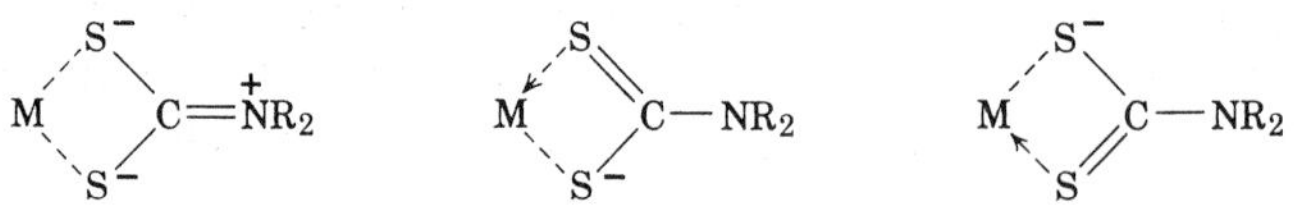

I II III

Then a decrease in the C$\overset{\cdots}{-}$N stretching frequency of these complexes may be interpreted as an indication of higher C—S and M—S bond orders. For *pyridine complexes*, Gill et al.[271] have found that the spectra are relatively insensitive to a change of metal.

The infrared spectra of metal chelate compounds of the more complex organic ligands shown in Fig. III-33 have been investigated. Only empirical band assignments are available for the spectra of these compounds because the structures are too complex to allow any theoretical approach. In the metal chelate compounds of *8-hydroxyquinoline and its derivatives*, Charles et al.[273] have noted that the C—O stretching frequency near 1100 cm^{-1} decreases slowly as the mass of the metal increases along the series Mg, Ca, Zn, Cd and Pb. A marked increase of the frequency, however, is observed along the series of transition metals Mn, Co, Ni and Cu, although the mass of the metal changes little along this series. Harkins and colleagues[276] have found that the band near 1250 cm^{-1} in metal

2-(*o*-hydroxyphenyl)-benzoxazoles shifts to a higher frequency along the series

$$Pb < Mn \approx Cd \approx Zn < Co < Ni < Mg < Cu$$

This order is the same as that of the stability constants for these divalent metals,[277] except Mg and Pb.

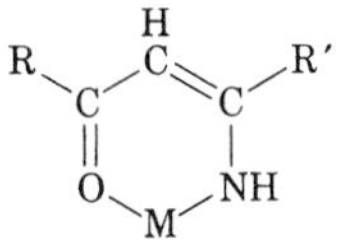

α,β-Unsaturated-β-ketoamine[272]

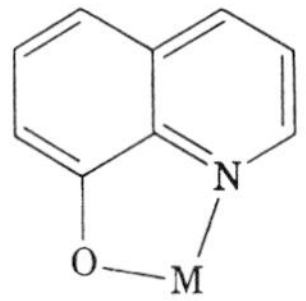

8-Hydroxyquinoline[273]

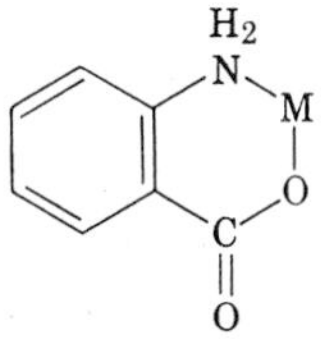

Anthranilic acid[274]

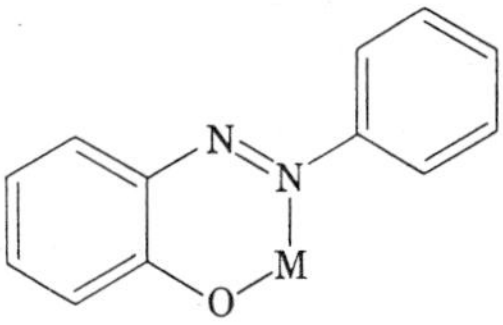

o-Hydroxyazobenzene[275]

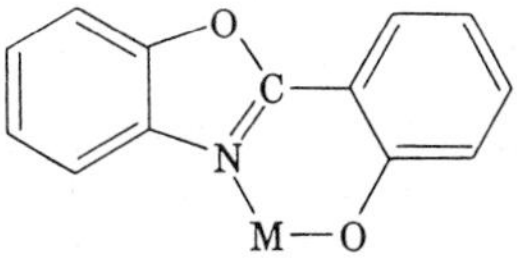

2-(*o*-Hydroxyphenyl)-benzoxazole[276]

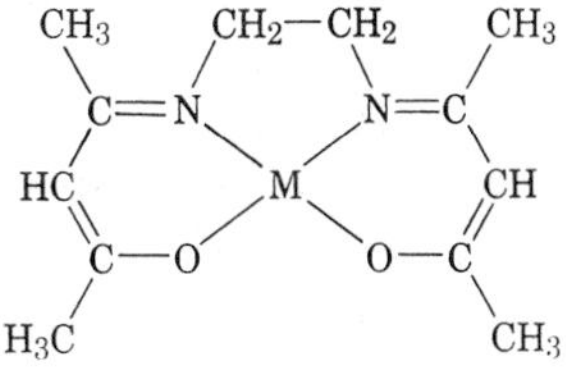

Bis-acetylacetone-ethylenediimine[278]

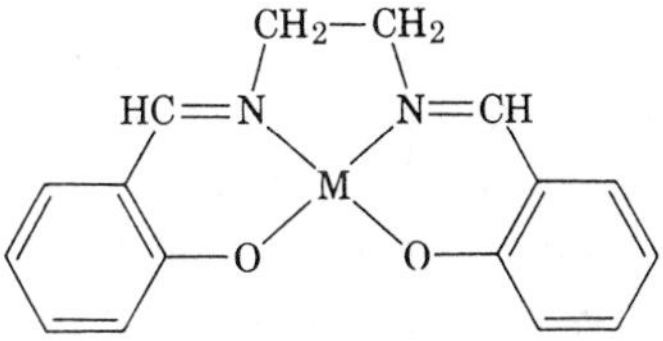

Bis-salicylaldehyde-ethylenediimine[278]

Fig. III-33. Structures of metal chelate compounds of various organic ligands.

The infrared spectra of metal complexes of imidazole derivatives[277a] and betaine[277b] have also been reported.

Ueno and Martell[278] have made extensive band assignments for the metal chelate compounds of bis-acetylacetone-ethylenediimine and bis-salicylaldehyde-ethylenediimine and have suggested that the metal-ligand stretching vibrations in these compounds appear in the range 580 to 430 cm^{-1} for the M—N and 640 to 500 cm^{-1} for the M—O stretching vibrations. The band at 565 cm^{-1} in oxygenated bis-salicylaldehyde-ethylenediimine Co(II) was attributed to the stretching mode of the bond between Co(II) and molecular oxygen.

III-17. COMPLEXES OF UNSATURATED HYDROCARBONS

In addition to the many coordination compounds discussed previously, there is a relatively new group of compounds in which the metal coordinates to the double or triple bond of an unsaturated hydrocarbon. They differ from other coordination compounds in that no localized coordinate bonds occur. The bonding arises mainly from the interaction of the $3d$ electrons of the metal with the delocalized π electrons of the ligand (Ref. I-35).

(1) Alkene and Alkyne Complexes

In early 1941, Taufer et al.[279] studied by means of Raman spectra the effect of adding Ag^+ ion to alkenes, alkynes and benzenes. They found that the C=C stretching bands of alkenes and C≡C stretching bands of alkynes are shifted to lower frequencies by about 65 and 120 cm^{-1}, respectively, upon adding Ag^+ ion. These results indicate that interaction of the Ag^+ ion with the C=C or C≡C bond of these compounds lowers the bond order, thus decreasing the frequency.

Such shifts of the bands to lower frequencies are more remarkable in Pt complexes. Chatt and Duncanson[280] used infrared spectra to elucidate the structure of Pt olefin complexes. Asymmetrical olefins such as propylene exhibit the C=C stretching band near 1647 cm^{-1}. This band is shifted to 1504 cm^{-1} in $K[PtCl_3(C_3H_6)]\cdot H_2O$. Although symmetrical olefins such as ethylene do not exhibit the C=C stretching band in the infrared spectrum, this vibration may become infrared active, if the field around the ethylene molecule becomes asymmetric through coordination. It was found, however, that the C=C stretching band cannot be observed even in complexes such as $K[PtCl_3(C_2H_4)]\cdot H_2O$. This result suggests that the ethylene molecule is symmetrically coordinated to the Pt atom as shown in Fig. III-34 (structure I). Later, proof of this arrangement of the olefin in the complex was demonstrated by x-ray analysis.[281]

By utilizing the observation that the free C=C group absorbs near 1650 cm^{-1} whereas the coordinated C=C group absorbs near 1500 cm^{-1}, Jonassen and co-workers[282] have been able to deduce the structure of metal olefin complexes. Since $[PtCl_2(C_{10}H_{12})]$ exhibits no free C=C stretching bands, both the C=C bonds of *dicyclopentadiene* ($C_{10}H_{12}$) must coordinate to the metal. The resulting structure is shown in Fig. III-34 (II). Similar studies were made by Alexander et al.[283] on the Pt(II) and Pd(II) complexes of *norbornadiene* (C_7H_8), which coordinates to the metal as a bidentate ligand. Recently, Hendra and Powell[284] concluded from infrared spectra that *1,5-hexadiene* (C_6H_{10}) forms a chelate ring of *gauche* conformation in $[PtCl_2(C_6H_{10})]$, $[PtI_2(C_6H_{10})]$ and $[PdCl_2(C_6H_{10})]$ but forms a bridged structure, shown in Fig. III-34 (III), in $K_2[Pt_2Cl_6(C_6H_{10})]$ and $[Cu_2Cl_2(C_6H_{10})]$. They also suggested that *1,5-cycloöctadiene* (C_8H_{12}) takes a "boat" conformation and chelates with the metal in $[PtCl_2(C_8H_{12})]$, $[PtI_2(C_8H_{12})]$ and $[PdCl_2(C_8H_{12})]$, whereas it takes a "chair" conformation

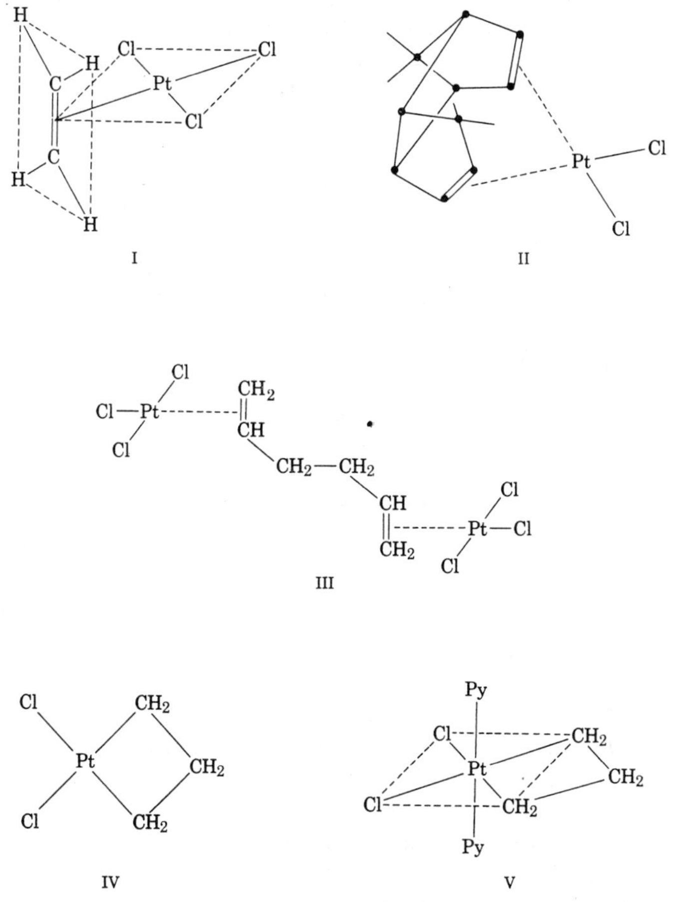

Fig. III-34. Structures of various olefin complexes.

and forms a polymer in $[CuCl(C_8H_{12})]$. *Cyclopropane* (C_3H_6) forms Pt(II) complexes because of its aromatic character. Using infrared spectra together with nuclear magnetic resonance spectra, Adams et al.[285] have deduced structure IV for $[PtCl_2(C_3H_6)]$ and structure V for $[PtCl_2(C_3H_6)(pyridine)_2]$.

Although previous investigators usually discussed only the C=C stretching bands of coordinated olefins, Powell and Sheppard[286] have compared all the observed bands of free and coordinated ethylene and have concluded that the frequency changes caused by coordination are only slight. Table III-27 is prepared from their data. It seems that the

TABLE III-27. VIBRATIONAL FREQUENCIES OF FREE AND COORDINATED ETHYLENE (CM^{-1})[286]

C_2H_4	$K_2[PtCl_3(C_2H_4)]\cdot H_2O$	Assignment
3106	3085	$\nu(CH)$
3019	3020	$\nu(CH)$
2990	2990	$\nu(CH)$
1623	1516	$\nu(C{=}C)$
1444	1428	$\delta_a(CH_2)$
1342	1402	$\delta_s(CH_2)$
949	1022	$\rho_w(CH_2)$
943	1010	
1027	975	$\rho_r(CH_2)$
810	841	$\rho_t(CH_2)$

C=C bond retains most of its double bond character in these compounds. Therefore structures involving only single bonds, such as

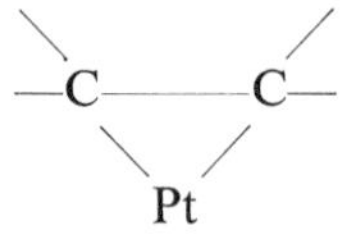

can be ruled out. Proton magnetic resonance studies[287] also indicate that the chemical shift of the ethylenic hydrogen of the complex is almost the same as that of free ethylene.

Chatt and co-workers[288] have studied *acetylene* complexes of the type $[Pt(P(C_6H_5)_3)_2(RC{\equiv}CR')]$, where R and R′ are alkyl groups. These compounds absorb near 1700 cm^{-1} rather than in the free C≡C stretching region near 2230 cm^{-1}. This may indicate that the triple bonds of these compounds have been reduced in strength almost to double bonds. More recently, Chatt et al.[289] also studied the infrared spectra of compounds of the types

$Na[PtCl_3L]$ and 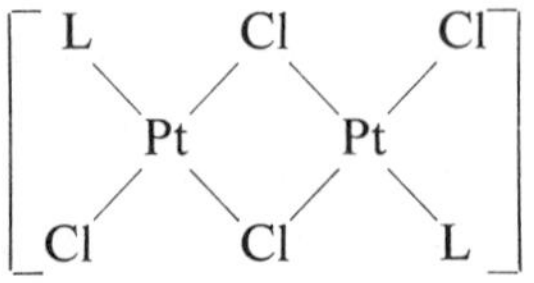

where L is an unsymmetrically substituted acetylene; they observed the C≡C stretching bands at 2025–2000 cm^{-1}. For $Na[PtCl_3$(ditertiarybutylacetylene)], only weak C≡C bands appear near 2000 cm^{-1}. This result seems to suggest a symmetrical coordination similar to that deduced for $K[PtCl_3$(ethylene)]. Markby and colleagues[290] have discussed the structure of $HCo_3(CO)_9 \cdot RC{\equiv}CH$ (R: alkyl group), using infrared spectra among other methods.

(2) Metal Sandwich Compounds

Since Kealy and Pauson[291] discovered ferrocene in 1951, a great number of compounds in which a metal is sandwiched between two aromatic

TABLE III-28. INFRARED FREQUENCIES AND BAND ASSIGNMENTS FOR $M(C_5H_5)_2$ COMPOUNDS (CM^{-1})[295]

		$Fe(C_5H_5)_2$	$Ru(C_5H_5)_2$[a]	$Ni(C_5H_5)_2$	Assignment
A_{2u}	ν_8	3085	3100	3075	ν(CH)
	ν_9	811	806	773	π(CH)
	ν_{10}	1108	1103	1110	ring def.
	ν_{11}	478	446	355	ν(M-ring)
E_{1u}	ν_{17}	3075	3100	3075	ν(CH)
	ν_{18}	1002	1002	1000	δ(CH)
	ν_{19}	834	835	800	π(CH)
	ν_{20}	1411	1413	1430	ν(CC)
	ν_{21}	492	528	355	ring tilt
	ν_{22}	170	(185)	(125)	δ(ring-M-ring)

[a] According to x-ray analysis,[293] $Ru(C_5H_5)_2$ belongs to the point group D_{5h}, in which the two cyclopentadienyl rings are in the eclipsed position.

rings have been prepared. Among the many sandwich compounds, *ferrocene* ($Fe(C_5H_5)_2$) is the best known. X-ray analyses of this compound have been made by several investigators,[292] and the $\mathbf{D}_{5d}$ structure in Fig. III-35 (structure I) has been deduced. A similar structure was also found for compounds of the type $M(C_5H_5)_2$ (M = Co, Ni, Mg, V, Mn, Cr, Os) from x-ray data.[293] Figure III-36 shows the infrared spectra of $Fe(C_5H_5)_2$ and $Ni(C_5H_5)_2$ obtained by Wilkinson et al.[294] Lippincott and Nelson[295] have made the most complete band assignments for the vibrational spectra of ferrocene. Table III-28 indicates the observed infrared frequencies and band assignments obtained. Of the vibrations listed in the table, the metal-ring vibration† is particularly interesting, since it gives a measure

† This may correspond to the metal-ligand stretching vibration in ordinary coordination compounds.

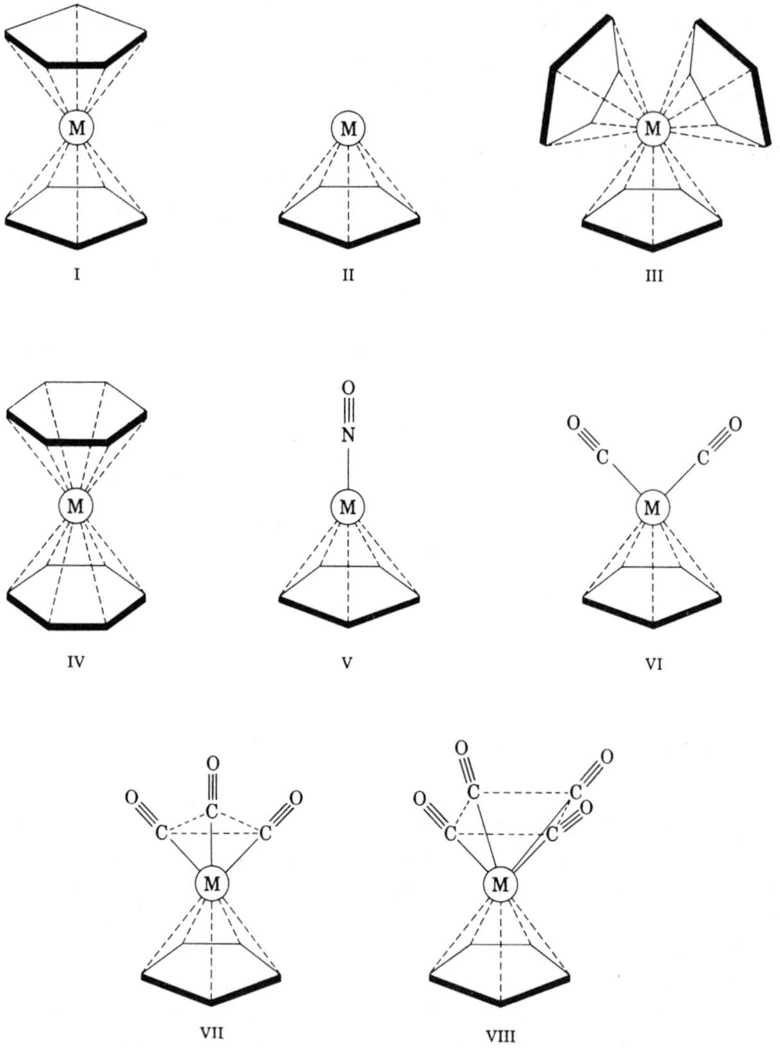

Fig. III-35. Structures of various sandwich-type compounds.

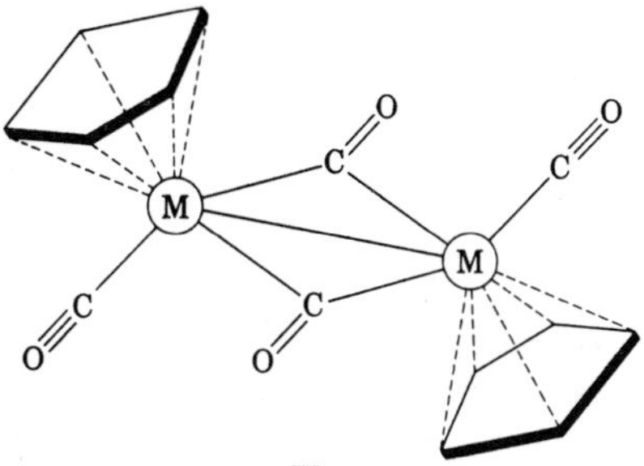

IX

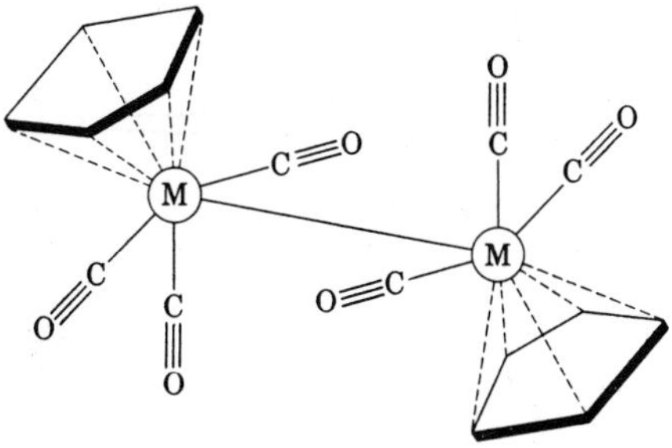

X

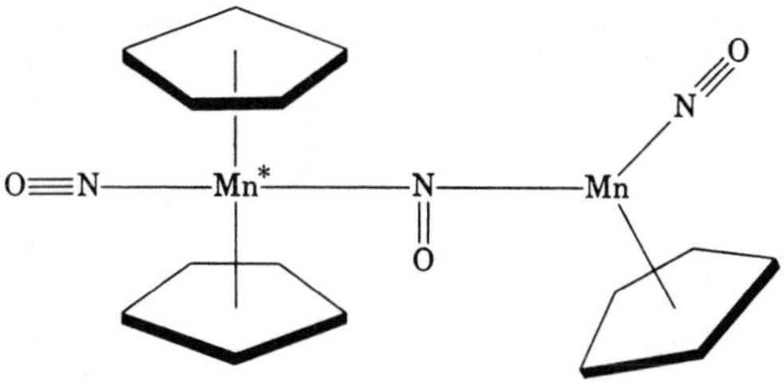

XI (One of the rings on Mn* is σ-bonded.)

Fig. III-35 (Continued).

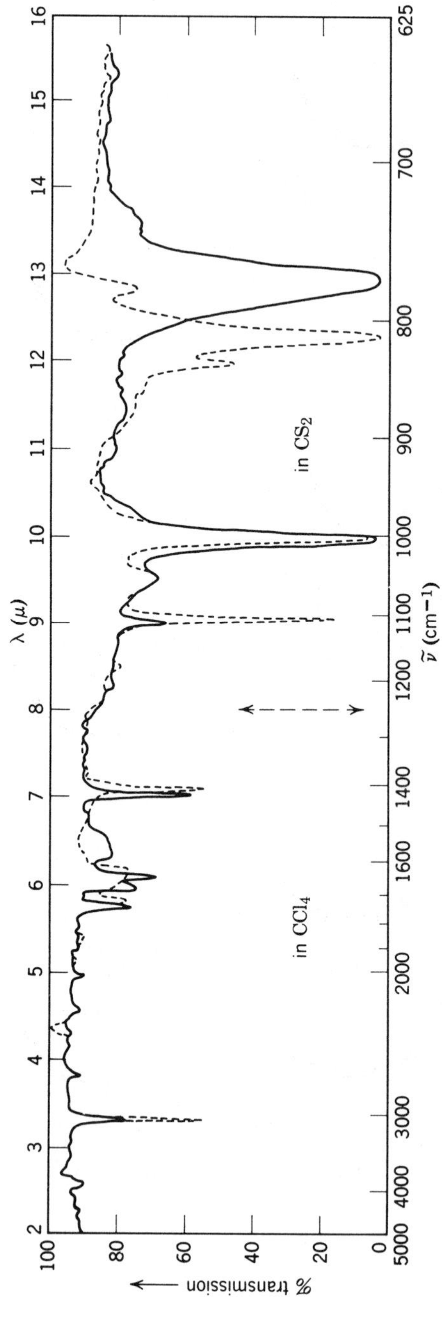

Fig. III-36. Infrared spectra of $Ni(C_5H_5)_2$ (solid line) and $Fe(C_5H_5)_2$ (broken line).[294,312]

of the magnitude of the interaction between the metal and the aromatic ring. The antisymmetric (infrared active) metal-ring vibrations appear at 478, 446 and 355 cm^{-1}, and the symmetric (Raman active) metal-ring vibrations appear at 303, 330 and 220 cm^{-1} in the Fe, Ru and Ni complexes, respectively. Recently, Fritz and Schneider[296] have made a detailed study of the infrared spectra of these compounds in the lower frequency region and estimated the metal-ring interaction force constants (10^5 dynes/cm) as

$$\begin{array}{ccccccccccccccc} Os & > & Fe & > & Ru & > & Cr & > & Co & \approx & V & \approx & Ni & \approx & Zn \\ 2.8 & & 2.7 & & 2.4 & & 1.6 & & & & 1.5 & & & & \end{array}$$

Recently, Winter et al.[297] studied the infrared dichroism of ferrocene, using a single crystal. The infrared spectra of compounds having the general formula $M(C_5H_5)_2$ have been reported by many other investigators.[298–301] If the valence of M in these compounds is more than 2+ the compound is a cation. Green and co-workers[302] have reported the infrared spectra of compounds of the type $M(C_5H_5)(C_5H_5R)$, where M is Rh or Co and C_5H_5R denotes cyclopentadiene rings substituted by R (R = H, D, CH_3 or CCl_3). The spectra of compounds of the type $Fe(C_5H_6)L$ (L = benzene or mesitylene) have also been reported by the same investigators.

Besides 1:2 (metal/ring) complexes, a number of 1:1 and 1:3 complexes are known. For example, Cotton and Reynolds[303] proposed structure II of Fig. III-35 for $Ti(C_5H_5)$ from a study of the vapor spectrum of this compound in the C—H stretching region. The spectrum of $Ti(C_5H_5)Cl_3$ is also available.[304] Reynolds and Wilkinson[305] obtained the spectrum of $[U(C_5H_5)_3]^+$, which is expected to have structure III. Since the interaction between the metal and the cyclopentadienyl ring is similar in all these compounds (π bonding), their infrared spectra are essentially the same. The spectrum of $Hg(C_5H_5)_2$ obtained by Wilkinson and Piper[306] is, however, markedly different from those of the π-bonded compounds just mentioned. In general, the spectrum is more complicated than that of the ferrocene type; this indicates the presence of direct interaction between the metal and the aromatic ring. They[315] suggested a structure in which the metal is σ-bonded to the rings as it is in diphenylmercury.

Fischer and Hafner[307] have prepared *dibenzene chromium*, $Cr(C_6H_6)_2$, and have suggested a ferrocene-like structure, on the basis of the infrared spectrum and magnetic measurements. Weiss and Fischer[308] have deduced structure IV of Fig. III-35 from x-ray analysis. Recently, Fritz et al.[309] and Snyder,[310] assuming $\mathbf{D}_{6h}$ symmetry, made complete band assignments for $Cr(C_6H_6)_2$. Table III-29 gives the observed infrared frequencies and band assignments obtained by Snyder. It was found that the metal-ring interaction force constant is 2.39×10^5 dynes/cm, which is slightly lower than that of ferrocene (2.7×10^5 dynes/cm). Fischer and Seus[311] have measured the infrared spectrum of the dibiphenyl chromium cation, $[Cr(C_{12}H_{10})_2]^+$.

There are many cyclopentadienyl compounds which are substituted with carbonyl, nitrosyl, alkyl and other groups. For example, Cotton et al.[312] have studied the infrared spectra of $Ni(C_5H_5)NO$, $Co(C_5H_5)(CO)_2$, $Mn(C_5H_5)(CO)_3$ and $V(C_5H_5)(CO)_4$ and have proposed structures V, VI, VII and VIII of Fig. III-35 for these compounds. The number of infrared active CO stretching modes of these compounds is in good agreement

TABLE III-29. INFRARED FREQUENCIES AND BAND ASSIGNMENTS FOR $Cr(C_6H_6)_2$ AND $Cr(C_6D_6)_2$ (CM^{-1})[310]

		$Cr(C_6H_6)_2$	$Cr(C_6D_6)_2$	Assignment†
A_{2u}	ν_1	970	931	ring def.
	ν_2	?	?	ν(CH)
	ν_{11}	796	669?	π(CH)
	ν_{22}	456	421	ν(M-ring)
E_{1u}	ν_{10}	1014	824	π(CH)
	ν_{18}	1002	803	δ(CH)
	ν_{19}	1430	1273	ν(CC)
	ν_{20}	3047	2278?	ν(CH)
	ν_{25}	492	481	ring tilt

† For the H compound.

with those predicted from the selection rule derived from a consideration of only the local symmetry of the $M(CO)_n$ portion of these molecules. For example, in $Mn(C_5H_5)(CO)_3$, only two CO stretching bands are expected from the C_{3v} symmetry of the $Mn(CO)_3$ group, and, in fact, only two bands are observed.

$Fe(C_5H_5)_2(CO)_2$ was first prepared by Hallam and Pauson,[313] who suggested that the metal and the rings are π-bonded. Piper and Wilkinson,[314] on the other hand, proposed that one ring is π-bonded and the other σ-bonded to the metal. Piper and Wilkinson[315] have demonstrated their structure to be correct by proton magnetic resonance studies and by infrared studies of compounds having the formula $[M(C_5H_5)\cdot(CO$ or $NO)_x\cdot R]$, where M = Cr, Fe, Mo or W, and R is an alkyl group.

Davison and co-workers[316] have reported the infrared spectra of compounds of the type $[M^n(C_5H_5)(CO)_3]^{n-1}$, where M is V^-, Cr^0, Mn^+ or Fe^{2+}, and have noted that the CO stretching frequency increases in that order of metals. This may imply that the M—C π bonding caused by the back donation of electrons from metal to CO group becomes weaker with increasing oxidation number of the metal. In a series of compounds of the type $[Fe(C_5H_5)(CO)_2L]$, where L is $(C_6H_5)_3Sb$, $(C_6H_5)_3As$, $(C_6H_5)_3P$ or CO, the CO stretching frequency increases along the same series. This may indicate that the M—C π bonding becomes weaker along this series. Winkhaus and colleagues[317] have obtained the infrared spectra of compounds of the type $[Mn(C_6H_6R)(CO)_3]$, where C_6H_6R represents cyclohexadienyl rings substituted by the alkyl group, R. Fischer[317a] has made a systematic study of the CO stretching frequency of compounds of the type $M(Ar)(CO)_3$, where M is Cr or Mn, and Ar represents an aromatic compound. Green and co-workers[302] have also reported the infrared spectra of compounds of the type $[Fe(Ar)(CO)_3]$ and $[Fe(Ar)(CO)_2]$, where Ar is norbornadiene, cyclopentadienone or some other group. The infrared spectra of $Cr(C_6H_6)(CO)_3$ and $Cr(C_6D_6)(CO)_3$ have been reported by Fritz and Manchot.[317b]

There are several cyclopentadienyl compounds which are polynuclear, having CO or NO bridges. The infrared spectrum of $[Fe_2(C_5H_5)_2(CO)_4]$ was first reported by Piper et al.[312] Mills[318] obtained structure IX of Fig. III-35 from x-ray analysis. Cotton and colleagues[319] discussed the spectrum of this compound on the basis of structure IX. The infrared spectra of $[Mo_2(C_5H_5)_2(CO)_6]$ and $[W_2(C_5H_5)_2(CO)_6]$ were obtained by Wilkinson.[320] Wilson and Shoemaker[321] obtained structure X from x-ray analysis. Recently, Abel et al.[322] have reported the infrared spectra of compounds of the type $[M_2(C_5H_4R)_2(CO)_6]$, where M represents Mo or W, and C_5H_4R represents cyclopentadienyl rings substituted by an alkyl group, R. Piper and Wilkinson[323] prepared $[Mn_2(C_5H_5)_3(NO)_3]$ and observed two NO stretching bands at 1732 and 1510 cm^{-1}. Attributing the former to the terminal and the latter to the bridging NO group, they proposed structure XI.

III-18. MISCELLANEOUS INTERACTIONS

(1) Molecular Compounds

A large number of molecular compounds are formed as a result of the reaction between an electron donor or Lewis base, A, and an electron acceptor or Lewis acid, B. Mulliken[324] developed a classification for the various molecular compounds based on quantum mechanics. Infrared studies of molecular compounds are useful for the elucidation of the force acting between the components. Some of the infrared work on inorganic molecular compounds is described briefly here.

In what follows, only the relative difference of acidity or basicity between A and B is important. If this difference is large, a charge-transfer occurs from A to B. In this case, infrared spectra can be interpreted on the basis of the ionic structure A^+B^-. For example,

$$NO_2F + BF_3 \rightarrow [NO_2]^+[BF_4]^- \qquad \text{(Ref. 325)}$$

$$N_2O_4 + 3SO_3 \rightarrow [NO_2]_2{}^+[S_3O_9]^{2-} \qquad \text{(Ref. 325}a\text{)}$$

$$N_2O_3 + 2BF_3 \rightarrow [NO]^+[N(OBF_3)_2]^- \qquad \text{(Ref. 326)}$$

$$NOCl + AlCl_3 \rightarrow [NO]^+[AlCl_4]^- \qquad \text{(Ref. II-311)}$$

$$SeCl_4 + AlCl_3 \rightarrow [SeCl_3]^+[AlCl_4]^- \qquad \text{(Ref. 327)}$$

If the difference is intermediate, a covalent molecular compound A—B is formed.

Table III-30 gives the frequencies of the coordinate bond stretching

TABLE III-30. VIBRATIONAL FREQUENCIES AND FORCE CONSTANTS OF COORDINATE BOND STRETCHING VIBRATIONS IN SOME MOLECULAR COMPOUNDS (CM^{-1})

Compound	Stretching Frequency (cm^{-1})	Force Constant† (10^5 dynes/cm)	References
$2(CH_3)_3N—AlH_3$	717 (IR)	4.22	328, 329
$H_3N—AlCl_3$	750 (R)	2.2	330, 231
$(CH_3)_3N—BH_3$	1255 (IR)	4.50	332
$(CH_3)_3N—BH_3$	676 (R)	2.79	333
$H_3N—BF_3$	—	4.40	334
$F_3P—BH_3$	607 (R)	—	335

† GVF field.

vibration and the corresponding force constants for some of these compounds. It is to be noted that AlH_3 and BH_3 exist only as molecular compounds.

Ketones form molecular compounds with a number of metal halides such as BF_3, $AlCl_3$ and $TiCl_4$. Susz and Chalandon[336] have found that the C═O stretching bands of ketones are shifted to lower frequencies upon formation of molecular compounds with metal halides. The same is true of the C═O stretching bands of *esters* bonded to metal halides.[336a] On the other hand, the C≡N stretching bands of *nitriles* are shifted to higher frequencies in molecular compounds with metal halides.[337–339a] In molecular compounds of *pyridine* with $TiCl_4$ and $ZrCl_4$, Rao[340] has found that some ring stretching frequencies decrease by 10–20 cm^{-1}, whereas some ring deformation frequencies increase by 20 cm^{-1}. For molecular compounds of pyridine with other metal halides, see Refs. 341–342*a*. Terenin and co-workers[343] have made an extensive study of the effect of molecular compound formation on infrared spectra. In molecular compounds of $POCl_3$ and $POBr_3$ with metal halides, Sheldon and Tyree[344] noted that the P=O stretching band is shifted to a lower frequency by complex formation. The bonding may occur in these complexes between the phosphoryl oxygen and the metal.[344a]

Pyridine also forms molecular compounds with *iodine*. Plyler and Mulliken[345] have found that the I—I stretching band at 213 cm^{-1} in the gaseous state is shifted to 184 cm^{-1} in the pyridine-I_2 complex. In addition, Zingaro and Witmer[346] have found that the 990 cm^{-1} band of pyridine (in-plane CH deformation) is shifted to a higher frequency. Using infrared spectra, Schmulbach and Drago[347] have obtained the equilibrium constant and other thermodynamic data for the reaction between dimethylacetamide and iodine.

Ether forms molecular compounds with HCl and HBr. Vidale and Taylor[348] have made a detailed study of the Raman spectra of these compounds and have found that in $(CH_3)_2O \cdot HCl$ the two skeletal stretching frequencies of the ether and the stretching frequency of HCl are lowered. The H—Cl stretching frequency is 2800 cm^{-1} in the gaseous state and about 2250 cm^{-1} in the ether complex.

Pullin and Pollock[349] have made the interesting observation that the C=O stretching (1715 cm^{-1}) and the CH_3—C—O bending (1225 cm^{-1}) bands of *acetone* are shifted to lower and higher frequencies, respectively, by adding $LiClO_4$ or $AgClO_4$. Thus, in acetone solutions of these salts, the C=O stretching band (as well as the CH_3—C—O bending band) splits into two peaks, one due to free acetone and the other due to molecular complexes such as $[Li(acetone)_2]^+$ and $[Ag(acetone)_2]^+$.

In "loose" molecular compounds such as benzene-$SbCl_3$ and benzene-$AgClO_4$, no marked band shifts of *benzene* are observed. Instead, the appearance of new lines and a redistribution of intensities are observed in the Raman spectrum.[350,351] Owing to a lowering of the symmetry of benzene, Daasch[352] has made a detailed study of the infrared spectra and thermodynamics of complexes of benzene and dioxane with $AgClO_4$, $SbCl_3$ and $HgCl_2$. He concluded that the complex $SbCl_3 \cdot \frac{1}{2}(C_6H_6)$ has $\mathbf{C}_{3v}$ symmetry in solution and $\mathbf{C}_{2v}$ symmetry in the solid state.

(2) Interactions in the Alkali Halide Pellet

The pressed pellet technique using alkali halide powder is widely employed to obtain the infrared spectra of solids. Several investigators have noted that the spectrum obtained by using this technique must be interpreted with caution. For example, Ketelaar et al.[353] have noted that the ν_3 frequency of the $[HF_2]^-$ ion is markedly sensitive to the kind of alkali halide used: 1599, 1570, 1527 and 1478 cm^{-1} in NaBr, KCl, KBr and KI, respectively. On the other hand, the spectra of $NaHF_2$, KHF_2 and NH_4HF_2 in KCl pellets are the same. These results imply the formation of a mixed crystal in which the halide ion is replaced by the $[HF_2]^-$ ion. Thus the surrounding alkali halide lattice induces a dipole moment in the $[HF_2]^-$ ion which results in the marked change in the ν_3 frequency. Jones and Chamberlain[354] have found that over a period of time the bands of $K[Au(CN)_2]$ at 2141 and 427 cm^{-1} are gradually replaced by new bands at 2154 and 448 cm^{-1} in KBr and KI pellets. This result also indicates the replacement of a Br—K—Br chain by the $[Au(CN)_2]^-$ ion. The $[Au(CN)_2]^-$ ion in the KBr pellet exhibits the same spectrum as that in the KI pellet; it differs in this respect from the $[HF_2]^-$ ion. Strasheim and Buijs[354a] have found that the ν_3 frequency of the $[NO_3]^-$ ion increases linearly with the lattice energy of the alkali halide used.

Meloche and Kalbus[355] have noted that the major factor involved in an exchange of anions between KBr and inorganic salts is the moisture adsorbed on the surface of the sample and of the KBr. According to Buchanan and Bowen,[355a] carefully prepared water-free alkali halide pellets of LiOH exhibit the infrared spectrum of $LiOH{\cdot}H_2O$ as soon as they absorb water vapor from the air. An alkali halide pellet, immediately after pressing, is in a stressed state. Vrátný[356] has noted that the rate of recovery from this stressed state is governed by the humidity of the environment of the pellet as well as by the duration of the evacuation process. Farmer[357] has studied the infrared spectra of *phenols* and *organic salts* in alkali halide pellets and has found that they are adsorbed on the surface of the alkali halide crystals through their hydroxyl groups. It is interesting to note that the carboxylic acids are adsorbed principally as monomers. Durie and Szewczyk[358] have made the unusual observation that non-hydroxylic compounds such as anthracene exhibit an abnormal OH stretching band (3400 cm^{-1}) in KCl pellets which is definitely not due to adsorbed moisture. They suggested that the interaction of water and KCl during grinding causes the formation of the $[OH]^-$ ions.

(3) Chemisorbed Molecules

Recent infrared studies of chemisorbed molecules afford valuable information on: (1) the structure of chemisorbed molecules and the surface structure of solid catalyst; (2) the interacting force between chemisorbed molecules and solid catalyst; (3) the mechanism of catalytic reaction. Some of this work will be described briefly.

Eischens and co-workers[359] have found that the band of free CO at 2141 cm^{-1} is shifted to 2128, 2070, 2053 and 2033 cm^{-1} when CO is adsorbed on the surface of metallic Cu, Pt, Pd and Ni, respectively. In

Ni and Pd, additional bands are observed at 1908 and 1916 cm^{-1}, respectively, possibly because of the existence of a bridged molecule such as

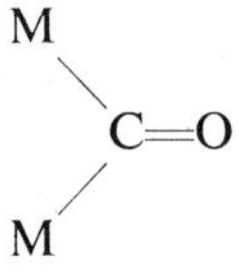

If the surface of the catalyst is homogeneous, the intensity of the band due to CO is expected to increase in proportion to the exposed area. If this does not occur, the surface may not be homogeneous. Using this principle, Eischens and colleagues have found that Pd is not homogeneous whereas Pt is homogeneous. For more recent work on chemisorbed CO, see Refs. 360–361*a*.

NH_3 molecules adsorbed on cracking catalysts exhibit both NH_3 and $[NH_4]^+$ absorption. Since the latter bands are much weaker than the former, Maples and Eischens[362] concluded that the surface structure of the catalyst is of the Lewis acid type and not of the Brönsted acid type.

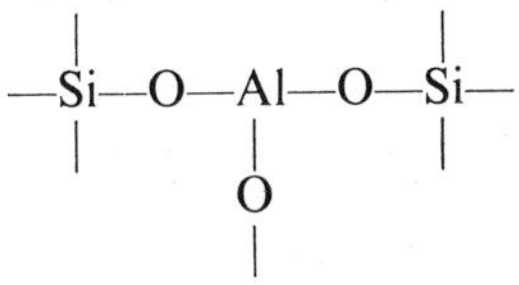

Lewis acid type

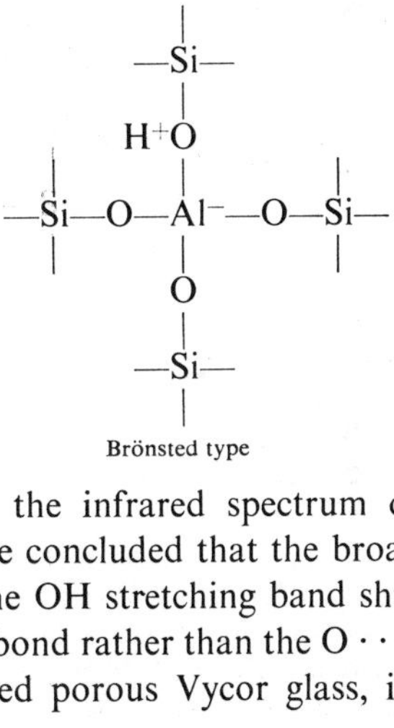

Brönsted type

Yates and co-workers[363] have studied the infrared spectrum of NH_3 adsorbed on porous silica glass and have concluded that the broad band observed at 2900–2850 cm^{-1} is due to the OH stretching band shifted by forming the O—H · · · N type hydrogen bond rather than the O · · · H—N type. If NH_3 is adsorbed on chlorinated porous Vycor glass, it reacts with the $\equiv$Si—Cl group and produces the aminated surface

$$\equiv Si—Cl + NH_3 = \equiv Si—NH_2 + HCl$$

which absorbs at 3520 and 3445 cm^{-1}. In addition, Folman[363a] has observed three bands at 3150, 3050 and 2805 cm^{-1} which are due to NH_4Cl on the surface formed during the process of amination.

Since chemisorbed molecules have lower symmetry than those in the free state, the appearance of new bands and the splitting of degenerate vibrations are anticipated. Sheppard and Yates[364] have found that the symmetry of CH_4, C_2H_4 and H_2 adsorbed on porous silica glass may be $\mathbf{C}_{3v}$, $\mathbf{C}_{2v}$ and $\mathbf{C}_{2v}$, respectively. The infrared spectra of chemisorbed olefins on silica-supported Ni have been studied by Pliskin and Eischens.[365] From the observation of the CH_2 and CH_3 deformation vibrations, it was found that ethylene molecules adsorbed on the catalyst exist predominantly as H_2C^*—C^*H_2 (the asterisk denotes an unpaired π electron) and are converted to H_2C^*—CH_3 by half-hydrogenation, whereas acetylene molecules are transformed readily into H_2C^*—CH_3 by self-hydrogenation. For investigations of other chemisorbed molecules, see Refs. 366–374.

References

1. I. Nakagawa and S. Mizushima, *Bull. Chem. Soc. Japan*, **28,** 589 (1955).
2. S. Mizushima, I. Nakagawa and J. V. Quagliano, *J. Chem. Phys.*, **23,** 1367 (1955).
3. J. Fujita, K. Nakamoto and M. Kobayashi, *J. Am. Chem. Soc.*, **78,** 3295 (1956).
4. A. Nakahara, Y. Saito and H. Kuroya, *Bull. Chem. Soc. Japan*, **25,** 331 (1952).
5. G. F. Svatos, C. Curran and J. V. Quagliano, *J. Am. Chem. Soc.*, **77,** 6159 (1955).
6. G. F. Svatos, D. M. Sweeny, S. Mizushima, C. Curran and J. V. Quagliano, *J. Am. Chem. Soc.*, **79,** 3313 (1957).
7. J. K. Wilmshurst, *Can. J. Chem.*, **38,** 467 (1960).
8. D. G. Hill and A. F. Rosenberg, *J. Chem. Phys.*, **22,** 148 (1954); **24,** 1219 (1956).
9. M. Kobayashi and J. Fujita, *J. Chem. Phys.*, **23,** 1354 (1955).
10. D. B. Powell and N. Sheppard, *J. Chem. Soc.*, **1956,** 3108.
11. K. Nakamoto and J. Fujita, unpublished.
12. K. Nakamoto, J. Fujita and H. Murata, *J. Am. Chem. Soc.*, **80,** 4817 (1958).
13. H. Block, *Trans. Faraday Soc.*, **55,** 867 (1959).
14. G. M. Barrow, R. H. Krueger and F. Basolo, *J. Inorg. & Nuclear Chem.*, **2,** 340 (1956).
15. E. P. Bertin, I. Nakagawa, S. Mizushima, T. J. Lane and J. V. Quagliano, *J. Am. Chem. Soc.*, **80,** 525 (1958).
16. F. A. Cotton, *Acta Chem. Scand.*, **10,** 1520 (1956).

16*a*. T. Shimanouchi and I. Nakagawa, *Spectrochim. Acta*, **18,** 89 (1962).

17. S. Mizushima, I. Nakagawa, M. J. Schmelz, C. Curran and J. V. Quagliano, *Spectrochim. Acta*, **13,** 31 (1958).
18. D. B. Powell, *J. Chem. Soc.*, **1956,** 4495.
19. G. W. Leonard, E. R. Lippincott, R. D. Nelson and D. E. Sellers, *J. Am. Chem. Soc.*, **77,** 2029 (1955).
20. I. Damaschun, *Z. physik. Chem.*, **B16,** 81 (1932).
21. J. P. Mathieu and S. J. Cornevin, *J. chim. phys.*, **36,** 271, 308 (1939).
22. S. Mizushima, I. Nakagawa and D. M. Sweeny, *J. Chem. Phys.*, **25,** 1006 (1956); I. Nakagawa, R. B. Penland, S. Mizushima, T. J. Lane and J. V. Quagliano, *Spectrochim. Acta*, **9,** 199 (1957).
23. K. Brodersen and H. J. Becher, *Chem. Ber.*, **89,** 1487 (1956).
24. K. Brodersen, *Z. anorg. u. allgem. Chem.*, **290,** 24 (1957).

25. J. Chatt, L. A. Duncanson and L. M. Venanzi, *J. Chem. Soc.*, **1955,** 4456, 4461; **1956,** 2712; *J. Inorg. & Nuclear Chem.*, **8,** 67 (1958).
26. L. A. Duncanson and L. M. Venanzi, *J. Chem. Soc.*, **1960,** 3841.
26*a*. D. M. Adams, J. Chatt and B. L. Shaw, *J. Chem. Soc.*, **1960,** 2047.
27. Y. Puget and C. Duval, *Compt. rend.*, **250,** 4141 (1960).
28. I. R. Beattie and H. J. V. Tyrrell, *J. Chem. Soc.*, **1956,** 2849.
29. J. P. Faust and J. V. Quagliano, *J. Am. Chem. Soc.*, **76,** 5346 (1954).
30. P. E. Merritt and S. E. Wiberley, *J. Phys. Chem.*, **59,** 55 (1955).
31. J. Chatt, L. A. Duncanson, B. M. Gatehouse, J. Lewis, R. S. Nyholm, M. L. Tobe, P. F. Todd and L. M. Venanzi, *J. Chem. Soc.*, **1959,** 4073.
32. M. L. Morris and D. H. Busch, *J. Am. Chem. Soc.*, **82,** 1521 (1960).
33. A. K. Majumdar, C. Duval and J. Lecomte, *Compt. rend.*, **247,** 302 (1958).
34. R. B. Penland, T. J. Lane and J. V. Quagliano, *J. Am. Chem. Soc.*, **78,** 887 (1956).
35. I. R. Beattie and D. P. N. Satchell, *Trans. Faraday Soc.*, **52,** 1590 (1956).
36. F. Basolo and G. S. Hammaker, *J. Am. Chem. Soc.*, **82,** 1001 (1960); *J. Inorg. Chem.*, **1,** 1 (1962).
37. B. M. Gatehouse, *J. Inorg. & Nuclear Chem.*, **8,** 79 (1958).
38. P. J. Lucchesi and W. A. Glasson, *J. Am. Chem. Soc.*, **78,** 1347 (1956).
39. C. Vassas-Dubuisson, *Compt. rend.*, **233,** 374 (1951); *J. chim. phys.*, **50,** 98 (1953).
40. A. Weil-Marchand, *Compt. rend.*, **242,** 93 (1956); **236,** 2147 (1953).
41. R. Aynard, *Compt. rend.*, **211,** 647 (1940); **236,** 1416 (1953).
42. A. Galy, *Compt. rend.*, **235,** 1504 (1952); J. Chapelle and A. Galy, *J. chim. phys.*, **50,** C93 (1953).
43. L. C. Mathieu and J. P. Mathieu, *Acta Cryst.*, **5,** 571 (1952).
44. J. Chapelle and A. Galy, *Compt. rend.*, **236,** 1653 (1953); **233,** 1181 (1951).
45. A. Weil-Marchand, *Compt. rend.*, **242,** 1791 (1956); **241,** 1456 (1955); **240,** 509 (1955).
46. R. Lafont, *Ann. phys.*, [13] **4,** 905 (1959); *J. chim. phys.*, **50,** C91 (1953); *Compt. rend.*, **244,** 1481 (1957).
46*a*. E. Schwarzmann and O. Glemser, *Z. anorg. u. allgem. Chem.*, **312,** 45 (1961).
46*b*. J. van der Elsken and D. W. Robinson, *Spectrochim. Acta*, **17,** 1249 (1961).
47. J. Fujita, K. Nakamoto and M. Kobayashi, *J. Am. Chem. Soc.*, **78,** 3963 (1956).
47*a*. I. Gamo, *Bull. Chem. Soc. Japan*, **34,** 760, 765, 1430, 1433 (1961).
48. G. Sartori, C. Furlani and A. Damiani, *J. Inorg. & Nuclear Chem.*, **8,** 119 (1958).
49. D. Scargill, *J. Chem. Soc.*, **1961,** 4440.
49*a*. K. Nakamoto, J. Fujita and Y. Morimoto, to be published.
50. K. Nakamoto, J. Fujita, S. Tanaka and M. Kobayashi, *J. Am. Chem. Soc.*, **79,** 4904 (1957).
51. J. Fujita, A. E. Martell and K. Nakamoto, *J. Chem. Phys.*, **36,** 339 (1962).
52. B. M. Gatehouse, S. E. Livingston and R. S. Nyholm, *J. Chem. Soc.*, **1958,** 3137.
53. B. M. Gatehouse, S. E. Livingston and R. S. Nyholm, *J. Chem. Soc.*, **1957,** 4222; *J. Inorg. & Nuclear Chem.*, **8,** 75 (1958).
54. E. Bannister and F. A. Cotton, *J. Chem. Soc.*, **1960,** 2276.
54*a*. C. G. Barraclough and M. L. Tobe, *J. Chem. Soc.*, **1961,** 1993.
55. E. P. Bertin, R. B. Penland, S. Mizushima, C. Curran and J. V. Quagliano, *J. Am. Chem. Soc.*, **81,** 3818 (1959).
55*a*. H. Siebert, *Z. anorg. u. allgem. Chem.*, **296,** 280 (1958); **298,** 51 (1959).
56. B. J. Hathaway and A. E. Underhill, *J. Chem. Soc.*, **1961,** 3091.
56*a*. M. E. Baldwin, *J. Chem. Soc.*, **1961,** 3123.
57. V. Caglioti, G. Sartori and M. Scrocco, *Atti accad. nazl. Lincei, Rend., Classe sci. fis., mat. e nat.*, **22,** 266 (1957).

58. G. B. Bonino and G. Fabbri, *Atti accad. nazl. Lincei, Rend., Classe sci. fis., mat. e nat.*, **20,** 414 (1956); **19,** 386 (1955); G. Fabbri, *ibid.*, **22,** 488 (1957); G. B. Bonino and O. Salvetti, *Ricerca sci.*, **26,** 3627 (1956).
59. O. Salvetti, *Ricerca sci.*, **29,** 1228 (1959).
60. E. F. Herington and W. Kynaston, *J. Chem. Soc.*, **1955,** 3555.
60*a*. G. Bor, *J. Inorg. & Nuclear Chem.*, **17,** 174 (1961).
61. W. P. Griffith and G. Wilkinson, *J. Chem. Soc.*, **1959,** 2757; *J. Inorg. & Nuclear Chem.*, **7,** 297 (1958).
62. M. F. A. El-Sayed and R. K. Sheline, *J. Inorg. & Nuclear Chem.*, **6,** 187 (1958).
63. M. F. A. El-Sayed and R. K. Sheline, *J. Am. Chem. Soc.*, **80,** 2047 (1958).
64. M. F. A. El-Sayed and R. K. Sheline, *J. Am. Chem. Soc.*, **78,** 702 (1956).
65. W. P. Griffith, F. A. Cotton and G. Wilkinson, *J. Inorg. & Nuclear Chem.*, **10,** 23 (1959).
66. L. H. Jones, *J. Chem. Phys.*, **29,** 463 (1958).
66*a*. L. H. Jones, *Spectrochim. Acta*, **17,** 188 (1961).
67. H. Poulet and J. P. Mathieu, *Spectrochim. Acta*, **15,** 932 (1959).
68. E. G. Brame, F. A. Johnson, E. M. Larsen and V. W. Meloche, *J. Inorg. & Nuclear Chem.*, **6,** 99 (1958).
69. G. B. Bonino and G. Fabbri, *Atti accad. nazl. Lincei, Rend., Classe sci. fis., mat. e nat.*, **20,** 566 (1956).
70. L. H. Jones, *J. Chem. Phys.*, **26,** 1578 (1957); **25,** 379 (1956).
71. D. M. Sweeny, I. Nakagawa, S. Mizushima and J. V. Quagliano, *J. Am. Chem. Soc.*, **78,** 889 (1956).
71*a*. R. L. McCullough, L. H. Jones and G. A. Crosby, *Spectrochim. Acta*, **16,** 929 (1960).
72. L. H. Jones, *J. Chem. Phys.*, **27,** 468 (1957); **21,** 1891 (1953); **22,** 1135 (1954).
73. H. Poulet and J. P. Mathieu, *Compt. rend.*, **248,** 2079 (1959).
74. L. H. Jones and R. A. Penneman, *J. Chem. Phys.*, **22,** 965 (1954).
75. R. A. Penneman and L. H. Jones, *J. Chem. Phys.*, **24,** 293 (1956).
76. R. A. Penneman and L. H. Jones, *J. Inorg. & Nuclear Chem.*, **20,** 19 (1961).
77. R. L. McCullough, L. H. Jones and R. A. Penneman, *J. Inorg. & Nuclear Chem.*, **13,** 286 (1960).
78. G. W. Chantry and R. A. Plane, *J. Chem. Phys.*, **33,** 736 (1960); **34,** 1268 (1961); **35,** 1027 (1961).
79. G. Emshwiller, *Compt. rend.*, **238,** 1414 (1954).
80. J. F. Keggin and F. D. Miles, *Nature*, **137,** 577 (1936).
81. L. H. Jones, *J. Chem. Phys.*, **27,** 665 (1957).
82. C. W. F. T. Pistorius, *Z. physik. Chem.*, **23,** 197 (1960).
83. V. Caglioti, G. Sartori and C. Furlani, *J. Inorg. & Nuclear Chem.*, **13,** 22 (1960); **8,** 87 (1958); *Rend. adunanza solenne, Accad. naz. Lincei*, VIII, **25,** 5 (1958).
84. S. Mizushima and I. Nakagawa, *Kagaku no Ryôiki*, **10,** 173 (1956).
84*a*. I. Nakagawa and T. Shimanouchi, *Spectrochim. Acta*, **18,** 101 (1962).
84*b*. L. H. Jones, *J. Mol. Spectroscopy*, **8,** 105 (1962); *J. Chem. Phys.*, **36,** 1209 (1962).
85. G. B. Bonino and O. Salvetti, *Atti accad. nazl. Lincei, Rend., Classe sci. fis., mat. e nat.*, **20,** 150 (1956).
86. P. Chiorboli and F. Cappellina, *Ann. chim. (Rome)*, **46,** 875 (1956); P. Chiorboli and E. Tedeschi, *Atti accad. nazl. Lincei, Rend., Classe sci. fis., mat. e nat.*, **22,** 44 (1957).
87. P. Chiorboli and C. Testa, *Ann. chim. (Rome)*, **47,** 639 (1957); P. Chiorboli, *J. Inorg: & Nuclear Chem.*, **8,** 133 (1958).

88. H. Stammreich and O. Sala, *Z. Elektrochem.*, **64,** 741 (1960); **65,** 149 (1961).
89. L. A. Woodward and H. F. Owen, *J. Chem. Soc.*, **1959,** 1055.
89*a*. R. Nast, H. Ruppert-Mesche and M. Helbig-Neubauer, *Z. anorg. u. allgem. Chem.*, **312,** 314 (1961).
89*b*. A. Haim and W. K. Wilmarth, *J. Am. Chem. Soc.*, **83,** 509 (1961).
89*c*. D. A. Dows, A. Haim and W. K. Wilmarth, *J. Inorg. & Nuclear Chem.*, **21,** 33 (1961).
90. G. Herzberg and C. Reid, *Discussions Faraday Soc.*, **9,** 92 (1950).
91. C. I. Beard and B. P. Dailey, *J. Chem. Phys.*, **18,** 1437 (1950).
92. Y. Takeuchi and Y. Saito, *Bull. Chem. Soc. Japan*, **29,** 320 (1957); Y. Saito, Y. Takeuchi and R. Pepinsky, *Z. Krist.*, **106,** 476 (1955).
93. P. C. H. Mitchell and R. J. P. Williams, *J. Chem. Soc.*, **1960,** 1912.
93*a*. J. Lewis, R. S. Nyholm and P. W. Smith, *J. Chem. Soc.*, **1961,** 4590.
94. M. M. Chamberlain and J. C. Bailar, *J. Am. Chem. Soc.*, **81,** 6412 (1959).
94*a*. M. E. Baldwin, *J. Chem. Soc.*, **1960,** 4369; **1961,** 471.
95. J. Chatt and L. A. Duncanson, *Nature*, **178,** 997 (1956).
96. J. Chatt, L. A. Duncanson, F. A. Hart and P. G. Owston, *Nature*, **181,** 43 (1958).
97. P. G. Owston and J. M. Rowe, *Acta Cryst.*, **13,** 253 (1960).
98. J. Chatt and F. A. Hart, *J. Chem. Soc.*, **1961,** 1416.
99. L. Cavalca, M. Nardelli and G. Fava, *Acta Cryst.*, **13,** 125 (1960).
100. E. H. Eyster and R. H. Gillet, *J. Chem. Phys.*, **8,** 369 (1940).
101. G. W. Bethke and M. K. Wilson, *J. Chem. Phys.*, **26,** 1118 (1957).
102. R. C. Taylor, *J. Chem. Phys.*, **26,** 1131; **27,** 979 (1957).
103. S. Sundaram and F. F. Cleveland, *J. Chem. Phys.*, **32,** 166 (1960).
104. R. D. Cowan, *J. Chem. Phys.*, **18,** 1101 (1950); **17,** 218 (1949).
105. L. H. Jones, *J. Chem. Phys.*, **28,** 1215 (1958); **23,** 2448 (1955); *J. Mol. Spectroscopy*, **5,** 133 (1960).
106. B. L. Crawford and P. C. Cross, *J. Chem. Phys.*, **6,** 525 (1938); B. L. Crawford and W. Horwitz, *ibid.*,**16,** 147 (1948).
107. C. W. F. T. Pistorius, *Spectrochim. Acta*, **15,** 717 (1959).
108. M. Bigorgne, *J. Inorg. & Nuclear Chem.*, **8,** 113 (1958); *Compt. rend.*, **246,** 1685 (1958).
109. H. Murata and K. Kawai, *J. Chem. Phys.*, **26,** 1355 (1957).
110. R. S. Nyholm and L. N. Short, *J. Chem. Soc.*, **1953,** 2670.
110*a*. H. Stammreich, K. Kawai, O. Sala and P. Krumholz, *J. Chem. Phys.*, **35,** 2168 (1961).
111. H. Stammreich, K. Kawai, Y. Tavares, P. Krumholz, J. Behmoiras and S. Bril, *J. Chem. Phys.*, **32,** 1482 (1960).
112. R. A. Friedel, I. Wender, S. L. Shufler and H. W. Sternberg, *J. Am. Chem. Soc.*, **77,** 3951 (1955).
113. W. F. Edgell, J. Huff, J. Thomas, H. Lehman, C. Angell and G. Asato, *J. Am. Chem. Soc.*, **82,** 1254 (1960).
114. W. G. Fateley and E. R. Lippincott, *Spectrochim. Acta*, **10,** 8 (1957); F. T. King and E. R. Lippincott, *J. Am. Chem. Soc.*, **78,** 4192 (1956).
115. C. W. F. T. Pistorius and P. C. Haarhoff, *J. Chem. Phys.*, **31,** 1439 (1959).
116. H. Stammreich, O. Sala and Y. Tavares, *J. Chem. Phys.*, **30,** 856 (1959).
117. H. Murata and K. Kawai, *J. Chem. Phys.*, **28,** 516 (1958).
118. F. A. Cotton, A. Danti, J. S. Waugh and R. W. Fessenden, *J. Chem. Phys.*, **29,** 1427 (1958).
119. R. K. Sheline and K. S. Pitzer, *J. Am. Chem. Soc.*, **72,** 1107 (1950).

120. M. F. O'Dwyer, *J. Mol. Spectroscopy*, **2,** 144 (1958).
121. N. J. Hawkins, H. C. Mattraw, W. W. Sabol and D. R. Carpenter, *J. Chem. Phys.*, **23,** 2422 (1955).
122. S. L. Shufler, H. W. Sternberg and R. A. Friedel, *J. Am. Chem. Soc.*, **78,** 2687 (1956).
123. A. Danti and F. A. Cotton, *J. Chem. Phys.*, **28,** 736 (1958).
124. H. Murata and K. Kawai, *J. Chem. Phys.*, **27,** 605 (1957); *Bull. Chem. Soc. Japan*, **33,** 1008 (1960).
125. H. W. Sternberg, I. Wender, R. A. Friedel and M. Orchin, *J. Am. Chem. Soc.*, **75,** 2717 (1953).
126. W. F. Edgell, C. Magee and G. Gallup, *J. Am. Chem. Soc.*, **78,** 4185, 4188 (1956).
127. F. A. Cotton, *J. Am. Chem. Soc.*, **80,** 4425 (1958).
128. F. A. Cotton and G. Wilkinson, *Chem. & Ind.* (*London*), **1956,** 1305.
129. W. F. Edgell and R. Summitt, *J. Am. Chem. Soc.*, **83,** 1772 (1961).
130. E. O. Bishop, J. L. Down, P. R. Emtage, R. E. Richards and G. Wilkinson, *J. Chem. Soc.*, **1959,** 2484.
131. W. E. Wilson, *Z. Naturforsch.*, **13b,** 349 (1958).
132. F. A. Cotton, J. L. Down and G. Wilkinson, *J. Chem. Soc.*, **1959,** 833.
132*a*. W. Beck, W. Hieber and G. Braun, *Z. anorg. u. allgem. Chem.*, **308,** 23 (1961).
133. J. W. Cable, R. S. Nyholm and R. K. Sheline, *J. Am. Chem. Soc.*, **76,** 3373 (1954).
134. H. W. Sternberg, I. Wender, R. A. Friedel and M. Orchin, *J. Am. Chem. Soc.*, **75,** 3148 (1953).
135. F. A. Cotton and R. R. Monchamp, *J. Chem. Soc.*, **1960,** 1882.
135*a*. G. Bor and L. Markó, *Spectrochim. Acta*, **15,** 747 (1959); **16,** 1105 (1960).
136. P. Corradini, *J. Chem. Phys.*, **31,** 1676 (1959).
137. E. O. Brimm, M. A. Lynch and W. J. Sesny, *J. Am. Chem. Soc.*, **76,** 3831 (1954).
138. F. A. Cotton, A. O. Liehr and G. Wilkinson, *J. Inorg. & Nuclear Chem.*, **2,** 141 (1956).
139. L. F. Dahl, E. Ishishi and R. E. Rundle, *J. Chem. Phys.*, **26,** 1750 (1957).
140. H. M. Powell and R. V. G. Ewens, *J. Chem. Soc.*, **1939,** 286.
141. R. K. Sheline, *J. Am. Chem. Soc.*, **73,** 1615 (1951).
142. F. A. Cotton and G. Wilkinson, *J. Am. Chem. Soc.*, **79,** 752 (1957).
143. O. S. Mills, *Chem. & Ind.* (*London*), **1957,** 73.
144. L. F. Dahl and R. E. Rundle, *J. Chem. Phys.*, **26,** 1751 (1957).
145. L. F. Dahl and R. E. Rundle, *J. Chem. Phys.*, **27,** 323 (1957).
145*a*. H. Stammreich, K. Kawai, O. Sala and P. Krumholz, *J. Chem. Phys.*, **35,** 2175 (1961).
146. R. J. Irving and E. A. Magnusson, *J. Chem. Soc.*, **1956,** 1860; **1958,** 2283.
147. E. W. Abel and G. Wilkinson, *J. Chem. Soc.*, **1959,** 1501.
147*a*. R. S. McDowell, W. D. Horrocks and J. T. Yates, *J. Chem. Phys.*, **34,** 530 (1961).
148. E. W. Abel, M. A. Bennett and G. Wilkinson, *J. Chem. Soc.*, **1959,** 2323.
149. H. L. Nigam, R. S. Nyholm and M. H. B. Stiddard, *J. Chem. Soc.*, **1960,** 1803; H. L. Nigam, R. S. Nyholm and D. V. R. Rao, *ibid.*, **1959,** 1397.
150. F. A. Cotton and R. V. Parish, *J. Chem. Soc.*, **1960,** 1440; F. A. Cotton and F. Zingales, *J. Am. Chem. Soc.*, **83,** 351 (1961).
150*a*. L. S. Meriwether and M. L. Fiene, *J. Am. Chem. Soc.*, **81,** 4200 (1959).
151. D. Seyferth and N. Kahlen, *J. Am. Chem. Soc.*, **82,** 1080 (1960).
152. R. E. Humphrey, *Spectrochim. Acta*, **17,** 93 (1961).
152*a*. L. E. Orgel, *J. Inorg. Chem.*, **1,** 25 (1962).
153. G. Winkhaus and G. Wilkinson, *J. Chem. Soc.*, **1961,** 602.
153*a*. W. Hieber and W. Beck, *Z. anorg. u. allgem. Chem.*, **305,** 265, 274 (1960).

153*b*. C. W. Garland and J. R. Wilt, *J. Chem. Phys.*, **36,** 1094 (1962).
153*c*. L. F. Dahl, C. Martell and D. L. Wampler, *J. Am. Chem. Soc.*, **83,** 1761 (1961).
154. J. Lewis, R. J. Irving and G. Wilkinson, *J. Inorg. & Nuclear Chem.*, **7,** 32, 38 (1958).
155. W. P. Griffith, J. Lewis and G. Wilkinson, *J. Chem. Soc.*, **1959,** 872, 1632, 1775; **1961,** 775.
156. E. P. Bertin, S. Mizushima, T. J. Lane and J. V. Quagliano, *J. Am. Chem. Soc.*, **81,** 3821 (1959).
157. A. Jahn, *Z. anorg. u. allgem. Chem.*, **301,** 301 (1959); W. Hieber and A. Jahn, *Z. Naturforsch.*, **13b,** 195 (1958).
158. T. C. Waddington and F. Klanberg, *Z. anorg. u. allgem. Chem.*, **304,** 185 (1960).
159. R. B. Penland, S. Mizushima, C. Curran and J. V. Quagliano, *J. Am. Chem. Soc.*, **79,** 1575 (1957).
160. A. Yamaguchi, T. Miyazawa, T. Shimanouchi and S. Mizushima, *Spectrochim. Acta*, **10,** 170 (1957).
161. T. J. Lane, A. Yamaguchi, J. V. Quagliano, J. A. Ryan and S. Mizushima, *J. Am. Chem. Soc.*, **81,** 3824 (1959).
162. A. Yamaguchi, R. B. Penland, S. Mizushima, T. J. Lane, C. Curran and J. V. Quagliano, *J. Am. Chem. Soc.*, **80,** 527 (1958).
163. T. J. Lane, D. N. Sen and J. V. Quagliano, *J. Chem. Phys.*, **22,** 1855 (1954).
164. F. A. Cotton, R. Francis and W. D. Horrocks, *J. Phys. Chem.*, **64,** 1534 (1960).
165. R. Francis and F. A. Cotton, *J. Chem. Soc.*, **1961,** 2078.
166. R. S. Drago and D. W. Meek, *J. Phys. Chem.*, **65,** 1446 (1961); D. W. Meek, D. K. Straub and R. S. Drago, *J. Am. Chem. Soc.*, **82,** 6013 (1960).
166*a*. J. Selbin, W. E. Bull and L. H. Holmes, *J. Inorg. & Nuclear Chem.*, **16,** 219 (1960).
167. F. A. Cotton, R. D. Barnes and E. Bannister, *J. Chem. Soc.*, **1960,** 2199; F. A. Cotton and D. M. L. Goodgame, *ibid.*, **1960,** 5267; **1961,** 2298, 3735; *J. Am. Chem. Soc.*, **82,** 5774 (1960).
168. M. Kobayashi, *J. Chem. Soc. Japan*, **64,** 648 (1943).
169. S. Mizushima, I. Ichishima, I. Nakagawa and J. V. Quagliano, *J. Phys. Chem.*, **59,** 293 (1955); J. V. Quagliano and S. Mizushima, *J. Am. Chem. Soc.*, **75,** 6084 (1953); D. M. Sweeny, S. Mizushima and J. V. Quagliano, *ibid.*, **77,** 6521 (1955).
170. D. B. Powell and N. Sheppard, *J. Chem. Soc.*, **1959,** 791.
171. H. Scouloud and C. H. Carlisle, *Acta Cryst.*, **6,** 651 (1953); *Nature*, **166,** 357 (1950).
172. L. N. Swink and M. Atoji, *Acta Cryst.*, **13,** 639 (1960).
173. D. B. Powell and N. Sheppard, *J. Chem. Soc.*, **1961,** 1112.
174. D. B. Powell and N. Sheppard, *J. Chem. Soc.*, **1959,** 3089; D. B. Powell, *Spectrochim. Acta*, **16,** 241 (1960); **17,** 68 (1961).
175. K. Brodersen, *Z. anorg. u. allgem. Chem.*, **298,** 142 (1959).
175*a*. G. Newman and D. B. Powell, *J. Chem. Soc.*, **1961,** 477.
176. G. Gordon and R. K. Birdwhistell, *J. Am. Chem. Soc.*, **81,** 3567 (1959).
177. F. H. Burstall and R. S. Nyholm, *J. Chem. Soc.*, **1952,** 3570; R. S. Nyholm and L. N. Short, *ibid.*, **1953,** 2670.
178. K. Nakamoto, *Advances in the Chemistry of the Coordination Compounds*, Macmillan, 1961.
179. D. H. Busch and J. C. Bailar, *J. Am. Chem. Soc.*, **78,** 1137 (1956).
180. A. A. Schilt and R. C. Taylor, *J. Inorg. & Nuclear Chem.*, **9,** 211 (1959).
181. A. A. Schilt, *J. Am. Chem. Soc.*, **81,** 2966 (1959).
182. R. C. Stoufer and D. H. Busch, *J. Am. Chem. Soc.*, **82,** 3491 (1960).
183. W. J. Stratton and D. H. Busch, *J. Am. Chem. Soc.*, **82,** 4834 (1960).
183*a*. R. A. Krause, N. B. Colthup and D. H. Busch, *J. Phys. Chem.*, **65,** 2216 (1961); P. E. Figgins and D. H. Busch, *J. Phys. Chem.*, **65,** 2236 (1961).

184. D. W. Thomas and A. E. Martell, *J. Am. Chem. Soc.*, **81,** 5111 (1959); **78,** 1338 (1956).
185. K. Ueno and A. E. Martell, *J. Phys. Chem.*, **60,** 934 (1956).
186. J. M. Goldstein, W. M. McNabb and J. F. Hazel, *J. Am. Chem. Soc.*, **78,** 3543 (1956).
187. R. E. Rundle and M. Parasol, *J. Chem. Phys.*, **20,** 1487 (1952).
188. K. Nakamoto, M. Margoshes and R. E. Rundle, *J. Am. Chem. Soc.*, **77,** 6480 (1955).
189. L. E. Godycki and R. E. Rundle, *Acta Cryst.*, **6,** 487 (1953).
190. J. Fujita, A. Nakahara and R. Tsuchida, *J. Chem. Phys.*, **23,** 1541 (1955).
191. A. Nakahara, *Bull. Chem. Soc. Japan*, **28,** 473 (1955); A. Nakahara, J. Fujita and R. Tsuchida, *ibid.*, **29,** 296 (1956).
192. E. Frasson, C. Panattoni and R. Zannetti, *Acta Cryst.*, **12,** 1027 (1959).
193. R. Blinc and D. Hadži, *J. Chem. Soc.*, **1958,** 4536; *Spectrochim. Acta*, **16,** 853 (1960).
194. C. Duval, J. Lecomte and F. Douvillé, *Bull. soc. chim. France*, **9,** 263 (1942); *Ann. phys.*, **17,** 5 (1942); A. Delay, C. Duval and J. Lecomte, *Compt. rend.*, **216,** 40 (1943); C. Duval, J. Lecomte and A. Delay, *Bull. soc. chim. France*, **11,** 180 (1944); C. Duval, H. Gerding and J. Lecomte, *Rec. trav. chim.*, **69,** 391 (1950).
195. M. J. Schmelz, I. Nakagawa, S. Mizushima and J. V. Quagliano, *J. Am. Chem. Soc.*, **81,** 287 (1959).
196. R. Theimer and O. Theimer, *Monatsh.*, **81,** 313 (1950).
197. R. E. Kagarise, *J. Phys. Chem.*, **59,** 271 (1955).
198. B. Ellis and H. Pyszora, *Nature*, **181,** 181 (1958).
199. W. H. Zachariasen, *J. Am. Chem. Soc.*, **62,** 1011 (1940).
200. V. Amirthalingam and V. M. Padmanabhan, *Acta Cryst.*, **11,** 896 (1958).
201. J. H. Talbot, *Acta Cryst.*, **6,** 720 (1953).
202. W. H. Zachariasen and H. A. Pettinger, *Acta Cryst.*, **12,** 526 (1959).
203. J. N. van Niekerk and F. R. L. Schoening, *Acta Cryst.*, **6,** 501 (1953).
204. J. N. van Niekerk and F. R. L. Schoening, *Acta Cryst.*, **6,** 227 (1953); *Nature*, **171,** 36 (1953).
205. W. H. Bragg and G. T. Morgan, *Proc. Roy. Soc. (London)*, **A104,** 437 (1923).
206. H. Koyama and Y. Saito, *Bull. Chem. Soc. Japan*, **127,** 113 (1954).
207. L. H. Jones and E. McLaren, *J. Chem. Phys.*, **22,** 1796 (1954).
208. J. K. Wilmshurst, *J. Chem. Phys.*, **23,** 2463 (1955).
209. K. Itoh and H. J. Bernstein, *Can. J. Chem.*, **34,** 170 (1956).
210. K. Nakamura, *J. Chem. Soc. Japan*, **79,** 1411, 1420 (1958).
211. K. Nakamoto, Y. Morimoto and A. E. Martell, *J. Am. Chem. Soc.*, **83,** 4528 (1961).
212. G. Costa, E. Pauluzzi and A. Puxeddu, *Gazz. chim. ital.*, **87,** 885 (1957).
213. J. D. S. Goulden, *Spectrochim. Acta*, **16,** 715 (1960).
214. M. Girard and J. Lecomte, *Compt. rend.*, **241,** 292 (1955); **240,** 415 (1955); C. Duval and J. Lecomte, *ibid.*, **219,** 483 (1944).
215. S. Kirschner and R. Kiesling, *J. Am. Chem. Soc.*, **82,** 4174 (1960).
216. Y. Kuroda and M. Kubo, *J. Phys. Chem.*, **64,** 759 (1960).
217. A. Miyake, *Bull. Chem. Soc. Japan*, **32,** 1381 (1959).
218. M. Tsuboi, K. Onishi, I. Nakagawa, T. Shimanouchi and S. Mizushima, *Spectrochim. Acta*, **12,** 253 (1958).
219. K. Fukushima, T. Onishi, T. Shimanouchi and S. Mizushima, *Spectrochim. Acta*, **14,** 236 (1959).
220. M. Tsuboi and T. Takenishi, *Bull. Chem. Soc. Japan*, **32,** 1044 (1959).
221. I. M. Klotz and D. M. Gruen, *J. Phys. Chem.*, **52,** 961 (1948).

222. H. W. Thompson, D. L. Nicholson and L. N. Short, *Discussions Faraday Soc.*, **9,** 222 (1950).
223. J. T. Edsall, *J. Chem. Phys.*, **4,** 1 (1936); **5,** 508 (1937); **6,** 124 (1938); **8,** 520 (1940); *J. Am. Chem. Soc.*, **65,** 1312, 1767 (1943); **72,** 474 (1950); **80,** 3807 (1958).
224. R. S. Krishnan and K. Balasubramanian, *Proc. Indian Acad. Sci.*, **48A,** 55, 138 (1958).
225. A. J. Stosick, *J. Am. Chem. Soc.*, **67,** 365 (1945).
226. B. M. Low, F. L. Hirshfeld and F. M. Richards, *J. Am. Chem. Soc.*, **81,** 4412 (1959).
227. A. Rosenberg, *Acta Chem. Scand.*, **10,** 840 (1956); **11,** 1390 (1957).
228. D. N. Sen, S. Mizushima, C. Curran and J. V. Quagliano, *J. Am. Chem. Soc.*, **77,** 211 (1955); S. Mizushima and J. V. Quagliano, *ibid.*, **75,** 4870 (1953); D. M. Sweeny, C. Curran and J. V. Quagliano, *ibid.*, **77,** 5508 (1955); A. J. Saraceno, I. Nakagawa, S. Mizushima, C. Curran and J. V. Quagliano, *ibid.*, **80,** 5018 (1958); D. Segnini, C. Curran and J. V. Quagliano, *Spectrochim. Acta*, **16,** 540 (1960); V. Moreno, K. Dittmer and J. V. Quagliano, *ibid.*, **16,** 1368 (1960).
229. C. Duval and J. Lecomte, *Compt. rend.*, **215,** 131 (1942); *Bull. soc. chim. France*, **10,** 180 (1943).
230. K. Nakamura, *J. Chem. Soc. Japan*, **80,** 113, 118 (1959).
231. D. H. Busch and J. C. Bailar, *J. Am. Chem. Soc.*, **75,** 4574 (1953); **78,** 716 (1956); M. L. Morris and D. H. Busch, *ibid.*, **78,** 5178 (1956); K. Swaminathan and D. H. Busch, *J. Inorg. & Nuclear Chem.*, **20,** 159 (1961); R. E. Sievers and J. C. Bailar, *J. Inorg. Chem.*, **1,** 174 (1962).
231*a*. D. Chapman, *J. Chem. Soc.*, **1955,** 1766.
232. T. Moeller, F. A. Moss and R. H. Marshall, *J. Am. Chem. Soc.*, **77,** 3182 (1955).
233. D. Sawyer and P. Paulsen, *J. Am. Chem. Soc.*, **80,** 1597 (1958); **81,** 816 (1959); **82,** 4191 (1960).
234. K. Nakamoto, Y. Morimoto and A. E. Martell, *J. Am. Chem. Soc.*, **84,** 2081 (1962).
235. S. Chaberek and A. E. Martell, *J. Am. Chem. Soc.*, **74,** 5052 (1952).
236. F. Douvillé, C. Duval and J. Lecomte, *Bull. soc. chim. France*, **9,** 548 (1942); *Compt. rend.*, **212,** 697 (1941).
237. H. Murata and K. Kawai, *J. Chem. Phys.*, **25,** 589, 796 (1956).
238. J. Fujita, K. Nakamoto and M. Kobayashi, *J. Phys. Chem.*, **61,** 1014 (1957).
239. M. J. Schmelz, T. Miyazawa, S. Mizushima, T. J. Lane and J. V. Quagliano, *Spectrochim. Acta*, **9,** 51 (1957).
240. R. Gaufrés and J. P. Mathieu, *Compt. rend.*, **248,** 81 (1959).
241. K. Kawai and H. Murata, *J. Chem. Soc. Japan*, **81,** 997 (1960).
242. J. Fujita, A. E. Martell and K. Nakamoto, *J. Chem. Phys.*, **36,** 324, 331 (1962).
243. G. A. Jeffrey and G. S. Parry, *J. Chem. Soc.*, **1952,** 4864.
244. J. van Niekerk and F. R. L. Schoening, *Acta Cryst.*, **4,** 35, 381 (1951).
245. K. Nakamoto and J. Fujita, to be published.
246. J. R. Barceló, *Spectrochim. Acta*, **10,** 245 (1958).
246*a*. Y. Kuroda, M. Kato and K. Sone, *Bull. Chem. Soc. Japan*, **34,** 877 (1961).
247. R. B. Roof, *Acta Cryst.*, **9,** 781 (1956).
248. M. Calvin and K. W. Wilson, *J. Am. Chem. Soc.*, **67,** 2003 (1945).
249. J. Lecomte, *Discussions Faraday Soc.*, **9,** 125 (1950); C. Duval, R. Freymann and J. Lecomte, *Bull. soc. chim. France*, **19,** 106 (1952); *Compt. rend.*, **231,** 272 (1950).
250. R. Mecke and E. Funck, *Z. Elektrochem.*, **60,** 1124 (1956).
251. K. Nakamoto and A. E. Martell, *J. Chem. Phys.*, **32,** 588 (1960).
252. K. Nakamoto, P. J. McCarthy, A. Ruby and A. E. Martell, *J. Am. Chem. Soc.*, **83,** 1066, 1272 (1961).
252*a*. K. E. Lawson, *Spectrochim. Acta*, **17,** 248 (1961).

252*b*. C. Djordjevic, *Spectrochim. Acta*, **17,** 448 (1961).
252*c*. J. P. Dismukes, L. H. Jones and J. C. Bailar, *J. Phys. Chem.*, **65,** 792 (1961).
253. L. J. Bellamy, G. S. Spicer and J. D. H. Strickland, *J. Chem. Soc.*, **1952,** 4653; L. J. Bellamy and R. F. Branch, *ibid.*, **1954,** 4487, 4491.
254. H. F. Holtzclaw and J. P. Collman, *J. Am. Chem. Soc.*, **79,** 3318 (1957).
255. R. West and R. Riley, *J. Inorg. & Nuclear Chem.*, **5,** 295 (1958).
256. R. M. Izatt, C. G. Haas, B. P. Block and W. C. Fernelius, *J. Phys. Chem.*, **58,** 1133 (1954).
257. K. Nakamoto, Y. Morimoto and A. E. Martell, *J. Am. Chem. Soc.*, **83,** 4533 (1961).
258. L. Sacconi, G. Caroti and P. Paoletti, *J. Chem. Soc.*, **1958,** 4257; *J. Inorg. & Nuclear Chem.*, **8,** 93 (1958).
259. A. E. Comyns, B. M. Gatehouse and E. Wait, *J. Chem. Soc.*, **1958,** 4655.
260. G. Sartori and G. Costa, *Z. Elektrochem.*, **63,** 105 (1959).
261. R. L. Belford, A. E. Martell and M. Calvin, *J. Inorg. & Nuclear Chem.*, **2,** 11 (1956).
262. R. P. Dryden and A. Winston, *J. Phys. Chem.*, **62,** 635 (1958).
263. J. J. Charette and P. Teyssié, *Spectrochim. Acta*, **16,** 689 (1960).
264. B. E. Bryant, J. C. Pariaud and W. C. Fernelius, *J. Org. Chem.*, **19,** 1889 (1954).
265. K. Nakamoto, Y. Morimoto and A. E. Martell, *J. Phys. Chem.*, **66,** 346 (1962).
265*a*. L. G. van Uitert, W. C. Fernelius and B. E. Douglas, *J. Am. Chem. Soc.*, **75,** 457, 2736 (1953).
266. L. A. Woodward and J. R. Hall, *Spectrochim. Acta*, **16,** 654 (1960).
267. F. A. Miller and G. L. Carlson, *Spectrochim. Acta*, **17,** 977 (1961).
268. F. A. Cotton and F. Zingales, *J. Am. Chem. Soc.*, **83,** 351 (1961).
269. I. Matsubara, *Bull. Chem. Soc. Japan*, **34,** 1710, 1719 (1961); **35,** 27 (1962); Y. Kinoshita, I. Matsubara and Y. Saito, *ibid.*, **32,** 741, 1216, 1221 (1959).
270. J. Chatt, L. A. Duncanson and L. M. Venanzi, Suomen Kemistilehti, **B29,** 75 (1956); *Nature*, **177,** 1042 (1956).
271. N. S. Gill, R. H. Nuttall, D. E. Scaife and D. W. A. Sharp, *J. Inorg. & Nuclear Chem.*, **18,** 79 (1961).
272. H. F. Holtzclaw, J. P. Collman and R. M. Alire, *J. Am. Chem. Soc.*, **80,** 1100 (1958).
273. R. C. Charles, H. Freiser, R. Friedel, L. E. Hilliard and W. D. Johnston, *Spectrochim. Acta*, **8,** 1 (1956).
274. A. G. Hill and C. Curran, *J. Phys. Chem.*, **64,** 1519 (1960).
275. K. Ueno, *J. Am. Chem. Soc.*, **79,** 3066 (1957).
276. T. R. Harkins, J. L. Walter, O. E. Harris and H. Freiser, *J. Am. Chem. Soc.*, **78,** 260 (1956).
277. D. P. Mellor and L. E. Maley, *Nature*, **159,** 379 (1947); **161,** 436 (1948).
277*a*. T. J. Lane, I. Nakagawa, J. L. Walter and A. J. Kandathil, *J. Inorg. Chem.*, **1,** 267 (1962).
277*b*. J. V. Quagliano, S. Kida and J. Fujita, *J. Am. Chem. Soc.*, **84,** 724 (1962).
278. K. Ueno and A. E. Martell, *J. Phys. Chem.*, **59,** 998 (1955); **60,** 1270 (1956).
279. H. J. Taufer, M. J. Murray and F. F. Cleveland, *J. Am. Chem. Soc.*, **63,** 3500 (1941).
280. J. Chatt and L. A. Duncanson, *J. Chem. Soc.*, **1953,** 2939.
281. J. N. Dempsey and N. C. Baenziger, *J. Am. Chem. Soc.*, **77,** 4984 (1955); J. R. Holden and N. C. Baenziger, *ibid.*, **77,** 4987 (1955).
282. J. R. Doyle and H. B. Jonassen, *J. Am. Chem. Soc.*, **78,** 3965 (1956); H. B. Jonassen and J. E. Field, *ibid.*, **79,** 1275 (1957); P. E. Slade and H. B. Jonassen, *ibid.*, **79,** 1277 (1957); H. B. Jonassen and W. B. Kirsh, *ibid.*, **79,** 1279 (1957).
283. R. A. Alexander, N. C. Baenziger, C. Carpenter and J. R. Doyle, *J. Am. Chem. Soc.*, **82,** 535 (1960).

284. P. J. Hendra and D. P. Powell, *Spectrochim. Acta*, **17,** 909, 913 (1961); **18,** 299 (1962).
285. D. M. Adams, J. Chatt, R. G. Guy and N. Sheppard, *J. Chem. Soc.*, **1961,** 738.
286. D. P. Powell and N. Sheppard, *Spectrochim. Acta*, **13,** 69 (1958).
287. D. P. Powell and N. Sheppard, *J. Chem. Soc.*, **1960,** 2519.
288. J. Chatt, G. A. Rowe and A. A. Williams, *Proc. Chem. Soc.* (*London*), **1957,** 208.
289. J. Chatt, R. G. Guy and L. A. Duncanson, *J. Chem. Soc.*, **1961,** 827.
290. R. Markby, I. Wender, R. A. Friedel, F. A. Cotton and H. W. Sternberg, *J. Am. Chem. Soc.*, **80,** 6529 (1958).
291. T. J. Kealy and P. L. Pauson, *Nature*, **168,** 1039 (1951).
292. E. O. Fischer and W. Pfab, *Z. Naturforsch.*, **7b,** 377 (1952); P. F. Eiland and R. Pepinsky, *J. Am. Chem. Soc.*, **74,** 4971 (1957); J. D. Dunitz and L. E. Orgel, *Nature*, **171,** 121 (1953).
293. W. Pfab and E. O. Fischer, *Z. anorg. u. allgem. Chem.*, **274,** 316 (1953); E. Weiss and E. O. Fischer, *ibid.*, **278,** 219 (1955); **284,** 69 (1956); *Z. Naturforsch.*, **10b,** 58 (1955); F. Jellinek, *ibid.*, **14b,** 737 (1959).
294. G. Wilkinson, P. L. Pauson and F. A. Cotton, *J. Am. Chem. Soc.*, **76,** 1970 (1954).
295. E. R. Lippincott and R. D. Nelson, *Spectrochim. Acta*, **10,** 307 (1958); *J. Chem. Phys.*, **21,** 1307 (1953); *J. Am. Chem. Soc.*, **77,** 4990 (1955).
296. H. P. Fritz and R. Schneider, *Chem. Ber.*, **93,** 1171 (1960).
297. W. K. Winter, B. Curnutte and S. E. Whitcomb, *Spectrochim. Acta*, **15,** 1085 (1959).
298. G. Wilkinson and J. M. Birmingham, *J. Am. Chem. Soc.*, **76,** 4281 (1954).
299. F. A. Cotton and G. Wilkinson, *Z. Naturforsch.*, **9b,** 417 (1954).
300. H. P. Fritz, *Chem. Ber.*, **92,** 780 (1959).
301. E. R. Lippincott, J. Xavier and D. Steele, *J. Am. Chem. Soc.*, **83,** 2262 (1961).
302. M. L. H. Green, L. Pratt and G. Wilkinson, *J. Chem. Soc.*, **1959,** 3753, 989.
303. F. A. Cotton and L. T. Reynolds, *J. Am. Chem. Soc.*, **80,** 269 (1958).
304. C. L. Sloan and W. A. Barber, *J. Am. Chem. Soc.*, **81,** 1364 (1959).
305. L. T. Reynolds and G. Wilkinson, *J. Inorg. & Nuclear Chem.*, **2,** 246 (1956).
306. G. Wilkinson and T. S. Piper, *J. Inorg. & Nuclear Chem.*, **2,** 32 (1956).
307. E. O. Fischer and W. Hafner, *Z. Naturforsch.*, **10b,** 665 (1955).
308. E. Weiss and E. O. Fischer, *Z. anorg. u. allgem. Chem.*, **286,** 142 (1956).
309. H. P. Fritz, W. Lüttke, H. Stammreich and R. Forneris, *Chem. Ber.*, **92,** 3246 (1959); *Spectrochim. Acta*, **17,** 1068 (1961).
310. R. G. Snyder, *Spectrochim. Acta*, **15,** 807 (1959).
311. E. O. Fischer and D. Seus, *Chem. Ber.*, **89,** 1809 (1956).
312. T. S. Piper, F. A. Cotton and G. Wilkinson, *J. Inorg. & Nuclear Chem.*, **1,** 165 (1955); F. A. Cotton, A. O. Liehr and G. Wilkinson, *ibid.*, **1,** 175 (1955).
313. B. F. Hallam and P. L. Pauson, *Chem. & Ind.* (*London*), **23,** 653 (1955).
314. T. S. Piper and G. Wilkinson, *Chem. & Ind.* (*London*), **23,** 1296 (1955).
315. T. S. Piper and G. Wilkinson, *J. Inorg. & Nuclear Chem.*, **3,** 104 (1956).
316. A. Davison, M. L. H. Green and G. Wilkinson, *J. Chem. Soc.*, **1961,** 3172.
317. G. Winkhaus, L. Pratt and G. Wilkinson, *J. Chem. Soc.*, **1961,** 3807.
317*a*. R. D. Fischer, *Chem. Ber.*, **93,** 165 (1960).
317*b*. H. P. Fritz and J. Manchot, *Spectrochim. Acta*, **18,** 171 (1962).
318. O. S. Mills, *Acta Cryst.*, **11,** 620 (1958).
319. F. A. Cotton, H. Stammreich and G. Wilkinson, *J. Inorg. & Nuclear Chem.*, **9,** 3 (1959).
320. G. Wilkinson, *J. Am. Chem. Soc.*, **76,** 209 (1954).

321. F. C. Wilson and D. P. Shoemaker, *J. Chem. Phys.*, **27,** 809 (1957); *Naturwiss.*, **43,** 57 (1956).
322. E. W. Abel, A. Singh and G. Wilkinson, *J. Chem. Soc.*, **1960,** 1321.
323. T. S. Piper and G. Wilkinson, *J. Inorg. & Nuclear Chem.*, **2,** 38 (1956).
324. R. S. Mulliken, *J. Am. Chem. Soc.*, **74,** 811 (1952).
325. D. Cook, S. J. Kuhn and G. A. Olah, *J. Chem. Phys.*, **33,** 1669 (1960).
325*a*. H. Gerding and K. Eriks, *Rec. trav. chim.*, **71,** 773 (1952); H. Gerding, J. W. M. Steeman and L. J. Revallier, *ibid.*, **69,** 944 (1950).
326. R. W. Sprague, A. B. Garrett and H. H. Sisler, *J. Am. Chem. Soc.*, **82,** 1059 (1960).
327. H. Gerding and H. Houtgraaf, *Rec. trav. chim.*, **73,** 759 (1954); H. Gerding, *ibid.*, **75,** 589 (1956).
328. W. Zeil, R. Dautel and W. Honsberg, *Z. Elektrochem.*, **60,** 1131 (1956).
329. G. Schomburg and E. G. Hoffmann, *Z. Elektrochem.*, **61,** 1110 (1957).
330. H. Gerding and H. Houtgraaf, *Rec. trav. chim.*, **74,** 15 (1955).
331. J. Goubeau and H. Siebert, *Z. anorg. u. allgem. Chem.*, **254,** 126 (1947).
332. B. Rice, R. J. Galiano and W. J. Lehmann, *J. Phys. Chem.*, **61,** 1222 (1957).
333. R. C. Taylor and C. L. Cluff, *Nature*, **182,** 390 (1958).
334. A. A. Babushkin, *Izvest. Akad. Nauk S.S.S.R., Ser. Fiz.*, **22,** 1131 (1958); A. A. Babushkin, I. F. Kovalev and V. M. Emelyanova, *Optika i Spektroskopiya*, **4,** 468 (1958).
335. R. C. Taylor and T. C. Bissot, *J. Chem. Phys.*, **25,** 780 (1956).
336. B. P. Susz and P. Chalandon, *Helv. Chim. Acta*, **41,** 1332, 697 (1958); B. P. Susz and A. Lachavanne, *ibid.*, **41,** 634 (1958); D. Cassimatis, P. Gagnaux and B. P. Susz, *ibid.*, **43,** 424 (1960).
336*a*. M. F. Lappert, *J. Chem. Soc.*, **1961,** 817.
337. G. S. Rao, *Z. anorg. u. allgem. Chem.*, **304,** 351 (1960).
338. H. J. Coerver and C. Curran, *J. Am. Chem. Soc.*, **80,** 3522 (1958).
339. W. Gerrard, M. F. Lappert, H. Pyszora and J. W. Wallis, *J. Chem. Soc.*, **1960,** 2182.
339*a*. T. L. Brown and M. Kubota, *J. Am. Chem. Soc.*, **83,** 4175 (1961).
340. G. S. Rao, *Z. anorg. u. allgem. Chem.*, **304,** 176 (1960).
341. H. Luther, D. Mootz and F. Radwitz, *J. prakt. Chem.*, [4] **5,** 242 (1958).
342. N. N. Greenwood and K. Wade, *J. Chem. Soc.*, **1960,** 1130.
342*a*. K. Dehnicke, *Z. anorg. u. allgem. Chem.*, **309,** 266 (1961).
343. A. Terenin, W. Filimonow and D. Bystrow, *Z. Elektrochem.*, **62,** 180 (1958); *Izvest. Akad. Nauk S.S.S.R., Ser. Fiz.*, **22,** 1100 (1958).
344. J. C. Sheldon and S. Y. Tyree, *J. Am. Chem. Soc.*, **80,** 4775 (1958); **81,** 2290 (1959).
344*a*. H. Gerding, J. A. Koningstein and E. R. van der Worm, *Spectrochim. Acta*, **16,** 881 (1960).
345. E. K. Plyler and R. S. Mulliken, *J. Am. Chem. Soc.*, **81,** 823 (1959).
346. R. A. Zingaro and W. B. Witmer, *J. Phys. Chem.*, **64,** 1705 (1960).
347. C. D. Schmulbach and R. S. Drago, *J. Am. Chem. Soc.*, **82,** 4484 (1960).
348. G. L. Vidale and R. C. Taylor, *J. Am. Chem. Soc.*, **78,** 294 (1956).
349. A. D. E. Pullin and J. M. Pollock, *Trans. Faraday Soc.*, **54,** 11 (1959).
350. S. S. Raskin, *Optika i Spektroskopiya*, **1,** 516 (1956).
351. E. F. Gross and I. M. Ginzburg, *Optika i Spektroskopiya*, **1,** 710 (1956).
352. L. W. Daasch, *Spectrochim. Acta*, **15,** 726 (1959); *J. Chem. Phys.*, **28,** 1005 (1958).
353. J. A. A. Ketelaar, C. Haas and J. van der Elsken, *J. Chem. Phys.*, **24,** 624 (1956); J. A. A. Ketelaar and J. van der Elsken, *ibid.*, **30,** 336 (1959).
354. L. H. Jones and M. M. Chamberlain, *J. Chem. Phys.*, **25,** 365 (1956).
354*a*. A. Strasheim and K. Buijs, *J. Chem. Phys.*, **34,** 691 (1961).

355. V. W. Meloche and G. E. Kalbus, *J. Inorg. & Nuclear Chem.*, **6,** 104 (1958).
355*a*. R. A. Buchanan and W. A. Bowen, *J. Chem. Phys.*, **34,** 348 (1961).
356. F. Vrátný, *J. Chem. Phys.*, **10,** 328 (1959).
357. V. C. Farmer, *Spectrochim. Acta*, **8,** 374 (1957).
358. R. A. Durie and J. Szewczyk, *Spectrochim. Acta*, **15,** 593 (1959).
359. R. P. Eischens, W. A. Pliskin and S. A. Francis, *J. Chem. Phys.*, **22,** 1786 (1954); *J. Phys. Chem.*, **60,** 194 (1956).
360. C. W. Garland, *J. Phys. Chem.*, **63,** 1422 (1959); J. T. Yates and C. W. Garland, *ibid.*, **65,** 617 (1961).
360*a*. C. E. O'Neill and D. J. C. Yates, *Spectrochim. Acta*, **17,** 953 (1961); *J. Phys. Chem.*, **65,** 901 (1961); D. J. C. Yates, *ibid.*, **65,** 746 (1961).
361. H. L. Pickering and H. C. Eckstrom, *J. Phys. Chem.*, **63,** 512 (1959).
361*a*. J. H. Taylor and C. H. Amberg, *Can. J. Chem.*, **39,** 535 (1961).
362. J. E. Maples and R. P. Eischens, *J. Phys. Chem.*, **58,** 1059 (1954); W. A. Pliskin and R. P. Eischens, *ibid.*, **59,** 1156 (1955).
363. D. J. C. Yates, N. Sheppard and C. L. Angell, *J. Chem. Phys.*, **23,** 1980 (1955).
363*a*. M. Folman, *Trans. Faraday Soc.*, **57,** 2000 (1961).
364. N. Sheppard and D. J. C. Yates, *Proc. Roy. Soc.* (*London*), **A238,** 69 (1957).
365. W. A. Pliskin and R. P. Eischens, *Spectrochim. Acta*, **8,** 302 (1956); *J. Chem. Phys.*, **24,** 482 (1956).
366. T. Yoshino, *J. Chem. Phys.*, **23,** 1564 (1955).
367. L. H. Little, *J. Phys. Chem.*, **63,** 1616 (1959); *J. Chem. Phys.*, **35,** 342 (1961).
368. G. Kragounis and O. Peter, *Z. Elektrochem.*, **63,** 1120 (1959).
369. M. Folman and D. J. C. Yates, *J. Phys. Chem.*, **63,** 183 (1959).
370. J. K. A. Clarke and A. D. E. Pullin, *Trans. Faraday Soc.*, **56,** 534 (1960).
371. L. H. Little, H. E. Klauser and C. H. Amberg, *Can. J. Chem.*, **39,** 421 (1961).
372. R. W. Hoffmann and G. W. Brindley, *J. Phys. Chem.*, **65,** 443 (1961).
373. W. A. Pliskin and R. P. Eischens, *Z. physik. Chem.*, **24,** 11 (1960).
374. S. Matsushita and T. Nakata, *J. Chem. Phys.*, **36,** 665 (1962).

Appendix

APPENDIX I

POINT GROUPS AND THEIR CHARACTER TABLES

The following are the character tables of the point groups which appear frequently in this book. The species (or the irreducible representations) of the point group are labeled according to the following rules: *A* and *B* denote non-degenerate species (one-dimensional representation). *A* represents the symmetric species (character = +1) with respect to rotation about the principal axis (chosen as z axis), whereas *B* represents the antisymmetric species (character = −1) with respect to rotation about the principal axis. *E* and *F* denote doubly degenerate (two-dimensional representation) and triply degenerate species (three-dimensional representation), respectively. If two species in the same point group differ in the character of *C* (other than the principal axis), they are distinguished by subscripts 1, 2, 3, ... If two species differ in the character of σ (other than σ_v), they are distinguished by ′ and ″. If two species differ in the character of *i*, they are distinguished by subscripts *g* and *u*. If these rules allow several different labels, *g* and *u* take precedence over 1, 2, 3, . . . , which in turn take precedence over ′ and ″. The labels of species of point groups $\mathbf{C}_{\infty v}$ and $\mathbf{D}_{\infty h}$ (linear molecules) are exceptional and are taken from the notation for the component of the electronic orbital angular momentum along the molecular axis.

$\mathbf{C}_s$	I	$\sigma(xy)$		
A'	$+1$	$+1$	T_x, T_y, R_z	$\alpha_{xx}, \alpha_{yy}, \alpha_{zz}, \alpha_{xy}$
A''	$+1$	-1	T_z, R_x, R_y	α_{yz}, α_{xz}

$\mathbf{C}_2$	I	$C_2(z)$		
A	$+1$	$+1$	T_z, R_z	$\alpha_{xx}, \alpha_{yy}, \alpha_{zz}, \alpha_{xy}$
B	$+1$	-1	T_x, T_y, R_x, R_y	α_{yz}, α_{xz}

$\mathbf{C}_{2v}$	I	$C_2(z)$	$\sigma_v(xz)$	$\sigma_v(yz)$		
A_1	$+1$	$+1$	$+1$	$+1$	T_z	$\alpha_{xx}, \alpha_{yy}, \alpha_{zz}$
A_2	$+1$	$+1$	-1	-1	R_z	α_{xy}
B_1	$+1$	-1	$+1$	-1	T_x, R_y	α_{xz}
B_2	$+1$	-1	-1	$+1$	T_y, R_x	α_{yz}

$\mathbf{C}_{3v}$	I	$2C_3(z)$	$3\sigma_v$		
A_1	$+1$	$+1$	$+1$	T_z	$\alpha_{xx} + \alpha_{yy}, \alpha_{zz}$
A_2	$+1$	$+1$	-1	R_z	
E	$+2$	-1	0	$(T_x, T_y), (R_x, R_y)$	$(\alpha_{xx} - \alpha_{yy}, \alpha_{xy}), (\alpha_{yz}, \alpha_{xz})$

$\mathbf{C}_{4v}$	I	$2C_4(z)$	$C_4^2 \equiv C_2''$	$2\sigma_v$	$2\sigma_d$		
A_1	$+1$	$+1$	$+1$	$+1$	$+1$	T_z	$\alpha_{xx} + \alpha_{yy}, \alpha_{zz}$
A_2	$+1$	$+1$	$+1$	-1	-1	R_z	
B_1	$+1$	-1	$+1$	$+1$	-1		$\alpha_{xx} - \alpha_{yy}$
B_2	$+1$	-1	$+1$	-1	$+1$		α_{xy}
E	$+2$	0	-2	0	0	$(T_x, T_y), (R_x, R_y)$	$(\alpha_{yz}, \alpha_{xz})$

$\mathbf{C}_{\infty v}$	I	$2C_\infty^{\phi}$	$2C_\infty^{2\phi}$	$2C_\infty^{3\phi}$	...	$\infty\sigma_v$		
Σ^+	$+1$	$+1$	$+1$	$+1$	...	$+1$	T_z	$\alpha_{xx}+\alpha_{yy}, \alpha_{zz}$
Σ^-	$+1$	$+1$	$+1$	$+1$	...	-1	R_z	
Π	$+2$	$2\cos\phi$	$2\cos 2\phi$	$2\cos 3\phi$	...	0	$(T_x, T_y), (R_x, R_y)$	$(\alpha_{yz}, \alpha_{xz})$
Δ	$+2$	$2\cos 2\phi$	$2\cos 2\cdot 2\phi$	$2\cos 3\cdot 2\phi$	...	0		$(\alpha_{xx}-\alpha_{yy}, \alpha_{xy})$
Φ	$+2$	$2\cos 3\phi$	$2\cos 2\cdot 3\phi$	$2\cos 3\cdot 3\phi$	...	0		
...	...	...	...	...	...	...		

$\mathbf{C}_{2h}$	I	$C_2(z)$	$\sigma_h(xy)$	i		
A_g	$+1$	$+1$	$+1$	$+1$	R_z	$\alpha_{xx}, \alpha_{yy}, \alpha_{zz}, \alpha_{xy}$
A_u	$+1$	$+1$	-1	-1	T_z	
B_g	$+1$	-1	-1	$+1$	R_x, R_y	α_{yz}, α_{xz}
B_u	$+1$	-1	$+1$	-1	T_x, T_y	

$\mathbf{D}_3$	I	$2C_3(z)$	$3C_2$		
A_1	$+1$	$+1$	$+1$		$\alpha_{xx}+\alpha_{yy}, \alpha_{zz}$
A_2	$+1$	$+1$	-1	T_z, R_z	
E	$+2$	-1	0	$(T_x, T_y), (R_x, R_y)$	$(\alpha_{xx}-\alpha_{yy}, \alpha_{xy}), (\alpha_{yz}, \alpha_{xz})$

$\mathbf{D}_{2d} \equiv \mathbf{V}_d$	I	$2S_4(z)$	$S_4^2 \equiv C_2''$	$2C_2$	$2\sigma_d$		
A_1	$+1$	$+1$	$+1$	$+1$	$+1$		$\alpha_{xx}+\alpha_{yy}, \alpha_{zz}$
A_2	$+1$	$+1$	$+1$	-1	-1	R_z	
B_1	$+1$	-1	$+1$	$+1$	-1		$\alpha_{xx}-\alpha_{yy}$
B_2	$+1$	-1	$+1$	-1	$+1$	T_z	α_{xy}
E	$+2$	0	-2	0	0	$(T_x, T_y), (R_x, R_y)$	$(\alpha_{yz}, \alpha_{xz})$

$\mathbf{D}_{3d}$	I	$2S_6(z)$	$2S_6^2 \equiv 2C_3$	$S_6^3 \equiv S_2 \equiv i$	$3C_2$	$3\sigma_d$		
A_{1g}	+1	+1	+1	+1	+1	+1		$\alpha_{xx} + \alpha_{yy}, \alpha_{zz}$
A_{1u}	+1	−1	+1	−1	+1	−1		
A_{2g}	+1	+1	+1	+1	−1	−1	R_z	
A_{2u}	+1	−1	+1	−1	−1	+1	T_z	
E_g	+2	−1	−1	+2	0	0	(R_x, R_y)	$(\alpha_{xx} - \alpha_{yy}, \alpha_{xy}), (\alpha_{yz}, \alpha_{xz})$
E_u	+2	+1	−1	−2	0	0	(T_x, T_y)	

$\mathbf{D}_{4d}$	I	$2S_8(z)$	$2S_8^2 \equiv 2C_4$	$2S_8^3$	$S_8^4 \equiv C_2''$	$4C_2$	$4\sigma_d$		
A_1	+1	+1	+1	+1	+1	+1	+1		$\alpha_{xx} + \alpha_{yy}, \alpha_{zz}$
A_2	+1	+1	+1	+1	+1	−1	−1	R_z	
B_1	+1	−1	+1	−1	+1	+1	−1		
B_2	+1	−1	+1	−1	+1	−1	+1	T_z	
E_1	+2	$+\sqrt{2}$	0	$-\sqrt{2}$	−2	0	0	(T_x, T_y)	
E_2	+2	0	−2	0	+2	0	0		$(\alpha_{xx} - \alpha_{yy}, \alpha_{xy})$
E_3	+2	$-\sqrt{2}$	0	$+\sqrt{2}$	−2	0	0	(R_x, R_y)	$(\alpha_{yz}, \alpha_{xz})$

$\mathbf{D}_{2h} \equiv \mathbf{V}_h$	I	$\sigma(xy)$	$\sigma(xz)$	$\sigma(yz)$	i	$C_2(z)$	$C_2(y)$	$C_2(x)$		
A_g	+1	+1	+1	+1	+1	+1	+1	+1		$\alpha_{xx}, \alpha_{yy}, \alpha_{zz}$
A_u	+1	−1	−1	−1	−1	+1	+1	+1		
B_{1g}	+1	+1	−1	−1	+1	+1	−1	−1	R_z	α_{xy}
B_{1u}	+1	−1	+1	+1	−1	+1	−1	−1	T_z	
B_{2g}	+1	−1	+1	−1	+1	−1	+1	−1	R_y	α_{xz}
B_{2u}	+1	+1	−1	+1	−1	−1	+1	−1	T_y	
B_{3g}	+1	−1	−1	+1	+1	−1	−1	+1	R_x	α_{yz}
B_{3u}	+1	+1	+1	−1	−1	−1	−1	+1	T_x	

$\mathbf{D}_{3h}$	I	$2C_3(z)$	$3C_2$	σ_h	$2S_3$	$3\sigma_v$		
A_1'	+1	+1	+1	+1	+1	+1		$\alpha_{xx}+\alpha_{yy}, \alpha_{zz}$
A_1''	+1	+1	+1	−1	−1	−1		
A_2'	+1	+1	−1	+1	+1	−1	R_z	
A_2''	+1	+1	−1	−1	−1	+1	T_z	
E'	+2	−1	0	+2	−1	0	(T_x, T_y)	$(\alpha_{xx}-\alpha_{yy}, \alpha_{xy})$
E''	+2	−1	0	−2	+1	0	(R_x, R_y)	$(\alpha_{yz}, \alpha_{xz})$

$\mathbf{D}_{4h}$	I	$2C_4(z)$	$C_4^2 \equiv C_2''$	$2C_2$	$2C_2'$	σ_h	$2\sigma_v$	$2\sigma_d$	$2S_4$	$S_2 \equiv i$		
A_{1g}	+1	+1	+1	+1	+1	+1	+1	+1	+1	+1		$\alpha_{xx}+\alpha_{yy}, \alpha_{zz}$
A_{1u}	+1	+1	+1	+1	+1	−1	−1	−1	−1	−1		
A_{2g}	+1	+1	+1	−1	−1	+1	−1	−1	+1	+1	R_z	
A_{2u}	+1	+1	+1	−1	−1	−1	+1	+1	−1	−1	T_z	
B_{1g}	+1	−1	+1	+1	−1	+1	+1	−1	−1	+1		$\alpha_{xx}-\alpha_{yy}$
B_{1u}	+1	−1	+1	+1	−1	−1	−1	+1	+1	−1		
B_{2g}	+1	−1	+1	−1	+1	+1	−1	+1	−1	+1		α_{xy}
B_{2u}	+1	−1	+1	−1	+1	−1	+1	−1	+1	−1		
E_g	+2	0	−2	0	0	−2	0	0	0	+2	(R_x, R_y)	$(\alpha_{yz}, \alpha_{xz})$
E_u	+2	0	−2	0	0	+2	0	0	0	−2	(T_x, T_y)	

$\mathbf{D}_{5h}$	I	$2C_5(z)$	$2C_5^2$	σ_h	$5C_2$	$5\sigma_v$	$2S_5$	$2S_5^3$		
A_1'	+1	+1	+1	+1	+1	+1	+1	+1		$\alpha_{xx}+\alpha_{yy}, \alpha_{zz}$
A_1''	+1	+1	+1	−1	+1	−1	−1	−1		
A_2'	+1	+1	+1	+1	−1	−1	+1	+1	R_z	
A_2''	+1	+1	+1	−1	−1	+1	−1	−1	T_z	
E_1'	+2	2 cos 72°	2 cos 144°	+2	0	0	+2 cos 72°	+2 cos 144°	(T_x, T_y)	
E_1''	+2	2 cos 72°	2 cos 144°	−2	0	0	−2 cos 72°	−2 cos 144°	(R_x, R_y)	$(\alpha_{yz}, \alpha_{xz})$
E_2'	+2	2 cos 144°	2 cos 72°	+2	0	0	+2 cos 144°	+2 cos 72°		$(\alpha_{xx}-\alpha_{yy}, \alpha_{xy})$
E_2''	+2	2 cos 144°	2 cos 72°	−2	0	0	−2 cos 144°	−2 cos 72°		

$\mathbf{D}_{6h}$	I	$2C_6(z)$	$2C_6^2 \equiv 2C_2$	$C_6^3 \equiv C_2''$	$3C_2$	$3C_2'$	σ_h	$3\sigma_v$	$3\sigma_d$	$2S_6$	$2S_3$	$S_6^3 \equiv S_2 \equiv i$		
A_{1g}	+1	+1	+1	+1	+1	+1	+1	+1	+1	+1	+1	+1		$\alpha_{xx} + \alpha_{yy}, \alpha_{zz}$
A_{1u}	+1	+1	+1	+1	+1	+1	−1	−1	−1	−1	−1	−1		
A_{2g}	+1	+1	+1	+1	−1	−1	+1	−1	−1	+1	+1	+1	R_z	
A_{2u}	+1	+1	+1	+1	−1	−1	−1	+1	+1	−1	−1	−1	T_z	
B_{1g}	+1	−1	+1	−1	+1	−1	−1	−1	+1	+1	−1	+1		
B_{1u}	+1	−1	+1	−1	+1	−1	+1	+1	−1	−1	+1	−1		
B_{2g}	+1	−1	+1	−1	−1	+1	−1	+1	−1	+1	−1	+1		
B_{2u}	+1	−1	+1	−1	−1	+1	+1	−1	+1	−1	+1	−1		
E_{1g}	+2	+1	−1	−2	0	0	−2	0	0	−1	+1	+2	(R_x, R_y)	$(\alpha_{yz}, \alpha_{xz})$
E_{1u}	+2	+1	−1	−2	0	0	+2	0	0	+1	−1	−2	(T_x, T_y)	
E_{2g}	+2	−1	−1	+2	0	0	+2	0	0	−1	−1	+2		$(\alpha_{xx} - \alpha_{yy}, \alpha_{xy})$
E_{2u}	+2	−1	−1	+2	0	0	−2	0	0	+1	+1	−2		

$\mathbf{D}_{\infty h}$	I	$2C_\infty^{\phi}$	$2C_\infty^{2\phi}$	$2C_\infty^{3\phi}$	…	σ_h	∞C_2	$\infty\sigma_v$	$2S_\infty^{\phi}$	$2S_\infty^{2\phi}$	…	$S_2 \equiv i$		
Σ_g^+	+1	+1	+1	+1	…	+1	+1	+1	+1	+1	…	+1		$\alpha_{xx} + \alpha_{yy}, \alpha_{zz}$
Σ_u^+	+1	+1	+1	+1	…	−1	−1	+1	−1	−1	…	−1	T_z	
Σ_g^-	+1	+1	+1	+1	…	+1	−1	−1	+1	+1	…	+1	R_z	
Σ_u^-	+1	+1	+1	+1	…	−1	+1	−1	−1	−1	…	−1		
Π_g	+2	$2\cos\phi$	$2\cos 2\phi$	$2\cos 3\phi$	…	−2	0	0	$-2\cos\phi$	$-2\cos 2\phi$	…	+2	(R_x, R_y)	$(\alpha_{yz}, \alpha_{xz})$
Π_u	+2	$2\cos\phi$	$2\cos 2\phi$	$2\cos 3\phi$	…	+2	0	0	$+2\cos\phi$	$+2\cos 2\phi$	…	−2	(T_x, T_y)	
Δ_g	+2	$2\cos 2\phi$	$2\cos 4\phi$	$2\cos 6\phi$	…	+2	0	0	$+2\cos 2\phi$	$+2\cos 4\phi$	…	+2		$(\alpha_{xx} - \alpha_{yy}, \alpha_{xy})$
Δ_u	+2	$2\cos 2\phi$	$2\cos 4\phi$	$2\cos 6\phi$	…	−2	0	0	$-2\cos 2\phi$	$-2\cos 4\phi$	…	−2		
Φ_g	+2	$2\cos 3\phi$	$2\cos 6\phi$	$2\cos 9\phi$	…	−2	0	0	$-2\cos 3\phi$	$-2\cos 4\phi$	…	+2		
Φ_u	+2	$2\cos 3\phi$	$2\cos 6\phi$	$2\cos 9\phi$	…	+2	0	0	$+2\cos 3\phi$	$+2\cos 4\phi$	…	−2		
…	…	…	…	…	…	…	…	…	…	…	…	…		

$\mathbf{T}_d$	I	$8C_3$	$6\sigma_d$	$6S_4$	$3S_4^2 \equiv 3C_2$		
A_1	+1	+1	+1	+1	+1		$\alpha_{xx} + \alpha_{yy} + \alpha_{zz}$
A_2	+1	+1	−1	−1	+1		
E	+2	−1	0	0	+2		$(\alpha_{xx} + \alpha_{yy} - 2\alpha_{zz}, \alpha_{xx} - \alpha_{yy})$
F_1	+3	0	−1	+1	−1	(R_x, R_y, R_z)	
F_2	+3	0	+1	−1	−1	(T_x, T_y, T_z)	$(\alpha_{xy}, \alpha_{yz}, \alpha_{xz})$

$\mathbf{O}_h$	I	$8C_3$	$6C_2$	$6C_4$	$3C_4^2 \equiv 3C_2''$	$S_2 \equiv i$	$6S_4$	$8S_6$	$3\sigma_h$	$6\sigma_d$		
A_{1g}	+1	+1	+1	+1	+1	+1	+1	+1	+1	+1		$\alpha_{xx} + \alpha_{yy} + \alpha_{zz}$
A_{1u}	+1	+1	+1	+1	+1	−1	−1	−1	−1	−1		
A_{2g}	+1	+1	−1	−1	+1	+1	−1	+1	+1	−1		
A_{2u}	+1	+1	−1	−1	+1	−1	+1	−1	−1	+1		
E_g	+2	−1	0	0	+2	+2	0	−1	+2	0		$(\alpha_{xx} + \alpha_{yy} - 2\alpha_{zz}, \alpha_{xx} - \alpha_{yy})$
E_u	+2	−1	0	0	+2	−2	0	+1	−2	0		
F_{1g}	+3	0	−1	+1	−1	+3	+1	0	−1	−1	(R_x, R_y, R_z)	
F_{1u}	+3	0	−1	+1	−1	−3	−1	0	+1	+1	(T_x, T_y, T_z)	
F_{2g}	+3	0	+1	−1	−1	+3	−1	0	−1	+1		$(\alpha_{xy}, \alpha_{yz}, \alpha_{xz})$
F_{2u}	+3	0	+1	−1	−1	−3	+1	0	+1	−1		

APPENDIX II

THE G AND F MATRIX ELEMENTS OF TYPICAL MOLECULES

In the following tables, F represents F matrix elements in the GVF field, whereas F^* denotes those in the UBF field. In the latter, $F' = -\frac{1}{10}F$ was assumed for all cases, and the *molecular tension* (see Ref. I-19) was ignored.

(1) Bent XY_2 Molecules (C_{2v})

A_1 species—infrared and Raman active

$$G_{11} = \mu_y + \mu_x(1 + \cos\alpha)$$

$$G_{12} = -\frac{\sqrt{2}}{r}\mu_x \sin\alpha$$

$$G_{22} = \frac{2}{r^2}[\mu_y + \mu_x(1 - \cos\alpha)]$$

$$F_{11} = f_r + f_{rr}$$

$$F_{12} = \sqrt{2}\, r f_{r\alpha}$$

$$F_{22} = r^2 f_\alpha$$

$$F_{11}^* = K + 2F\sin^2\frac{\alpha}{2}$$

$$F_{12}^* = (0.9)\sqrt{2}\, rF\sin\frac{\alpha}{2}\cos\frac{\alpha}{2}$$

$$F_{22}^* = r^2\left[H + F\left\{\cos^2\frac{\alpha}{2} + (0.1)\sin^2\frac{\alpha}{2}\right\}\right]$$

B_2 species—infrared and Raman active

$$G = \mu_y + \mu_x(1 - \cos\alpha)$$

$$F = f_r - f_{rr}$$

$$F^* = K - (0.2)F\cos^2\frac{\alpha}{2}$$

(2) Pyramidal XY_3 Molecules (C_{3v})

A_1 species—infrared and Raman active

$$G_{11} = \mu_y + (1 + 2\cos\alpha)\mu_x$$

$$G_{12} = -\frac{2}{r}\frac{(1 + 2\cos\alpha)(1 - \cos\alpha)}{\sin\alpha}\mu_x$$

$$G_{22} = \frac{2}{r^2}\left(\frac{1 + 2\cos\alpha}{1 + \cos\alpha}\right)[\mu_y + 2\mu_x(1 - \cos\alpha)]$$

$$F_{11} = f_r + 2f_{rr}$$

$$F_{12} = r(2f_{r\alpha} + f_{r\alpha}')$$

$$F_{22} = r^2(f_\alpha + 2f_{\alpha\alpha})$$

$$F_{11}^* = K + 4F\sin^2\frac{\alpha}{2}$$

$$F_{12}^* = (1.8)rF\sin\frac{\alpha}{2}\cos\frac{\alpha}{2}$$

$$F_{22}^* = r^2\left[H + F\left\{\cos^2\frac{\alpha}{2} + (0.1)\sin^2\frac{\alpha}{2}\right\}\right]$$

E species—infrared and Raman active

$$G_{11} = \mu_y + \mu_x(1 - \cos\alpha)$$

$$G_{12} = -\frac{1}{r}\frac{(1 - \cos\alpha)^2}{\sin\alpha}\mu_x$$

$$G_{22} = \frac{1}{r^2(1 + \cos\alpha)}[(2 + \cos\alpha)\mu_y + (1 - \cos\alpha)^2\mu_x]$$

$$F_{11} = f_r - f_{rr}$$

$$F_{12} = r(-f_{r\alpha} + f_{r\alpha}')$$

$$F_{22} = r^2(f_\alpha - f_{\alpha\alpha})$$

$$F_{11}^* = K + \left[\sin^2\frac{\alpha}{2} - (0.3)\cos^2\frac{\alpha}{2}\right]F$$

$$F_{12}^* = (0.9)rF\sin\frac{\alpha}{2}\cos\frac{\alpha}{2}$$

$$F_{22}^* = r^2\left[H + F\left\{\cos^2\frac{\alpha}{2} + (0.1)\sin^2\frac{\alpha}{2}\right\}\right]$$

$f_{r\alpha}$ denotes interaction between Δr and $\Delta\alpha$ having a common bond (e.g., Δr_1 and $\Delta\alpha_{12}$ or $\Delta\alpha_{31}$).
$f_{r\alpha}'$ denotes interaction between Δr and $\Delta\alpha$ having no common bonds (e.g., Δr_1 and $\Delta\alpha_{23}$); see Fig. I-10*c*.

(3) Tetrahedral XY_4 Molecules (T_d)

A_1 species—Raman active

$$G = \mu_y$$
$$F = f_r + 3f_{rr}$$
$$F^* = K + 4F$$

E species—Raman active

$$G = \frac{3\mu_y}{r^2}$$
$$F = r^2(f_\alpha - 2f_{\alpha\alpha} + f_{\alpha\alpha}')$$
$$F^* = r^2(H + 0.37F)$$

F_2 species—infrared and Raman active

$$G_{11} = \mu_y + \tfrac{4}{3}\mu_x$$
$$G_{12} = -\frac{8}{3r}\mu_x$$
$$G_{22} = \frac{1}{r^2}(\tfrac{16}{3}\mu_x + 2\mu_y)$$
$$F_{11} = f_r - f_{rr}$$
$$F_{12} = \sqrt{2}\, r(f_{r\alpha} - f_{r\alpha}')$$
$$F_{22} = r^2(f_\alpha - f_{\alpha\alpha}')$$
$$F_{11}^* = K + \tfrac{6}{5}F$$
$$F_{12}^* = \tfrac{3}{5}rF$$
$$F_{22}^* = r^2(H + \tfrac{1}{2}F)$$

$f_{\alpha\alpha}$ denotes interaction between two $\Delta\alpha$ having a common bond.
$f_{\alpha\alpha}'$ denotes interaction between two $\Delta\alpha$ having no common bond.

(4) Square-Planar XY_4 Molecules (D_{4h})

A_{1g} species—Raman active

$$G = \mu_y$$
$$F = f_r + 2f_{rr} + f_{rr}'$$
$$F^* = K + 2F$$

B_{1g} species—Raman active

$$G = \mu_y$$
$$F = f_r - 2f_{rr} + f_{rr}'$$
$$F^* = K - 0.2F$$

B_{2g} species—Raman active

$$G = \frac{4\mu_y}{r^2}$$
$$F = r^2(f_\alpha - 2f_{\alpha\alpha} + f_{\alpha\alpha}')$$
$$F^* = r^2(H + 0.55F)$$

E_u species—infrared active

$$G_{11} = 2\mu_x + \mu_y$$
$$G_{12} = -\frac{2\sqrt{2}}{r}\mu_x$$
$$G_{22} = \frac{2}{r^2}(\mu_y + 2\mu_x)$$
$$F_{11} = f_r - f_{rr}'$$
$$F_{12} = \sqrt{2}\, r(f_{r\alpha} - f_{r\alpha}')$$
$$F_{22} = r^2(f_\alpha - f_{\alpha\alpha}')$$
$$F_{11}^* = K + 0.9F$$
$$F_{12}^* = -\sqrt{2}\, r(0.45)F$$
$$F_{22}^* = r^2(H + 0.55F)$$

f_{rr} denotes interaction between two Δr having a common bond. f_{rr}' denotes interaction between two Δr having no common bond. In addition, a square-planar XY_4 molecule has two out-of-plane vibrations in A_{2u} and B_{1u} species.

(5) Octahedral XY_6 Molecules (O_h)

A_{1g} species—Raman active

$$G = \mu_y$$
$$F = f_r + 4f_{rr} + f_{rr}'$$
$$F^* = K + 4F$$

E_g species—Raman active

$$G = \mu_y$$
$$F = f_r - 2f_{rr} + f_{rr}'$$
$$F^* = K + 0.7F$$

F_{1u} species—infrared active

$$G_{11} = \mu_y + 2\mu_x$$
$$G_{12} = -\frac{4}{r}\mu_y$$
$$G_{22} = \frac{2}{r^2}(\mu_y + 4\mu_x)$$
$$F_{11} = f_r - f_{rr}'$$
$$F_{12} = 2rf_{r\alpha}$$
$$F_{22} = r^2(f_\alpha + 2f_{\alpha\alpha})$$
$$F_{11}^* = K + 1.8F$$
$$F_{12}^* = 0.9rF$$
$$F_{22}^* = r^2(H + 0.55F)$$

F_{2g} species—Raman active

$$G = \frac{4\mu_y}{r^2}$$
$$F = r^2(f_\alpha - 2f_{\alpha\alpha}')$$
$$F^* = r^2(H + 0.55F)$$

F_{2u} species—inactive

$$G = \frac{2\mu_y}{r^2}$$
$$F = r^2(f_\alpha - 2f_{\alpha\alpha})$$
$$F^* = r^2(H + 0.55F)$$

f_{rr} denotes interaction between two Δr perpendicular to each other, whereas f_{rr}' denotes those between two Δr on the same straight line. $f_{\alpha\alpha}$ denotes interaction between two $\Delta\alpha$ perpendicular to each other, whereas $f_{\alpha\alpha}'$ denotes those between two $\Delta\alpha$ on the same plane.

APPENDIX III

A NORMAL COORDINATE ANALYSIS OF METAL ACETYLACETONATES

A procedure for carrying out a normal coordinate analysis of a complex system is described below using bis-acetylacetonato-Cu(II) as an example (Ref. 251 of Part III).

(1) Selection of Molecular Models

In order to carry out a normal coordinate analysis of a complex molecule such as bis-acetylacetonato-Cu(II), it is desirable to simplify the system by making reasonable assumptions. Although the compound is a 1:2 (metal/ligand) complex having a square-planar configuration around the central metal, a simple 1:1 complex model may be sufficient as a first approximation. This assumption is reasonable for most of the vibrations, since coupling between two ligands is expected to be small. Such coupling may be appreciable, however, for the Cu—O stretching and O—Cu—O bending modes which have the central metal as a common atom. The magnitude of coupling can be found by comparing the results of calculations on 1:1 and 1:2 complex models using the same set of force constants. It has been found for metal oxalato complexes (Ref. III-242) that the metal-oxygen stretching force constants in square-planar complexes is overestimated by 10–15% if the 1:1 complex model is employed.

The 1:1 complex model of bis-acetylacetonato-Cu(II) is shown in Fig. 1. This model consists of nine atoms if the methyl group is assumed to be a single atom having the same mass as the methyl group. Furthermore, it belongs to the point group $\mathbf{C}_{2v}$ since, according to the results of x-ray analysis (Ref. III-247), the chelate ring is planar and symmetrical.

(2) Classification of Normal Vibrations and Internal Coordinates

The 1:1 complex model shown in Fig. 1 has twenty-one normal vibrations ($3 \times 9 - 6 = 21$). By the method given in Sec. I-7, they are grouped into four species ($8A_1 + 2A_2 + 4B_1 + 7B_2$) of the point group $\mathbf{C}_{2v}$. Since the in-plane vibrations ($8A_1 + 7B_2$) are separable from the out-of-plane vibrations ($2A_2 + 4B_1$), and since the former are more important than the latter, only fifteen in-plane vibrations will be calculated here. Figure 1 also indicates twenty-one internal coordinates (see Sec. I-8) for the fifteen in-plane vibrations. Apparently, six redundant conditions are involved in this set of internal coordinates.

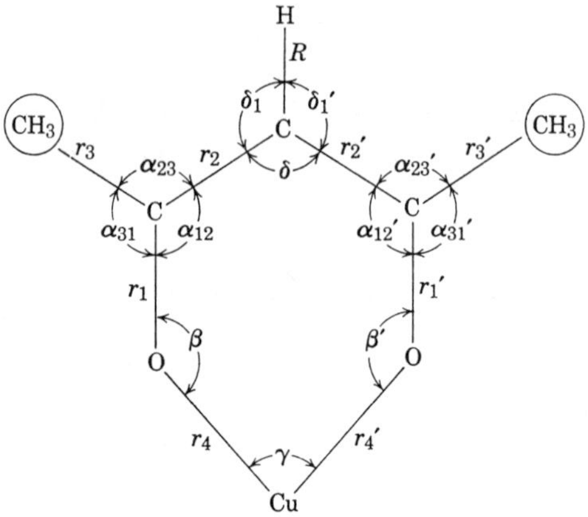

Fig. 1.

(3) Construction of Original G and F Matrices

As a first step, the **G** matrix is constructed, the twenty-one internal coordinates being used as the basis. The result is shown in Table 1, where $A_1, \ldots, B_1 \ldots$, etc., represents **G** matrix elements which are calculated by the methods given in Sec. I-10. Table 2 shows the corresponding **F** matrix in terms of the GVF potential field. Some interaction force constants are assumed to be zero because they are not taken into consideration in the UBF field, which will be introduced later.

(4) Removal of Redundancies and Utilization of Symmetry Properties

Four of the six redundant conditions involved in the present set of internal coordinates are obvious (see Sec. I-8). They are

$$\Delta\alpha_{12} + \Delta\alpha_{23} + \Delta\alpha_{31} = 0$$

$$\Delta\alpha_{12}' + \Delta\alpha_{23}' + \Delta\alpha_{31}' = 0$$

$$\Delta\delta + \Delta\delta_1 + \Delta\delta_1' = 0$$

$$\Delta\delta + \Delta\alpha_{12} + \Delta\alpha_{12}' + \Delta\beta + \Delta\beta' + \Delta\gamma = 0$$

However, the remaining two redundant conditions (one in A_1 and one in B_2) are rather difficult to write explicitly. In such a case, it is better to

TABLE 1

G	r_1	r_1'	r_2	r_2'	r_3	r_3'	r_4	r_4'	R	α_{12}	α_{23}	α_{31}	α_{12}'	α_{23}'	α_{31}'	δ	δ_1	δ_1'	β	β'	γ
r_1	A_1		A_6		A_6		A_7			B_1	D_1	B_2				C_1	C_1'		B_3		C_2
r_1'		A_1		A_6		A_6		A_7					B_1	D_1	B_2	C_1		C_1'		B_3	C_2
r_2			A_2	A_6	A_6				A_6	B_4	B_2	D_2	C_1	C_1'		B_1	B_5	D_5	C_3		
r_2'				A_2		A_6			A_6	C_1	C_1'		B_4	B_2	D_2	B_1	D_5	B_5		C_3	
r_3					A_3					D_3	B_1	B_4				C_1'	C_1		C_3'		
r_3'						A_3							D_3	B_1	B_4	C_1'		C_1		C_3'	
r_4							A_4			C_4		C_4'							B_6	C_5	B_7
r_4'								A_4					C_4		C_4'				C_5	B_6	B_7
R									A_5	C_1'	C_1		C_1'	C_1		D_4	B_1	B_1			
α_{12}										E_1	F_1	F_2	H_1	H_1'		G_1	G_2	I_1	G_3		H_2
α_{23}											E_2	F_3	H_1'	H_1		G_4	G_5	I_1'	I_2		
α_{31}												E_3				I_3	I_3'		G_6		H_2'
α_{12}'													E_1	F_1	F_2	G_1	I_1	G_2		E_3	H_2
α_{23}'														E_2	F_3	G_4	I_1'	G_5		I_2	
α_{31}'					(Symmetrical)										E_3	I_3		I_3'		G_6	H_2'
δ																E_4	F_4	F_4	H_3	H_3	
δ_1																	E_5	F_5	H_3'		
δ_1'																		E_5		H_3'	
β																			E_6		G_7
β'																				E_6	G_7
γ																					E_7

TABLE 2

F	r_1	r_1'	r_2	r_2'	r_3	r_3'	r_4	r_4'	R	α_{12}	α_{23}	α_{31}	α_{12}'	α_{23}'	α_{31}'	δ	δ_1	δ_1'	β	β'	γ
r_1	f_1		f_1^2		f_1^3		f_1^4			f_1^{12}		f_1^{31}							f_1^β		
r_1'		f_1		f_1^2		f_1^3		f_1^4					f_1^{12}		f_1^{31}					f_1^β	
r_2			f_2	f_2^2	f_2^3				f_2^R	f_2^{12}	f_2^{23}					f_2^δ	$f_2^{\delta_1}$				
r_2'				f_2		f_2^3			f_2^R				f_2^{12}	f_2^{23}		f_2^δ		$f_2^{\delta_1}$			
r_3					f_3						f_3^{23}	f_3^{31}									
r_3'						f_3								f_3^{23}	f_3^{31}						
r_4							f_4	f_4^4											f_4^β		f_4^γ
r_4'								f_4												f_4^β	f_4^γ
R									f_5								$f_R^{\delta_1}$	$f_R^{\delta_1}$			
α_{12}										f_{12}											
α_{23}											f_{23}										
α_{31}												f_{31}									
α_{12}'													f_{12}								
α_{23}'														f_{23}							
α_{31}'							(Symmetrical)								f_{31}						
δ																f_δ					
δ_1																	f_{δ_1}				
δ_1'																		f_{δ_1}			
β																			f_β		
β'																				f_β	
γ																					f_γ

Suitable bond distances must be multipled to bending force constants and to interaction force constants between stretching and solve the secular equations of the form $|\mathbf{GF} - \mathbf{E}\lambda| = 0$, including redundancies. This method, in turn, may be used as a check of the calculations, since these redundancies must yield exact *zero frequencies* in the final results.

Removal of four redundancies can be accomplished as follows. At first, the **G** and **F** matrices shown in Tables 1 and 2 are transformed through the relations

$$\mathbf{G}_{\mathrm{I}} = \mathbf{T}\mathbf{G}\tilde{\mathbf{T}}$$

$$\mathbf{F}_{\mathrm{I}} = \tilde{\mathbf{T}}^{-1}\mathbf{F}\mathbf{T}^{-1}$$

which are slightly different from those given in Eqs. 11.13 of Sec. I-11. This difference is due to the fact that the transformation matrix **T** shown in Table 3 is not orthogonal. Through this coordinate transformation, three rows and columns (s_{10}, s_{13} and s_{16}) in the $\mathbf{G}_{\mathrm{I}}$ matrix become zero. A similar result can be obtained for the $\mathbf{F}_{\mathrm{I}}$ matrix simply by deleting the corresponding rows and columns.

The next step is to remove the redundancy concerning the sum of all the six angles in the ring. This process and the factoring of the matrices, using symmetry properties, can be accomplished simultaneously by means of a coordinate transformation given in Eqs. 11.13 of Sec. I-11.

$$\mathbf{G}_{\mathrm{II}} = \mathbf{U}\mathbf{G}_{\mathrm{I}}\tilde{\mathbf{U}}$$

$$\mathbf{F}_{\mathrm{II}} = \mathbf{U}\mathbf{F}_{\mathrm{I}}\tilde{\mathbf{U}}$$

The **U** matrix used for this purpose is shown in Table 4. Through this coordinate transformation, the row and column of S_{13} become zero in the $\mathbf{G}_{\mathrm{II}}$ matrix. The same result is obtained for the $\mathbf{F}_{\mathrm{II}}$ matrix by deleting the corresponding row and column. If rows and columns are rearranged as shown in Table 5, it is seen that the eighteenth order $\mathbf{G}_{\mathrm{I}}$ matrix is factored into one ninth order (A_1) and one eighth order (B_2) matrix. Tables 6 and 7 tabulate the final $\mathbf{G}_{\mathrm{II}}$ and $\mathbf{F}_{\mathrm{II}}$ matrix elements thus obtained.

(5) Conversion of the GVF to UBF Force Constants

The final $\mathbf{F}_{\mathrm{II}}$ matrix elements given in Table 7 involve thirty GVF force constants which are difficult to determine from experiment. As stated in Sec. I-12, the number of force constants can be reduced considerably by using the UBF field. Through Eqs. 12.4 and 12.5 of Sec. I-12, the thirty GVF force constants can be represented by the combinations of nineteen UBF force constants. Furthermore, most of these UBF force constants can be estimated a priori from those of other compounds having

TABLE 3

T	r_1	r_1'	r_2	r_2'	r_3	r_3'	r_4	r_4'	R	α_{12}	α_{23}	α_{31}	α_{12}'	α_{23}'	α_{31}'	δ	δ_1	δ_1'	β	β'	γ
s_1	+1																				
s_2		+1																			
s_3			+1																		
s_4				+1																	
s_5					+1												Zero				
s_6						+1															
s_7							+1														
s_8								+1													
s_9									+1												
s_{10}										+1	+1	+1									
s_{11}										+1	0	0									
s_{12}										0	+1	−1									
s_{13}													+1	+1	+1						
s_{14}													+1	0	0						
s_{15}													0	+1	−1						
s_{16}																+1	+1	+1			
s_{17}						Zero										+1	0	0			
s_{18}																0	+1	−1			
s_{19}																			+1		
s_{20}																				+1	
s_{21}																					+1

U	s_1	s_2	s_3	s_4	s_5	s_6	s_7	s_8	s_9	s_{12}	s_{15}	s_{18}	s_{11}	s_{14}	s_{19}	s_{20}	s_{21}	s_{17}	
$S_1(A_1)$	$\frac{+1}{\sqrt{2}}$	$\frac{+1}{\sqrt{2}}$																	ν_s(C⋯O)
$S_2(B_2)$	$\frac{+1}{\sqrt{2}}$	$\frac{-1}{\sqrt{2}}$																	ν_{as}(C⋯O)
$S_3(A_1)$			$\frac{+1}{\sqrt{2}}$	$\frac{+1}{\sqrt{2}}$															ν_s(C⋯C)
$S_4(B_2)$			$\frac{+1}{\sqrt{2}}$	$\frac{-1}{\sqrt{2}}$															ν_{as}(C⋯C)
$S_5(A_1)$					$\frac{+1}{\sqrt{2}}$	$\frac{+1}{\sqrt{2}}$								Zero					ν_s(C—R)
$S_6(B_2)$					$\frac{+1}{\sqrt{2}}$	$\frac{-1}{\sqrt{2}}$													ν_{as}(C—R)
$S_7(A_1)$							$\frac{+1}{\sqrt{2}}$	$\frac{+1}{\sqrt{2}}$											ν_s(Cu—O)
$S_8(B_2)$							$\frac{+1}{\sqrt{2}}$	$\frac{-1}{\sqrt{2}}$											ν_{as}(Cu—O)
$S_9(A_1)$									+1										ν(C—H)
$S_{10}(A_1)$										$\frac{+1}{\sqrt{2}}$	$\frac{+1}{\sqrt{2}}$								δ_s(C—R)
$S_{11}(B_2)$										$\frac{+1}{\sqrt{2}}$	$\frac{-1}{\sqrt{2}}$								δ_{as}(C—R)
$S_{12}(B_2)$												+1							δ(C—H)
S_{13}													$\frac{+1}{\sqrt{6}}$	$\frac{+1}{\sqrt{6}}$	$\frac{+1}{\sqrt{6}}$	$\frac{+1}{\sqrt{6}}$	$\frac{+1}{\sqrt{6}}$	$\frac{+1}{\sqrt{6}}$	redundancy
$S_{14}(A_1)$					Zero								$\frac{+1}{2}$	$\frac{+1}{2}$	$\frac{-1}{2}$	$\frac{-1}{2}$			ring def.
$S_{15}(B_2)$													$\frac{+1}{2}$	$\frac{-1}{2}$	$\frac{+1}{2}$	$\frac{-1}{2}$			ring def.
$S_{16}(B_2)$													$\frac{+1}{2}$	$\frac{-1}{2}$	$\frac{-1}{2}$	$\frac{+1}{2}$			ring def.
$S_{17}(A_1)$													$\frac{-1}{\sqrt{12}}$	$\frac{-1}{\sqrt{12}}$	$\frac{-1}{\sqrt{12}}$	$\frac{-1}{\sqrt{12}}$	$\frac{+2}{\sqrt{12}}$	$\frac{+2}{\sqrt{12}}$	ring def.
$S_{18}(A_1)$																	$\frac{+1}{\sqrt{2}}$	$\frac{-1}{\sqrt{2}}$	ring def.

TABLE 5

G_{II}	A_1 species									B_2 species							
	S_1	S_3	S_5	S_7	S_9	S_{10}	S_{14}	S_{17}	S_{18}	S_2	S_4	S_6	S_8	S_{11}	S_{12}	S_{15}	S_{16}
S_1	G_{11}	G_{12}	G_{13}	G_{14}	G_{15}	G_{16}	G_{17}	G_{18}	G_{19}								
S_3		G_{22}	G_{23}	G_{24}	G_{25}	G_{26}	G_{27}	G_{28}	G_{29}								
S_5			G_{33}	G_{34}	G_{35}	G_{36}	G_{37}	G_{38}	G_{39}								
S_7				G_{44}	G_{45}	G_{46}	G_{47}	G_{48}	G_{49}								
S_9					G_{55}	G_{56}	G_{57}	G_{58}	G_{59}					Zero			
S_{10}						G_{66}	G_{67}	G_{68}	G_{69}								
S_{14}	(Symmetrical)						G_{77}	G_{78}	G_{79}								
S_{17}								G_{88}	G_{89}								
S_{18}									G_{99}								
S_2										G_{11}	G_{12}	G_{13}	G_{14}	G_{15}	G_{16}	G_{17}	G_{18}
S_4											G_{22}	G_{23}	G_{24}	G_{25}	G_{26}	G_{27}	G_{28}
S_6												G_{33}	G_{34}	G_{35}	G_{36}	G_{37}	G_{38}
S_8					Zero								G_{44}	G_{45}	G_{46}	G_{47}	G_{48}
S_{11}														G_{55}	G_{56}	G_{57}	G_{58}
S_{12}											(Symmetrical)				G_{66}	G_{67}	G_{68}
S_{15}																G_{77}	G_{78}
S_{16}																	G_{88}

TABLE 6. G MATRIX ELEMENTS

A_1 Species

$G_{11} = \mu_C + \mu_O, \quad G_{12} = G_{13} = -(1/2)\mu_C, \quad G_{14} = -(1/\sqrt{2})\mu_O, \quad G_{15} = 0,$
$G_{16} = (\sqrt{3}/2)\mu_C(\rho_{r_2} + 2\rho_{r_3}), \quad G_{17} = (1/2\sqrt{2})(\sqrt{2}\mu_O\rho_{r_4} - \sqrt{3}\mu_C\rho_{r_2}),$
$G_{18} = (\sqrt{3}/2)(\sqrt{3/2}\,\mu_C\rho_{r_2} + \mu_O\rho_{r_4}), \quad G_{19} = (1/\sqrt{2})(\mu_O\rho_{r_4} - \sqrt{3/2}\,\mu_C\rho_{r_2}),$
$G_{22} = (3/2)\,\mu_C, \quad G_{23} = -(1/2)\mu_C, \quad G_{24} = 0, \quad G_{25} = -(1/\sqrt{2})\mu_C,$
$G_{26} = -(\sqrt{3}/2)\mu_C(\rho_{r_1} + \rho_{r_2} + 2\rho_{r_3}), \quad G_{27} = (\sqrt{3}/2\sqrt{2})\mu_C(\rho_{r_2} - 2\rho_{r_1}),$
$G_{28} = -(3/2\sqrt{2})\mu_C\rho_{r_2}, \quad G_{29} = (\sqrt{3}/2)\mu_C\rho_{r_2}, \quad G_{33} = \mu_C + \mu_R, \quad G_{34} = G_{35} = 0$
$G_{36} = (\sqrt{3}/2)\mu_C(\rho_{r_1} - \rho_{r_2}), \quad G_{37} = (\sqrt{3}/2\sqrt{2})\mu_C(2\rho_{r_1} + \rho_{r_2}),$
$G_{38} = -(3/2\sqrt{2})\mu_C\rho_{r_2}, \quad G_{39} = (\sqrt{3}/2)\mu_C\rho_{r_2}, \quad G_{44} = \mu_O + \mu_M, \quad G_{45} = 0,$
$G_{46} = (1/\sqrt{2})\mu_O\rho_{r_1}, \quad G_{47} = (1/\sqrt{2})(\sqrt{2}\mu_O\rho_{r_1} - \mu_M\rho_{r_4}), \quad G_{48} = -(3/\sqrt{6})\mu_M\rho_{r_4},$
$G_{49} = -\mu_M\rho_{r_4}, \quad G_{55} = \mu_C + \mu_H, \quad G_{56} = (\sqrt{3/2})\mu_C\rho_{r_2}, \quad G_{57} = -(\sqrt{3}/2)\mu_C\rho_{r_2},$
$G_{58} = (3/2)\mu_C\rho_{r_2}, \quad G_{59} = -(\sqrt{3/2})\mu_C\rho_{r_2},$
$G_{66} = \mu_O\rho_{r_1}^{\,2} + 4\mu_R\rho_{r_3}^{\,2} + \mu_C\{\rho_{r_1}^{\,2} + (5/2)\rho_{r_2}^{\,2} + 4\rho_{r_3}^{\,2} - \rho_{r_1}\rho_{r_2} + 2\rho_{r_2}\rho_{r_3}$
$\quad + 2\rho_{r_1}\rho_{r_3}\},$
$G_{67} = (1/\sqrt{2})\mu_C\{2\rho_{r_1}^{\,2} - (1/2)\rho_{r_1}\rho_{r_2} - \rho_{r_2}\rho_{r_3} + 2\rho_{r_1}\rho_{r_3} - (5/2)\rho_{r_2}^{\,2}\}$
$\quad + (1/\sqrt{2})\mu_O\{2\rho_{r_1}^{\,2} + (1/\sqrt{2})\rho_{r_1}\rho_{r_4}\},$
$G_{68} = (1/\sqrt{6})\mu_C\{-(3/2)\rho_{r_1}\rho_{r_2} + 3\rho_{r_2}\rho_{r_3} + (15/2)\rho_{r_2}^{\,2}\} + (\sqrt{3}/2)\mu_O\rho_{r_1}\rho_{r_4},$
$G_{69} = (1/\sqrt{2})\mu_O\rho_{r_1}\rho_{r_4} - (1/2)\mu_C\rho_{r_2}(5\rho_{r_2} + 2\rho_{r_3} - \rho_{r_1}),$
$G_{77} = (1/2)\mu_M\rho_{r_4}^{\,2} + \mu_C\{(5/4)\rho_{r_2}^{\,2} + 2\rho_{r_1}^{\,2} + \rho_{r_1}\rho_{r_2}\}$
$\quad + \mu_O\{2\rho_{r_1}^{\,2} + (1/2)\rho_{r_4}^{\,2} + \sqrt{2}\rho_{r_1}\rho_{r_4}\},$
$G_{78} = (1/2\sqrt{3})[3\mu_M\rho_{r_4}^{\,2} + \mu_O\{(3\rho_{r_4}^{\,2} + (6/\sqrt{2})\rho_{r_1}\rho_{r_4}\} - \mu_C\{(15/2)\rho_{r_2}^{\,2} + 3\rho_{r_1}\rho_{r_2}\}],$
$G_{79} = (1/\sqrt{2})[\mu_C\{(5/2)\rho_{r_2}^{\,2} + \rho_{r_1}\rho_{r_2}\} + \mu_O(\rho_{r_4}^{\,2} + \sqrt{2}\rho_{r_1}\rho_{r_4}) + \mu_M\rho_{r_4}^{\,2}],$
$G_{88} = (3/2)\{(\mu_M + \mu_O)\rho_{r_4}^{\,2} + (5/2)\mu_C\rho_{r_2}^{\,2}\},$
$G_{89} = (\sqrt{3}/\sqrt{2})\{(\mu_M + \mu_O)\rho_{r_4}^{\,2} - (5/2)\mu_C\rho_{r_2}^{\,2}\},$
$G_{99} = (\mu_M + \mu_O)\rho_{r_4}^{\,2} + (5/2)\mu_C\rho_{r_2}^{\,2}$

TABLE 6 (Continued)

B_2 Species
$G_{11} = G_{11}{}^{A_1}$, $G_{12} = G_{13} = G_{12}{}^{A_1}$, $G_{14} = G_{14}{}^{A_1}$, $G_{15} = G_{16}{}^{A_1}$,
$G_{16} = -(\sqrt{3/2})\mu_C\rho_{r_2}$, $G_{17} = -(1/2)\{(\sqrt{6}/2)\mu_C\rho_{r_2} + \mu_O\rho_{r_4}\}$,
$G_{18} = -(1/2)\{(\sqrt{6}/2)\mu_C\rho_{r_2} - \mu_O\rho_{r_4}\}$, $G_{22} = (5/2)\mu_C$, $G_{23} = G_{23}{}^{A_1}$, $G_{24} = 0$,
$G_{25} = -(\sqrt{3/2})\mu_C(\rho_{r_1} - \rho_{r_2} + 2\rho_{r_3})$, $G_{26} = -(\sqrt{3/2})\mu_C(2\rho_R + \rho_{r_2})$,
$G_{27} = -(\sqrt{3}/2\sqrt{2})\mu_C\rho_{r_2}$, $G_{28} = -(\sqrt{3/2})\mu_C\{\rho_{r_1} + (1/2)\rho_{r_2}\}$, $G_{33} = G_{33}{}^{A_1}$,
$G_{34} = 0$, $G_{35} = G_{36}{}^{A_1}$, $G_{36} = (\sqrt{3/2})\mu_C\rho_{r_2}$, $G_{37} = (\sqrt{3}/2\sqrt{2})\mu_C\rho_{r_2}$,
$G_{38} = G_{37}{}^{A_1}$, $G_{44} = G_{44}{}^{A_1}$, $G_{45} = G_{46}{}^{A_1}$, $G_{46} = 0$, $G_{47} = -(1/\sqrt{2})\mu_M\rho_{r_4}$,
$G_{48} = (1/\sqrt{2})(\mu_M\rho_{r_4} + \sqrt{2}\mu_O\rho_{r_1})$,
$G_{55} = 4\mu_R\rho_{r_3}{}^2 + \mu_O\rho_{r_1}{}^2 + \mu_C\{\rho_{r_1}{}^2 + (3/2)\rho_{r_2}{}^2 + 4\rho_{r_3}{}^2 - \rho_{r_1}\rho_{r_2} + 2\rho_{r_2}\rho_{r_3} + 2\rho_{r_1}\rho_{r_3}\}$
$G_{56} = (1/\sqrt{2})\mu_C\rho_{r_2}(\rho_{r_1} - 3\rho_{r_2} - 2\rho_{r_3} - 2\rho_R)$,
$G_{57} = (1/\sqrt{2})[\mu_C\{(1/2)\rho_{r_1}\rho_{r_2} - \rho_{r_2}\rho_{r_3} - (3/2)\rho_{r_2}{}^2\} - (1/\sqrt{2})\mu_O\rho_{r_1}\rho_{r_4}]$,
$G_{58} = (1/\sqrt{2})[\mu_C(2\rho_{r_1}\rho_{r_3} - \rho_{r_2}\rho_{r_3} - (1/2)\rho_{r_1}\rho_{r_2} + 2\rho_{r_1}{}^2 - (3/2)\rho_{r_2}{}^2)$ $+ \mu_O\{2\rho_{r_1}{}^2 + (1/\sqrt{2})\rho_{r_1}\rho_{r_4}\}]$,
$G_{66} = 4\mu_H\rho_R{}^2 + \mu_C(4\rho_R{}^2 + 3\rho_{r_2}{}^2 + 4\rho_R\rho_{r_2})$, $G_{67} = \mu_C\rho_{r_2}\{\rho_R + (3/2)\rho_{r_2}\}$,
$G_{68} = \mu_C\rho_{r_2}\{\rho_{r_1} + \rho_R + (3/2)\rho_{r_2}\}$,
$G_{77} = (1/2)\{(3/2)\mu_C\rho_{r_2}{}^2 + (\mu_O + \mu_M)\rho_{r_4}{}^2\}$
$G_{78} = (1/2)[\mu_C\{(3/2)\rho_{r_2}{}^2 + \rho_{r_1}\rho_{r_2}\} - \mu_M\rho_{r_4}{}^2 - \mu_O(\rho_{r_4}{}^2 + \sqrt{2}\rho_{r_1}\rho_{r_4})]$,
$G_{88} = (1/2)[\mu_C\{4\rho_{r_1}{}^2 + 2\rho_{r_1}\rho_{r_2} + (3/2)\rho_{r_2}{}^2\} + \mu_M\rho_{r_4}{}^2$ $+ \mu_O(4\rho_{r_1}{}^2 + 2\sqrt{2}\rho_{r_1}\rho_{r_4} + \rho_{r_4}{}^2)]$

μ_C, μ_H, μ_O, μ_R and μ_M are reciprocal masses of C, H, O, R(CH_3) and M(Cu), respectively. ρ_{r_1}, ρ_{r_2}, ρ_{r_3}, ρ_R and ρ_{r_4} are reciprocals of the bond distances of C⩦O, C⩦C, C—R(CH_3), C—H and M(Cu)—O, respectively.

TABLE 7. F MATRIX ELEMENTS

A_1 Species

$F_{11} = f_1, \quad F_{12} = f_1^{\,2}, \quad F_{13} = f_1^{\,3}, \quad F_{14} = f_1^{\,4}, \quad F_{15} = 0, \quad F_{16} = -\tfrac{1}{2}f_1^{\,31},$

$F_{17} = (1/\sqrt{2})(f_1^{\,12} - \tfrac{1}{2}f_1^{\,31} - f_1^{\,\beta}), \quad F_{18} = -(1/\sqrt{6})(f_1^{\,12} - \tfrac{1}{2}f_1^{\,31} + f_1^{\,\beta}),$

$F_{19} = 0, \quad F_{22} = f_2 + f_2^{\,2}, \quad F_{23} = f_2^{\,3}, \quad F_{24} = 0, \quad F_{25} = \sqrt{2}f_2^{\,\mathrm{R}}, \quad F_{26} = \tfrac{1}{2}f_2^{\,23},$

$F_{27} = (1/\sqrt{2})(f_2^{\,12} - \tfrac{1}{2}f_2^{\,23}), \quad F_{28} = -(1/\sqrt{6})(f_2^{\,12} - \tfrac{1}{2}f_2^{\,23} - 2f_2^{\,\delta} + f_2^{\,\delta_1}),$

$F_{29} = \tfrac{1}{2}f_2^{\,\delta_1} - f_2^{\,\delta}, \quad F_{33} = f_3, \quad F_{34} = F_{35} = 0, \quad F_{36} = \tfrac{1}{2}(f_3^{\,23} - f_3^{\,31}),$

$F_{37} = -(1/2\sqrt{2})(f_3^{\,23} + f_3^{\,31}), \quad F_{38} = (1/2\sqrt{6})(f_3^{\,23} + f^{31}), \quad F_{39} = 0,$

$F_{44} = f_4 + f_4^{\,4}, \quad F_{45} = F_{46} = 0, \quad F_{47} = -(1/\sqrt{2})f_4^{\,\beta},$

$F_{48} = (1/\sqrt{6})(2f_4^{\,\gamma} - f_4^{\,\beta}), \quad F_{49} = f_4^{\,\gamma}, \quad F_{55} = f_5, \quad F_{56} = F_{57} = 0,$

$F_{58} = -(1/\sqrt{3})f_{\mathrm{R}}^{\,\delta_1}, \quad F_{59} = (1/\sqrt{2})f_{\mathrm{R}}^{\,\delta_1}, \quad F_{66} = \tfrac{1}{4}(f_{23} + f_{31}),$

$F_{67} = (1/4\sqrt{2})(f_{31} - f_{23}), \quad F_{68} = -(1/4\sqrt{6})(f_{31} - f_{23}), \quad F_{69} = 0,$

$F_{77} = \tfrac{1}{2}[f_\beta + \tfrac{1}{4}(4f_{12} + f_{23} + f_{31})], \quad F_{78} = (1/2\sqrt{3})[f_\beta - \tfrac{1}{4}(4f_{12} + f_{23} + f_{31})],$

$F_{79} = 0, \quad F_{88} = \tfrac{1}{6}[f_{12} + \tfrac{1}{4}(f_{23} + f_{31}) + f_\beta + 2(f_\gamma + f_\delta) + f_{\delta_1}],$

$F_{89} = (1/\sqrt{6})(f_\gamma - f_\delta - \tfrac{1}{2}f_{\delta_1}), \quad F_{99} = \tfrac{1}{3}(f_\gamma + f_\delta + \tfrac{1}{2}f_{\delta_1})$

B_2 Species

$F_{11} = F_{11}^{\,A_1}, \quad F_{12} = F_{12}^{\,A_1}, \quad F_{13} = F_{13}^{\,A_1}, \quad F_{14} = F_{14}^{\,A_1}, \quad F_{15} = F_{16}^{\,A_1}, \quad F_{16} = 0,$

$F_{17} = (1/\sqrt{2})(f_1^{\,12} - \tfrac{1}{2}f_1^{\,31} + f_1^{\,\beta}), \quad F_{18} = F_{17}^{\,A_1}, \quad F_{22} = f_2 - f_2^{\,2}, \quad F_{23} = F_{23}^{\,A_1},$

$F_{24} = 0, \quad F_{25} = F_{26}^{\,A_1}, \quad F_{26} = (1/\sqrt{2})f_2^{\,\delta_1}, \quad F_{27} = F_{28} = F_{27}^{\,A_1}, \quad F_{33} = F_{33}^{\,A_1},$

$F_{34} = 0, \quad F_{35} = F_{36}^{\,A_1}, \quad F_{36} = 0, \quad F_{37} = F_{38} = F_{37}^{\,A_1}, \quad f_{44} = f_4 - f_4^{\,4},$

$F_{45} = F_{46} = 0, \quad F_{47} = (1/\sqrt{2})f_4^{\,\beta}, \quad F_{48} = -(1/\sqrt{2})f_4^{\,\beta}, \quad F_{55} = F_{66}^{\,A_1}, \quad F_{56} = 0,$

$F_{57} = F_{58} = F_{67}^{\,A_1}, \quad F_{66} = \tfrac{1}{2}f_{\delta_1}, \quad F_{67} = F_{68} = 0, \quad F_{77} = F_{77}^{\,A_1},$

$F_{78} = \tfrac{1}{2}[\tfrac{1}{4}(4f_{12} + f_{23} + f_{31}) - f_\beta]. \quad F_{88} = F_{77}^{\,A_1}$

TABLE 8

$$f_1 = K_1 + (t_1^2F_1' + s_1^2F_1) + (t_2^2F_3' + s_2^2F_3) + (t_3^2F_4' + s_3^2F_4)$$
$$f_2 = K_2 + (t_4^2F_1' + s_4^2F_1) + (t_5^2F_6' + s_5^2F_6) + (t_6^2F_2' + s_6^2F_2) + (t_7^2F_7' + s_7^2F_7)$$
$$f_3 = K_3 + (t_8^2F_3' + s_8^2F_3) + (t_9^2F_2' + s_9^2F_2)$$
$$f_4 = K_4 + (t_{10}^2F_4' + s_{10}^2F_4) + (t_{11}^2F_5' + s_{11}^2F_5)$$

$f_1^2 = -t_1t_4F_1' + s_1s_4F_1$	$f_1^3 = -t_2t_8F_3' + s_2s_8F_3$
$f_1^4 = -t_3t_{10}F_4' + s_3s_{10}F_4$	$f_2^2 = -t_5^2F_6' + s_5^2F_6$
$f_2^3 = -t_6t_9F_2' + s_6s_9F_2$	$f_2^R = -t_7t_{12}F_7' + s_7s_{12}F_7$
$f_4^4 = -t_{11}^2F_5' + s_{11}^2F_5$	$f_{12} = H_1 - s_1s_4F_1' + t_1t_4F_1$
$f_{23} = H_2 - s_6s_9F_2' + t_6t_9F_2$	$f_{31} = H_3 - s_2s_8F_3' + t_2t_8F_3$
$f_\delta = H_\delta - s_5^2F_6' + t_5^2F_6$	$f_\beta = H_\beta - s_3s_{10}F_4' + t_3t_{10}F_4$
$f_\gamma = H_\gamma - s_{11}^2F_5' + t_{11}^2F_5$	$f_{\delta_1} = H_{\delta_1} - s_7s_{12}F_7' + t_7t_{12}F_7$
$f_1^{12} = t_1s_4F_1' + t_4s_1F_1$	$f_1^{31} = t_2s_8F_3' + t_8s_2F_3$
$f_1^\beta = t_3s_{10}F_4' + t_{10}s_3F_4$	$f_2^{12} = t_4s_1F_1' + t_1s_4F_1$
$f_2^{23} = t_6s_9F_2' + t_9s_6F_2$	$f_2^\delta = t_5s_5F_6' + t_5s_5F_6$
$f_2^{\delta_1} = t_7s_{12}F_7' + t_{12}s_7F_7$	$f_3^{23} = t_9s_6F_2' + t_6s_9F_2$
$f_3^{31} = t_8s_2F_3' + t_2s_8F_3$	$f_R^{\delta_1} = t_{12}s_7F_7' + t_7s_{12}F_7$
$f_4^\beta = t_{10}s_3F_4' + t_3s_{10}F_4$	$f_4^\gamma = t_{11}s_{11}F_5' + t_{11}s_{11}F_5$

Here

$t_1 = (r_2 \sin \alpha_{12})/q_{C\cdots O}$	$t_2 = (r_3 \sin \alpha_{31})/q_{R\cdots O}$
$t_3 = (r_3 \sin \beta)/q_{C\cdots M}$	$t_4 = (r_1 \sin \alpha_{12})/q_{C\cdots O}$
$t_5 = (r_2 \sin \delta)/q_{C\cdots C}$	$t_6 = (r_3 \sin \alpha_{23})/q_{C\cdots R}$
$t_7 = (R \sin \delta_1)/q_{C\cdots H}$	$t_8 = (r_1 \sin \alpha_{31})/q_{R\cdots O}$
$t_9 = (r_2 \sin \alpha_{23})/q_{C\cdots R}$	$t_{10} = (r_1 \sin \beta)/q_{C\cdots M}$
$t_{11} = (r_4 \sin \gamma)/q_{O\cdots O}$	$t_{12} = (r_2 \sin \delta_1)/q_{C\cdots H}$
$s_1 = (r_1 - r_2 \cos \alpha_{12})/q_{C\cdots O}$	$s_2 = (r_1 - r_3 \cos \alpha_{31})/q_{R\cdots O}$
$s_3 = (r_1 - r_4 \cos \beta)/q_{C\cdots M}$	$s_4 = (r_2 - r_1 \cos \alpha_{12})/q_{C\cdots O}$
$s_5 = \{r_2(1 - \cos \delta)\}/q_{C\cdots C}$	$s_6 = (r_2 - r_3 \cos \alpha_{23})/q_{C\cdots R}$
$s_7 = (r_2 - R \cos \delta_1)/q_{C\cdots H}$	$s_8 = (r_3 - r_1 \cos \alpha_{31})/q_{C\cdots O}$
$s_9 = (r_3 - r_2 \cos \alpha_{23})/q_{C\cdots R}$	$s_{10} = (r_4 - r_1 \cos \beta)/q_{C\cdots M}$
$s_{11} = \{r_4(1 - \cos \gamma)\}/q_{O\cdots O}$	$s_{12} = (R - r_2 \cos \delta_1)/q_{C\cdots H}$

$q_{i\cdots j}$ is the distance between non-bonded atoms, i and j.

structures similar to those of metal acetylacetonates. Table 8 summarizes the relations between the GVF and UBF force constants.

(6) High Frequency Separation

The frequency of the C—H stretching vibration (S_9) in the A_1 species is much higher than those of other vibrations. In such a case, it is possible to reduce the order of the matrix by the *high frequency separation* technique (Ref. I-12). This can be done by correcting each $\mathbf{G}_{II}$ (A_1) element according to the relation

$$G^*_{ij} = G_{ij} - \frac{G_{9i}G_{j9}}{G_{99}} \qquad (G^* \text{ denotes a new element})$$

and separating the row and column corresponding to S_9 both from the $\mathbf{G}_{II}$ and from the $\mathbf{F}_{II}$ matrices.

(7) Solution of the Secular Equations

Numerical values of all the matrix elements are now calculated using the parameters in Table 9. The final forms of the matrices thus obtained are shown in Table 10. The next step is to solve two eighth order secular equations of the type $|\mathbf{GF} - \mathbf{E}\lambda| = 0$, using the methods mentioned in Sec. I-13. Here, the Frame method† is used to obtain the coefficients of the expanded algebraic equation of the form

$$|\mathbf{GF} - \mathbf{E}\lambda| = \lambda^n - c_1\lambda^{n-1} - c_2\lambda^{n-2} - \cdots - c_k\lambda^{n-k} - \cdots - c_{n-1}\lambda - c_n = 0$$

The first coefficient c_1 is given by

$$c_1 = \text{trace } (\mathbf{GF})$$

Here trace (**GF**) means the sum of the diagonal elements of the matrix **GF**. The second coefficient c_2 is given by

$$c_2 = \text{trace } [(\mathbf{GF})(\mathbf{GF})_1/2]$$

where

$$(\mathbf{GF})_1 = (\mathbf{GF}) - c_1\mathbf{E}$$

In general, the kth coefficient c_k is given by

$$c_k = \text{trace } [(\mathbf{GF})(\mathbf{GF})_{k-1}/k]$$

where

$$(\mathbf{GF})_{k-1} = (\mathbf{GF})(\mathbf{GF})_{k-2} - c_{k-1}\mathbf{E}$$

Thus all the coefficients are calculated successively. According to this

† For the proof of this method, see Ref. I-10*a*.

TABLE 9

Bond Distances and Angles

$r_1 = 1.28$ A, $r_2 = 1.39$ A, $r_3 = 1.53$ A, $r_4 = 1.95$ A, $\alpha_{12} = \alpha_{12}' = 120°$, $\alpha_{23} = \alpha_{23}' = 120°$, $\alpha_{31} = \alpha_{31}' = 120°$, $\beta = 135°$, $\gamma = 90°$, $\delta = 120°$

Masses of Constituent Atoms

H = 1.008, C = 12.010, O = 16.0000, Cu = 63.54

Force Constants (10^5 dynes/cm)

Stretching	Bending	Repulsive
$K_1 = K(C\cdots O) = 7.20^a$	$H_1 = H(\Delta\alpha_{12}) = 0.24$	$F_1 = F(C\cdots O) = 0.50^a$
$K_2 = K(C\cdots C) = 5.46^b$	$H_2 = H(\Delta\alpha_{23}) = 0.25$	$F_2 = F(C\cdots CH_3) = 0.40$
$K_3 = K(C—CH_3) = 3.30^a$	$H_3 = H(\Delta\alpha_{31}) = 0.31^a$	$F_3 = F(O\cdots CH_3) = 0.50^a$
$K_4 = K(Cu—O) = 2.25$	$H_\beta = H(\Delta\beta) = 0.05$	$F_4 = F(C\cdots Cu) = 0.05$
	$H_\gamma = H(\Delta\gamma) = 0.05$	$F_5 = F(O\cdots O) = 0.05$
	$H_\delta = H(\Delta\delta) = 0.33^b$	$F_6 = F(C\cdots C) = 0.37^b$
	$H_{\delta_1} = H(\Delta\delta_1) = 0.20^b$	$F_7 = F(C\cdots H) = 0.54^b$

Force constants superscripted were taken from (*a*) the acetate anion (Ref. III-210) and (*b*) benzene [Y. Kakiuchi, *Bull. Chem. Soc. Japan*, **26**, 260 (1953)]. F' was taken as $-\frac{1}{10}F$ for all the repulsive force constants.

TABLE 10

$G(A_1)$	S_1	S_3	S_5	S_7	S_{10}	S_{14}	S_{17}	S_{18}
S_1	0.145757	−0.041629	−0.041629	−0.044194	0.146125	−0.020654	0.091288	−0.029209
S_3		0.121663	−0.041629	0	−0.198439	−0.045823	−0.058611	0.047856
S_5			0.149768	0	0.004458	0.116342	−0.063530	0.051872
S_7				0.078238	0.034527	0.043121	−0.009885	−0.008071
S_{10}					0.564131	0.081592	0.166787	−0.100769
S_{14}						0.321783	−0.081000	0.145315
S_{17}							0.184949	−0.100611
S_{18}								0.123298
$G(B_2)$	S_2	S_4	S_6	S_{12}	S_8	S_{11}	S_{15}	S_{16}
S_2	0.145757	−0.041629	−0.041629	−0.073359	−0.044194	0.146125	−0.052705	−0.020654
S_4		0.208143	−0.041629	−0.262190	0	−0.098710	−0.036680	−0.116342
S_6			0.149768	0.073359	0	0.004458	0.036680	0.116342
S_{12}				4.038769	0	−0.192120	0.120097	0.166892
S_8					0.078238	0.034527	−0.005707	0.054535
S_{11}						0.526045	−0.069364	0.108523
S_{15}							0.042606	0.027722
S_{16}								0.302740

$F(A_1)$	S_1	S_3	S_5	S_7	S_{10}	S_{14}	S_{17}	S_{18}
S_1	7.926739	0.387189	0.386053	0.043007	−0.127510	0.073036	−0.060030	0
S_3		7.094988	0.309663	0	0.109942	0.110457	−0.011788	−0.063668
S_5			3.986550	0	−0.025943	−0.183522	0.105956	0
S_7				2.344978	0	−0.018646	0.025059	0.043875
S_{10}					0.432485	0.020343	−0.011745	0
S_{14}						0.650391	−0.287329	0
S_{17}							0.698178	−0.348953
S_{18}								0.722072
$F(B_2)$	S_2	S_4	S_6	S_{12}	S_8	S_{11}	S_{15}	S_{16}
S_2	7.926739	0.387189	0.386053	0	0.043007	−0.127510	0.103975	0.073036
S_4		6.521488	0.309663	0.193409	0	0.109942	0.110457	0.110457
S_6			3.986550	0	0	−0.025943	−0.183522	−0.183522
S_{12}				0.279522	0	0	0	0
S_8					2.289978	0	0.018646	−0.018646
S_{11}						0.432485	0.020343	0.020343
S_{15}							0.650391	0.497668
S_{16}								0.650391

method, the last matrix, $(\mathbf{GF})_n$, must be zero, since otherwise the coefficient c_{n+1} becomes non-zero. Therefore this method provides a good way of checking the results of the calculations.

As stated previously, both the A_1 and the B_2 species involve one redundant condition in each species. Thus the final coefficient c_8 becomes zero in each species. The seventh order polynomial equations thus obtained are shown in Table 11. If they are solved by a conventional method,

TABLE 11

A_1 Species
$\lambda^7 - 3.32380555\lambda^6 + 3.88326770\lambda^5 - 1.98336379\lambda^4 + 0.45752398\lambda^3 - 0.04573440\lambda^2 + 0.00177012\lambda - 0.00002154 = 0$
B_2 Species
$\lambda^7 - 4.53845130\lambda^6 + 7.77558535\lambda^5 - 6.28517913\lambda^4 + 2.47627227\lambda^3 - 0.45589981\lambda^2 + 0.03533807\lambda - 0.00094092 = 0$

seven λ values (eigenvalues) are obtained for each equation. By use of Eq. 13.1 of Sec. I-13 ($\tilde{\nu} = 1303.16\sqrt{\lambda}$), they are converted to $\tilde{\nu}$ (cm^{-1}) and can then be compared with the observed frequencies. These are shown in Table 12. The agreement between calculated and observed values is seen to be satisfactory in view of the complexity of the system.

(8) Theoretical Band Assignments

As stated in Sec. I-16, the concept of a group frequency is not applicable to metal acetylacetonates. In order to make theoretical band assignments, it is first necessary to calculate the eigenvector for each eigenvalue obtained above. According to the Frame method, the eigenvector $\mathbf{l}_N$ for the eigenvalue λ_N is obtained as follows: The matrices obtained previously are combined according to the expression

$$(\mathbf{GF})_{n-1} + \lambda_N(\mathbf{GF})_{n-2} + \cdots + \lambda_N^{n-2}(\mathbf{GF})_1\lambda_N^{n-1}\mathbf{E}$$

Any column of the resulting matrix is an eigenvector for λ_N. If a similar calculation is made for each eigenvalue, and if all the eigenvectors are assembled columnwise, the $\mathbf{L}$ matrix is obtained. It should be noted,

TABLE 12

	Calc. (λ)†		Calc. (cm^{-1})†	Obs. (cm^{-1})‡
A_1	λ_1	1.44423226	1566	1554 1534
	λ_2	0.92144658	1251	1274
	λ_3	0.51368941	934	937
	λ_4	0.25453608	657	684
	λ_5	0.12316057	457	455
	λ_6	0.04376737	273	—
	λ_7	0.02297328	197	—
B_2	λ_8	1.49664458	1594	1580
	λ_9	1.32355890	1499	1464
	λ_{10}	0.88307662	1225	1190
	λ_{11}	0.45753876	881	937
	λ_{12}	0.23449893	631	654
	λ_{13}	0.08198174	373	—
	λ_{14}	0.06115177	320	—

† This result was slightly improved later (see Ref. III-252).

‡ The methyl group vibrations and the out-of-plane vibrations are not listed in the table.

however, that the **L** matrix thus obtained must be normalized to satisfy the relation†

$$\tilde{\mathbf{L}}\mathbf{F}\mathbf{L} = \mathbf{\Lambda}$$

where $\mathbf{\Lambda}$ is a diagonal matrix whose elements are eigenvalues.

† As shown in Eq. 10.1 of Part I,

$$V = \tfrac{1}{2}\tilde{\mathbf{R}}\mathbf{F}\mathbf{R}$$

and, according to Eq. 16.1,

$$\mathbf{R} = \mathbf{L}\mathbf{Q} \quad \text{and} \quad \tilde{\mathbf{R}} = \tilde{\mathbf{Q}}\tilde{\mathbf{L}}$$

By combining these two equations,

$$V = \tfrac{1}{2}\tilde{\mathbf{Q}}\tilde{\mathbf{L}}\mathbf{F}\mathbf{L}\mathbf{Q} \tag{a}$$

On the other hand, the potential energy may be written

$$V = \tfrac{1}{2}\tilde{\mathbf{Q}}\mathbf{\Lambda}\mathbf{Q} \tag{b}$$

using normal coordinates. A comparison of Eqs. (a) and (b) shows that

$$\tilde{\mathbf{L}}\mathbf{F}\mathbf{L} = \mathbf{\Lambda}$$

The relation $\mathbf{L}\mathbf{G}^{-1}\mathbf{L} = \mathbf{E}$ is also obtained by comparing Eq. 10.3,

$$T = \tfrac{1}{2}\dot{\tilde{\mathbf{R}}}\mathbf{G}^{-1}\dot{\mathbf{R}} = \tfrac{1}{2}\dot{\tilde{\mathbf{Q}}}\tilde{\mathbf{L}}\mathbf{G}^{-1}\mathbf{L}\dot{\mathbf{Q}} \tag{c}$$

with

$$T = \tfrac{1}{2}\dot{\tilde{\mathbf{Q}}}\mathbf{E}\dot{\mathbf{Q}} \tag{d}$$

For Eqs. (b) and (d), see Ref. I-12.

TABLE 13

$L(A_1)$	Q_1	Q_2	Q_3	Q_4	Q_5	Q_6	Q_7
S_1	0.34875823	−0.10326347	0.11319624	0.01473210	0.01684428	−0.01007628	−0.00521610
S_3	−0.22159279	−0.25209728	0.07995148	−0.00236838	0.04773561	0.01737290	0.00379353
S_5	−0.08401884	0.31033448	0.17550510	−0.09810698	0.07734993	0.00173729	0.00142257
S_7	−0.08782376	0.06108937	−0.11445542	0.17240977	0.14022715	−0.06150006	−0.02323538
S_{10}	0.54829039	0.29656226	−0.15726757	0.25237258	0.13359889	0.26337314	−0.01849346
S_{14}	−0.06515297	0.31609303	0.27529680	0.33225510	−0.04092492	−0.03196613	0.16976050
S_{17}	0.30149302	−0.06694619	−0.18200581	−0.06185878	0.10520076	−0.00694916	0.20390228
S_{18}	−0.16276397	0.02580151	0.26843958	0.11568916	−0.07406620	0.01876273	0.06923194

$L(B_2)$	Q_8	Q_9	Q_{10}	Q_{11}	Q_{12}	Q_{13}	Q_{14}
S_2	−0.21780685	−0.27176833	0.13953392	−0.06571584	0.01054932	−0.01533913	0.01798470
S_4	0.42154243	−0.10687875	0.11488231	−0.07093823	0.02305434	−0.01596827	−0.00221323
S_6	−0.05241283	0.16996592	−0.18461200	−0.28822292	−0.00995072	0.02046216	0.02140040
S_{12}	−0.61966163	1.43628907	1.25530940	−0.09964928	0.07317693	0.02732282	−0.00250949
S_8	0.04557170	0.08171613	−0.07550578	0.08948194	0.20509055	−0.00548254	0.11702255
S_{11}	−0.33059548	−0.27451907	−0.04446630	−0.10683392	0.50004096	0.19596337	−0.19917361
S_{15}	−0.01748075	0.15371392	−0.08216036	0.01881444	−0.09282826	0.00575217	−0.05371013
S_{16}	−0.21600230	0.19611470	−0.21648704	−0.14309305	0.23479100	−0.30537451	−0.04262653

Normalization of the **L** matrix can be carried out as follows. If the relation above is written for one eigenvalue λ_N, there results

$$\lambda_N = \tilde{\mathbf{l}}_N \mathbf{F} \mathbf{l}_N = \sum_{ij} l_{Ni} F_{ij} l_{jN} = \sum_{ij} F_{ij} l_{iN} l_{jN}$$

Let a non-orthogonal eigenvector and a normalizing factor be represented by $\mathbf{l}_N'$ and k_N, respectively. Then

$$\mathbf{l}_N = k_N \mathbf{l}_N'$$

By putting this relation into the previous one, k_N becomes

$$k_N = \sqrt{\frac{\lambda_N}{\sum_{ij} F_{ij} l_{iN}' l_{jN}'}}$$

Thus the **L** matrix can be normalized by multiplying each $\mathbf{l}_N'$ eigenvector by k_N. The normalized **L** matrices thus obtained are shown in Table 13.

TABLE 14

A_1	λ_1	λ_2	λ_3	λ_4	λ_5	λ_6	λ_7
S_1	1.000	0.188	0.827	0.023	0.049	0.027	0.007
S_3	0.361	1.000	0.369	0.000	0.351	0.071	0.004
S_5	0.029	0.852	1.000	0.535	0.517	0.000	0.000
S_7	0.019	0.019	0.250	0.971	1.000	0.296	0.044
S_{10}	0.135	0.084	0.087	0.384	0.167	1.000	0.005
S_{14}	0.003	0.144	0.401	1.000	0.024	0.022	0.646
S_{17}	0.066	0.007	0.188	0.037	0.168	0.001	1.000
S_{18}	0.020	0.001	0.424	0.135	0.086	0.009	0.119
Assign-ment	ν(C⋯O)	ν(C⋯C) ν(C—R)	ν(C—R) ν(C⋯O)	ring def. ν(Cu—O)	ν(Cu—O)	δ(C—R)	ring def.
B_2	λ_8	λ_9	λ_{10}	λ_{11}	λ_{12}	λ_{13}	λ_{14}
S_2	0.324	1.000	0.351	0.103	0.008	0.031	0.082
S_4	1.000	0.127	0.195	0.099	0.032	0.027	0.001
S_6	0.009	0.197	0.309	1.000	0.004	0.028	0.058
S_{12}	0.093	0.985	1.000	0.008	0.014	0.003	0.000
S_8	0.004	0.026	0.030	0.055	0.890	0.001	1.000
S_{11}	0.041	0.056	0.002	0.015	1.000	0.274	0.547
S_{15}	0.000	0.026	0.010	0.001	0.052	0.000	0.060
S_{16}	0.026	0.043	0.001	0.040	0.332	1.000	0.038
Assign-ment	ν(C⋯C)	ν(C⋯O) δ(C—H)	δ(C—H)	ν(C—R)	δ(C—R) ν(Cu—O)	ring def.	ν(Cu—O)

According to the results shown in Table 13, the largest term in the eigenvector $\mathbf{l}_1$ is in S_{10} (the C—R bending mode). Since the frequency of the normal vibration associated with Q_1 is about 1550 cm^{-1}, it is too high for the C—R bending mode. Thus the **L** matrix itself is not suitable for making band assignments. As stated in Sec. I-16, the potential energy distribution, $F_{ii}L_i^2\lambda_N$, gives a better measure for the contribution from the individual internal coordinates. Table 14 shows the relative values of $F_{ii}L_i^2\lambda_N$ in internal symmetry coordinates, S_i, for the normal vibration associated with the normal coordinate Q_N. Terms of relatively large contribution to the normal vibration are underlined in each column. Finally, the band assignments obtained from these calculations are shown at the bottom of each column.

APPENDIX IV

A CONVERSION TABLE FOR λ, WAVE NUMBER AND WAVELENGTH

λ $(= 4\pi^2c^2\tilde{\nu}^2)$ is related to $\tilde{\nu}(\text{cm}^{-1})$ by Eq. 13.1 of Sec. I-13.

λ	$\tilde{\nu}$ (cm^{-1})	λ_w (μ)	λ	$\tilde{\nu}$ (cm^{-1})	λ_w (μ)
0.01	130.32	76.74	0.33	748.61	13.36
0.02	184.29	54.26	0.34	759.87	13.16
0.03	225.71	44.30	0.35	770.96	12.97
0.04	260.63	38.37	0.36	781.90	12.79
0.05	291.40	34.32	0.37	792.68	12.62
0.06	319.21	31.33	0.38	803.32	12.45
0.07	344.78	29.00	0.39	813.82	12.29
0.08	368.59	27.13	**0.40**	**824.19**	**12.13**
0.09	390.95	25.58	0.41	834.43	11.98
0.10	**412.10**	**24.27**	0.42	844.54	11.84
0.11	432.21	23.14	0.43	854.54	11.70
0.12	451.43	22.15	0.44	864.42	11.57
0.13	469.86	21.28	0.45	874.19	11.44
0.14	487.60	20.51	0.46	883.85	11.31
0.15	504.71	19.81	0.47	893.40	11.19
0.16	521.26	19.18	0.48	902.86	11.08
0.17	537.31	18.61	0.49	912.21	10.96
0.18	552.88	18.09	**0.50**	**921.47**	**10.85**
0.19	568.03	17.60	0.51	930.64	10.75
0.20	**582.79**	**17.16**	0.52	939.72	10.64
0.21	597.18	16.75	0.53	948.71	10.54
0.22	611.24	16.36	0.54	957.62	10.44
0.23	624.97	16.00	0.55	966.45	10.35
0.24	638.42	15.66	0.56	975.20	10.25
0.25	651.58	15.35	0.57	983.86	10.16
0.26	664.48	15.05	0.58	992.46	10.08
0.27	677.14	14.77	0.59	1000.98	9.99
0.28	689.57	14.50	**0.60**	**1009.42**	**9.91**
0.29	701.77	14.25	0.61	1017.80	9.83
0.30	**713.77**	**14.01**	0.62	1026.11	9.75
0.31	725.57	13.78	0.63	1034.35	9.67
0.32	737.18	13.57	0.64	1042.53	9.59

λ	$\tilde{\nu}$ (cm^{-1})	λ_w (μ)	λ	$\tilde{\nu}$ (cm^{-1})	λ_w (μ)
0.65	1050.64	9.52	1.07	1348.00	7.42
0.66	1058.69	9.45	1.08	1354.28	7.38
0.67	1066.68	9.37	1.09	1360.54	7.35
0.68	1074.61	9.31	**1.10**	**1366.77**	**7.32**
0.69	1082.49	9.24	1.11	1372.96	7.28
0.70	**1090.30**	**9.17**	1.12	1379.13	7.25
0.71	1098.06	9.11	1.13	1385.28	7.22
0.72	1105.77	9.04	1.14	1391.39	7.19
0.73	1113.42	8.98	1.15	1397.48	7.16
0.74	1121.02	8.92	1.16	1403.55	7.12
0.75	1128.57	8.86	1.17	1409.58	7.09
0.76	1136.07	8.80	1.18	1415.59	7.06
0.77	1143.52	8.74	1.19	1421.58	7.03
0.78	1150.92	8.69	**1.20**	**1427.54**	**7.01**
0.79	1158.27	8.63	1.21	1433.48	6.98
0.80	**1165.58**	**8.58**	1.22	1439.39	6.95
0.81	1172.84	8.53	1.23	1445.27	6.92
0.82	1180.06	8.47	1.24	1451.14	6.89
0.83	1187.24	8.42	1.25	1456.98	6.86
0.84	1194.37	8.37	1.26	1462.79	6.84
0.85	1201.45	8.32	1.27	1468.59	6.81
0.86	1208.50	8.27	1.28	1474.36	6.78
0.87	1215.51	8.23	1.29	1480.10	6.76
0.88	1222.47	8.18	**1.30**	**1485.83**	**6.73**
0.89	1229.40	8.13	1.31	1491.53	6.70
0.90	**1236.29**	**8.09**	1.32	1497.22	6.68
0.91	1243.14	8.04	1.33	1502.88	6.65
0.92	1249.95	8.00	1.34	1508.52	6.63
0.93	1256.72	7.96	1.35	1514.13	6.60
0.94	1263.46	7.91	1.36	1519.73	6.58
0.95	1270.16	7.87	1.37	1525.31	6.56
0.96	1276.83	7.83	1.38	1530.87	6.53
0.97	1283.46	7.79	1.39	1536.40	6.51
0.98	1290.06	7.75	**1.40**	**1541.92**	**6.49**
0.99	1296.63	7.71	1.41	1547.42	6.46
1.00	**1303.16**	**7.67**	1.42	1552.89	6.44
1.01	1309.66	7.64	1.43	1558.35	6.42
1.02	1316.13	7.60	1.44	1563.79	6.39
1.03	1322.56	7.56	1.45	1569.21	6.37
1.04	1328.97	7.52	1.46	1574.61	6.35
1.05	1335.34	7.49	1.47	1580.00	6.33
1.06	1341.69	7.45	1.48	1585.36	6.31

λ	$\tilde{\nu}$ (cm^{-1})	λ_w (μ)	λ	$\tilde{\nu}$ (cm^{-1})	λ_w (μ)
1.49	1590.71	6.29	1.91	1801.00	5.55
1.50	**1596.04**	**6.27**	1.92	1805.71	5.54
1.51	1601.35	6.24	1.93	1810.41	5.52
1.52	1606.64	6.22	1.94	1815.09	5.51
1.53	1611.92	6.20	1.95	1819.76	5.50
1.54	1617.18	6.18	1.96	1824.42	5.48
1.55	1622.42	6.16	1.97	1829.07	5.47
1.56	1627.65	6.14	1.98	1833.71	5.45
1.57	1632.85	6.12	1.99	1838.33	5.44
1.58	1638.05	6.10	**2.00**	**1842.95**	**5.43**
1.59	1643.22	6.09	2.01	1847.55	5.41
1.60	**1648.38**	**6.07**	2.02	1852.14	5.40
1.61	1653.52	6.05	2.03	1856.72	5.39
1.62	1658.65	6.03	2.04	1861.28	5.37
1.63	1663.76	6.01	2.05	1865.84	5.36
1.64	1668.86	5.99	2.06	1870.39	5.35
1.65	1673.94	5.97	2.07	1874.92	5.33
1.66	1679.00	5.96	2.08	1879.44	5.32
1.67	1684.05	5.94	2.09	1883.96	5.31
1.68	1689.09	5.92	**2.10**	**1888.46**	**5.30**
1.69	1694.11	5.90	2.11	1892.95	5.28
1.70	**1699.11**	**5.89**	2.12	1897.43	5.27
1.71	1704.10	5.87	2.13	1901.90	5.26
1.72	1709.08	5.85	2.14	1906.36	5.25
1.73	1714.04	5.83	2.15	1910.81	5.23
1.74	1718.99	5.82	2.16	1915.25	5.22
1.75	1723.92	5.80	2.17	1919.67	5.21
1.76	1728.84	5.78	2.18	1924.09	5.20
1.77	1733.74	5.77	2.19	1928.50	5.19
1.78	1738.63	5.75	**2.20**	**1932.90**	**5.17**
1.79	1743.51	5.74	2.21	1937.29	5.16
1.80	**1748.37**	**5.72**	2.22	1941.66	5.15
1.81	1753.22	5.70	2.23	1946.03	5.14
1.82	1758.06	5.69	2.24	1950.39	5.13
1.83	1762.88	5.67	2.25	1954.74	5.12
1.84	1767.69	5.66	2.26	1959.08	5.10
1.85	1772.49	5.64	2.27	1963.41	5.09
1.86	1777.27	5.63	2.28	1967.73	5.08
1.87	1782.04	5.61	2.29	1972.04	5.07
1.88	1786.80	5.60	**2.30**	**1976.34**	**5.06**
1.89	1791.55	5.58	2.31	1980.63	5.05
1.90	**1796.28**	**5.57**	2.32	1984.91	5.04

λ	$\tilde{\nu}$ (cm^{-1})	λ_w (μ)	λ	$\tilde{\nu}$ (cm^{-1})	λ_w (μ)
2.33	1989.19	5.03	2.75	2161.05	4.63
2.34	1993.45	5.02	2.76	2164.97	4.62
2.35	1997.71	5.01	2.77	2168.89	4.61
2.36	2001.95	5.00	2.78	2172.80	4.60
2.37	2006.19	4.98	2.79	2176.71	4.59
2.38	2010.42	4.97	**2.80**	**2180.60**	**4.59**
2.39	2014.64	4.96	2.81	2184.49	4.58
2.40	**1018.85**	**4.95**	2.82	2188.38	4.57
2.41	2023.05	4.94	2.83	2192.25	4.56
2.42	2027.24	4.93	2.84	2196.12	4.55
2.43	2031.42	4.92	2.85	2199.99	4.55
2.44	2035.60	4.91	2.86	2203.84	4.54
2.45	2039.77	4.90	2.87	2207.69	4.53
2.46	2043.93	4.89	2.88	2211.54	4.52
2.47	2048.08	4.88	2.89	2215.37	4.51
2.48	2052.22	4.87	**2.90**	**2219.20**	**4.51**
2.49	2056.35	4.86	2.91	2223.02	4.50
2.50	**2060.48**	**4.85**	2.92	2226.84	4.49
2.51	2064.59	4.84	2.93	2230.65	4.48
2.52	2068.70	4.83	2.94	2234.45	4.48
2.53	2072.80	4.82	2.95	2238.25	4.47
2.54	2076.89	4.81	2.96	2242.04	4.46
2.55	2080.98	4.81	2.97	2245.82	4.45
2.56	2085.06	4.80	2.98	2249.60	4.45
2.57	2089.12	4.79	2.99	2253.37	4.44
2.58	2093.18	4.78	**3.00**	**2257.14**	**4.43**
2.59	2097.24	4.77	3.01	2260.90	4.42
2.60	**2101.28**	**4.76**	3.02	2264.65	4.42
2.61	2105.32	4.75	3.03	2268.40	4.41
2.62	2109.35	4.74	3.04	2272.14	4.40
2.63	2113.37	4.73	3.05	2275.87	4.39
2.64	2117.38	4.72	3.06	2279.60	4.39
2.65	2121.39	4.71	3.07	2283.32	4.38
2.66	2125.39	4.71	3.08	2287.04	4.37
2.67	2129.38	4.70	3.09	2290.75	4.37
2.68	2133.36	4.69	**3.10**	**2294.45**	**4.36**
2.69	2137.34	4.68	3.11	2298.15	4.35
2.70	**2141.31**	**4.67**	3.12	2301.84	4.34
2.71	2145.27	4.66	3.13	2305.52	4.34
2.72	2149.23	4.65	3.14	2309.20	4.33
2.73	2153.17	4.64	3.15	2312.88	4.32
2.74	2157.11	4.64	3.16	2316.55	4.32

λ	$\tilde{\nu}$ (cm^{-1})	λ_w (μ)	λ	$\tilde{\nu}$ (cm^{-1})	λ_w (μ)
3.17	2320.21	4.31	3.59	2469.13	4.05
3.18	2323.87	4.30	**3.60**	**2472.57**	**4.04**
3.19	2327.52	4.30	3.61	2476.00	4.04
3.20	**2331.16**	**4.29**	3.62	3479.43	4.03
3.21	2334.80	4.28	3.63	2482.85	4.03
3.22	2338.44	4.28	3.64	2486.27	4.02
3.23	2342.06	4.27	3.65	2489.68	4.02
3.24	2345.69	4.26	3.66	2493.09	4.01
3.25	2349.30	4.26	3.67	2496.49	4.01
3.26	2352.92	4.25	3.68	2499.89	4.00
3.27	2356.52	4.24	3.69	2503.29	3.99
3.28	2360.12	4.24	**3.70**	**2506.68**	**3.99**
3.29	2363.72	4.23	3.71	2510.06	3.98
3.30	**2367.31**	**4.22**	3.72	2513.44	3.98
3.31	2370.89	4.22	3.73	2516.82	3.97
3.32	2374.47	4.21	3.74	2520.19	3.97
3.33	2378.04	4.21	3.75	2523.56	3.96
3.34	2381.61	4.20	3.76	2526.92	3.96
3.35	2385.17	4.19	3.77	2530.28	3.95
3.36	2388.73	4.19	3.78	2533.63	3.95
3.37	2392.28	4.18	3.79	2636.98	3.94
3.38	2395.83	4.17	**3.80**	**2540.33**	**3.94**
3.39	2399.37	4.17	3.81	2543.67	3.93
3.40	**2402.91**	**4.16**	3.82	2547.00	3.93
3.41	2406.44	4.16	3.83	2550.33	3.92
3.42	2409.96	4.15	3.84	2553.66	3.92
3.43	2413.49	4.14	3.85	2556.98	3.91
3.44	2417.00	4.14	3.86	2560.30	3.91
3.45	2420.51	4.13	3.87	2563.62	3.90
3.46	2424.02	4.13	3.88	2566.93	3.90
3.47	2427.52	4.12	3.89	2570.23	3.89
3.48	2431.01	4.11	**3.90**	**2573.53**	**3.89**
3.49	2434.50	4.11	3.91	2576.83	3.88
3.50	**2437.99**	**4.10**	3.92	2580.12	3.88
3.51	2441.47	4.10	3.93	2583.41	3.87
3.52	2444.94	4.09	3.94	2586.70	3.87
3.53	2448.41	4.08	3.95	2589.98	3.86
3.54	2451.88	4.08	3.96	2593.25	3.86
3.55	2455.34	4.07	3.97	2596.53	3.85
3.56	2458.80	4.07	3.98	2599.79	3.85
3.57	2462.25	4.06	3.99	2603.06	3.84
3.58	2465.69	4.06	**4.00**	**2606.32**	**3.84**

λ	$\tilde{\nu}$ (cm^{-1})	λ_w (μ)	λ	$\tilde{\nu}$ (cm^{-1})	λ_w (μ)
4.01	2609.57	3.83	4.43	2742.83	3.65
4.02	2612.83	3.83	4.44	2745.93	3.64
4.03	2616.07	3.82	4.45	2749.02	3.64
4.04	2619.32	3.82	4.46	2752.10	3.63
4.05	2622.56	3.81	4.47	2755.19	3.63
4.06	2625.79	3.81	4.48	2758.27	3.63
4.07	2629.03	3.80	4.49	2761.35	3.62
4.08	2632.25	3.80	**4.50**	**2764.42**	**3.62**
4.09	2635.48	3.79	4.51	2767.49	3.61
4.10	**2638.70**	**3.79**	4.52	2770.55	3.61
4.11	2641.91	3.79	4.53	2773.62	3.61
4.12	2645.12	3.78	4.54	2776.68	3.60
4.13	2648.33	3.78	4.55	2779.73	3.60
4.14	2651.54	3.77	4.56	2782.79	3.59
4.15	2654.74	3.77	4.57	2785.84	3.59
4.16	2657.93	3.76	4.58	2788.88	3.59
4.17	2661.13	3.76	4.59	2791.93	3.58
4.18	2664.32	3.75	**4.60**	**2794.97**	**3.58**
4.19	2667.50	3.75	4.61	2798.00	3.57
4.20	**2670.68**	**3.74**	4.62	2801.04	3.57
4.21	2673.86	3.74	4.63	2804.06	3.57
4.22	2677.03	3.74	4.64	2807.09	3.56
4.23	2680.20	3.73	4.65	2810.11	3.56
4.24	2683.37	3.73	4.66	2813.13	3.55
4.25	2686.53	3.72	4.67	2816.15	3.55
4.26	2689.69	3.72	4.68	2819.16	3.55
4.27	2692.85	3.71	4.69	2822.18	3.54
4.28	2696.00	3.71	**4.70**	**2825.18**	**3.54**
4.29	2699.14	3.70	4.71	2828.19	3.54
4.30	**2702.29**	**3.70**	4.72	2831.19	3.53
4.31	2705.43	3.70	4.73	2834.18	3.53
4.32	2708.57	3.69	4.74	2837.18	3.52
4.33	2711.70	3.69	4.75	2840.17	3.52
4.34	2714.83	3.68	4.76	2843.16	3.52
4.35	2717.95	3.68	4.77	2846.14	3.51
4.36	2721.08	3.68	4.78	2849.12	3.51
4.37	2724.20	3.67	4.79	2852.10	3.51
4.38	2727.31	3.67	**4.80**	**2855.08**	**3.50**
4.39	2730.42	3.66	4.81	2858.05	3.50
4.40	**2733.53**	**3.66**	4.82	2861.02	3.50
4.41	2736.63	3.65	4.83	2863.99	3.49
4.42	2739.74	3.65	4.84	2866.95	3.49

λ	$\tilde{\nu}$ (cm^{-1})	λ_w (μ)	λ	$\tilde{\nu}$ (cm^{-1})	λ_w (μ)
4.85	2869.91	3.48	6.35	3283.86	3.05
4.86	2872.87	3.48	6.40	3296.76	3.03
4.87	2875.82	3.48	6.45	3309.61	3.02
4.88	2878.77	3.47	6.50	3322.42	3.01
4.89	2881.72	3.47	6.55	3335.17	3.00
4.90	**2884.67**	**3.47**	6.60	3347.88	2.99
4.91	2887.61	3.46	6.65	3360.53	2.98
4.92	2890.55	3.46	6.70	3373.14	2.96
4.93	2893.48	3.46	6.75	3385.71	2.95
4.94	2896.42	3.45	6.80	3398.22	2.94
4.95	2899.35	3.45	6.85	3410.69	2.93
4.96	2902.27	3.45	6.90	3423.12	2.92
4.97	2905.20	3.44	6.95	3435.50	2.91
4.98	2908.12	3.44	**7.00**	**3447.84**	**2.90**
4.99	2911.04	3.44	7.05	3460.13	2.89
5.00	**2913.95**	**3.43**	7.10	3472.38	2.88
5.05	2928.49	3.41	7.15	3484.58	2.87
5.10	2942.95	3.40	7.20	3496.74	2.86
5.15	2957.34	3.38	7.25	3508.86	2.85
5.20	2971.66	3.37	7.30	3520.94	2.84
5.25	2985.91	3.35	7.35	3532.98	2.83
5.30	3000.10	3.33	7.40	3544.98	2.82
5.35	3014.22	3.32	7.45	3556.93	2.81
5.40	3028.27	3.30	7.50	3568.85	2.80
5.45	3042.26	3.29	7.55	3580.73	2.79
5.50	3056.18	3.27	7.60	3592.56	2.78
5.55	3070.04	3.26	7.65	3604.36	2.77
5.60	3083.84	3.24	7.70	3616.12	2.77
5.65	3097.57	3.23	7.75	3627.84	2.76
5.70	3111.25	3.21	7.80	3639.53	2.75
5.75	3124.87	3.20	7.85	3651.17	2.74
5.80	3138.42	3.19	7.90	3662.78	2.73
5.85	3151.92	3.17	7.95	3674.35	2.72
5.90	3165.36	3.16	**8.00**	**3685.89**	**2.71**
5.95	3178.75	3.15	8.05	3697.39	2.70
6.00	**3192.08**	**3.13**	8.10	3708.86	2.70
6.05	3205.35	3.12	8.15	3720.29	2.69
6.10	3218.57	3.11	8.20	3731.68	2.68
6.15	3231.73	3.09	8.25	3743.04	2.67
6.20	3244.84	3.08	8.30	3754.37	2.66
6.25	3257.90	3.07	8.35	3765.66	2.66
6.30	3270.90	3.06	8.40	3776.91	2.65

λ	$\tilde{\nu}$ (cm^{-1})	λ_w (μ)	λ	$\tilde{\nu}$ (cm^{-1})	λ_w (μ)
8.45	3788.14	2.64	9.25	3963.40	2.52
8.50	3799.33	2.63	9.30	3974.10	2.52
8.55	3810.49	2.62	9.35	3984.77	2.51
8.60	3821.61	2.62	9.40	3995.41	2.50
8.65	3832.71	2.61	9.45	4006.02	2.50
8.70	3843.77	2.60	9.50	4016.61	2.49
8.75	3854.80	2.59	9.55	4027.16	2.48
8.80	3865.80	2.59	9.60	4037.69	2.48
8.85	3876.76	2.58	9.65	4048.19	2.47
8.90	3887.70	2.57	9.70	4058.67	2.46
8.95	3898.60	2.57	9.75	4069.11	2.46
9.00	**3909.48**	**2.56**	9.80	4079.53	2.45
9.05	3920.32	2.55	9.85	4089.93	2.45
9.10	3931.14	2.54	9.90	4100.30	2.44
9.15	3941.92	2.54	9.95	4110.64	2.43
9.20	3952.68	2.53	**10.00**	**4120.95**	**2.43**

APPENDIX V

GROUP FREQUENCY CHARTS

The data cited in this book were used in the preparation of the following group frequency charts. For the physical meaning of group frequency, see Sec. I-16.

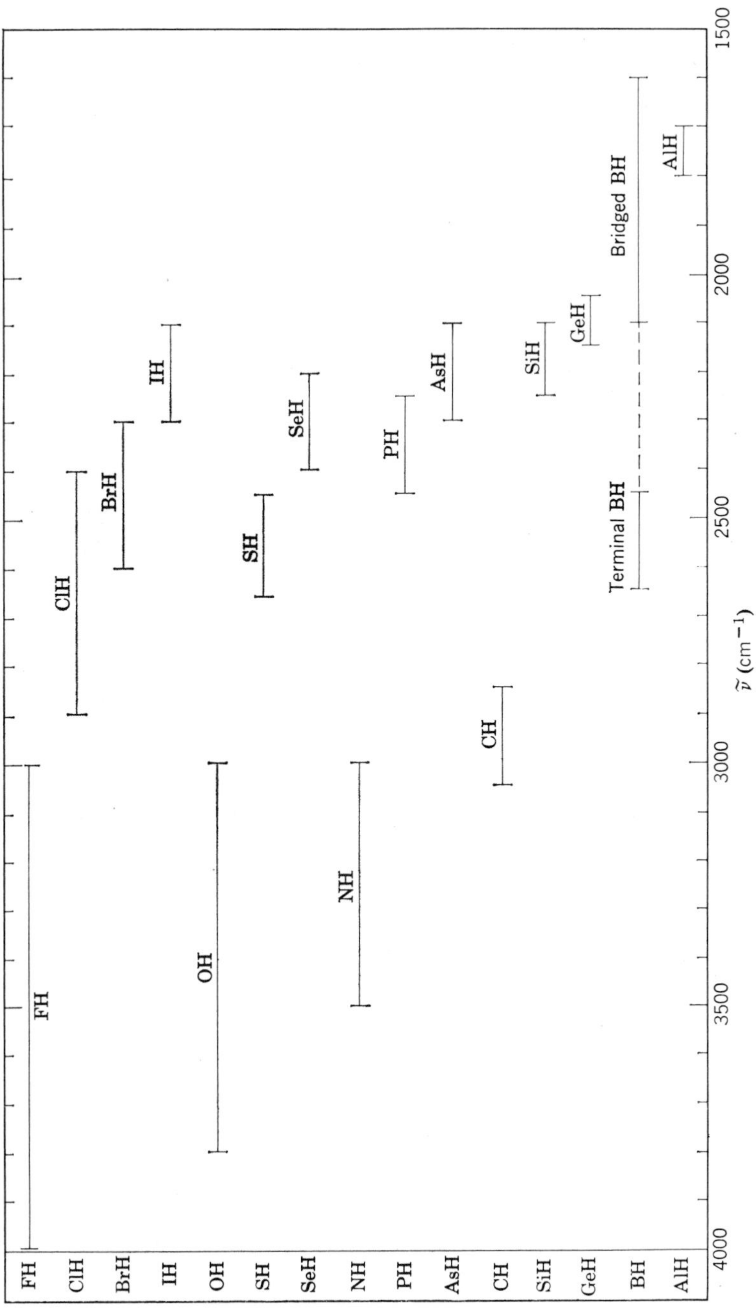

(*a*) Hydrogen stretching frequencies

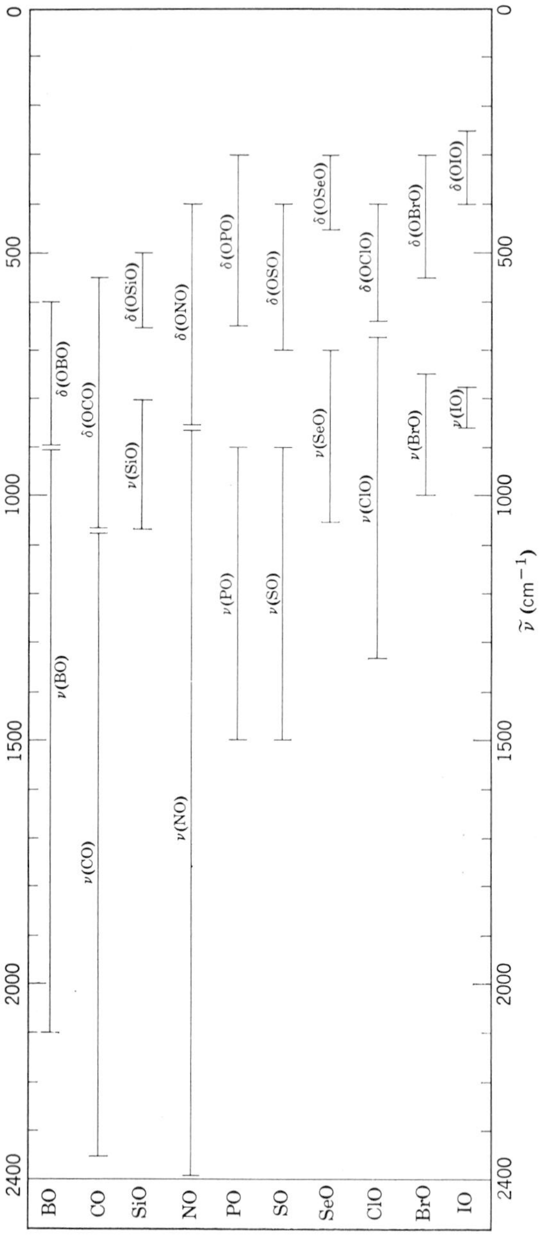

(*b*) Oxygen stretching and bending frequencies

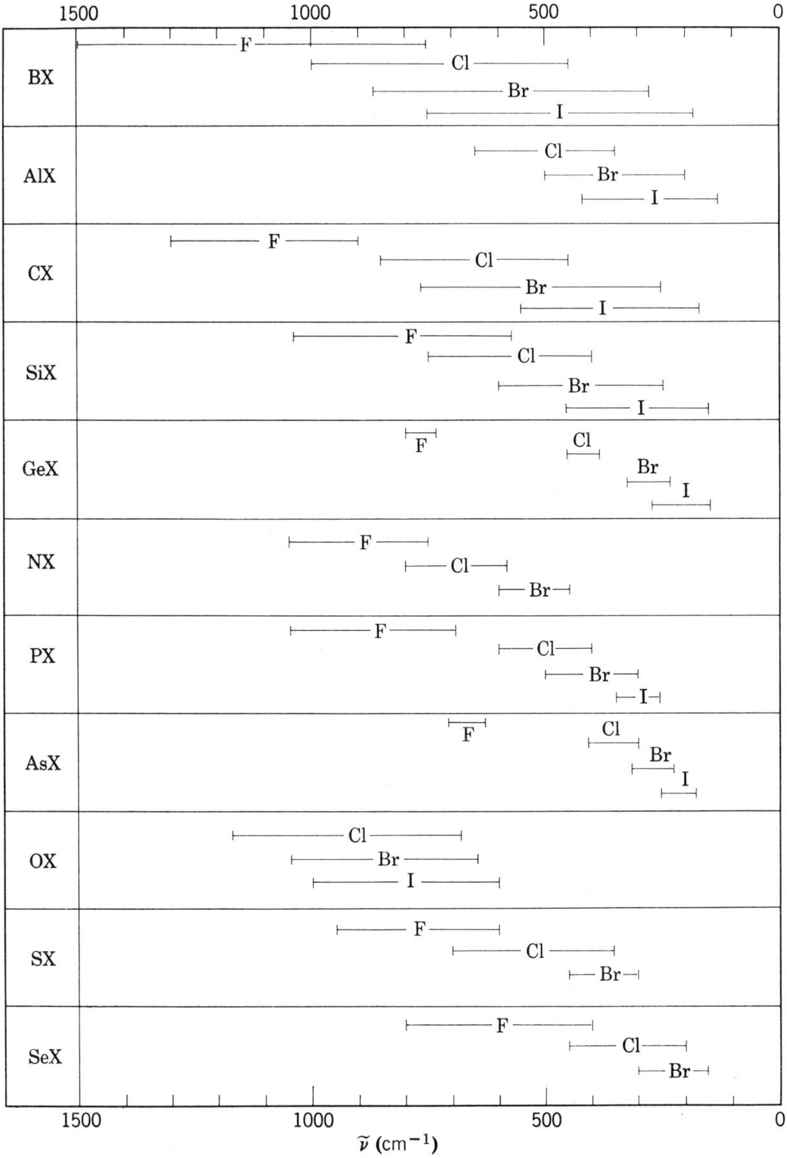

(c) Halogen (X) stretching frequencies

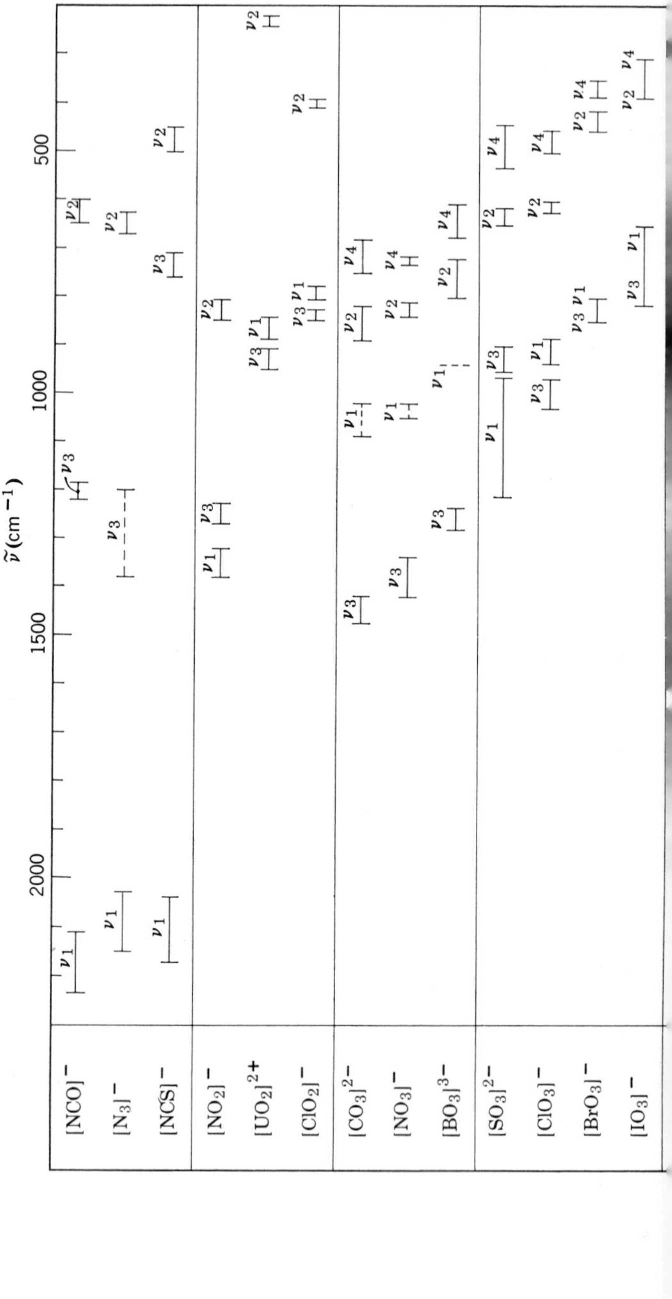
$\tilde{\nu}$ (cm^{-1})
500
1000
1500
2000
$[NCO]^-$
$[N_3]^-$
$[NCS]^-$
$[NO_2]^-$
$[UO_2]^{2+}$
$[ClO_2]^-$
$[CO_3]^{2-}$
$[NO_3]^-$
$[BO_3]^{3-}$
$[SO_3]^{2-}$
$[ClO_3]^-$
$[BrO_3]^-$
$[IO_3]^-$

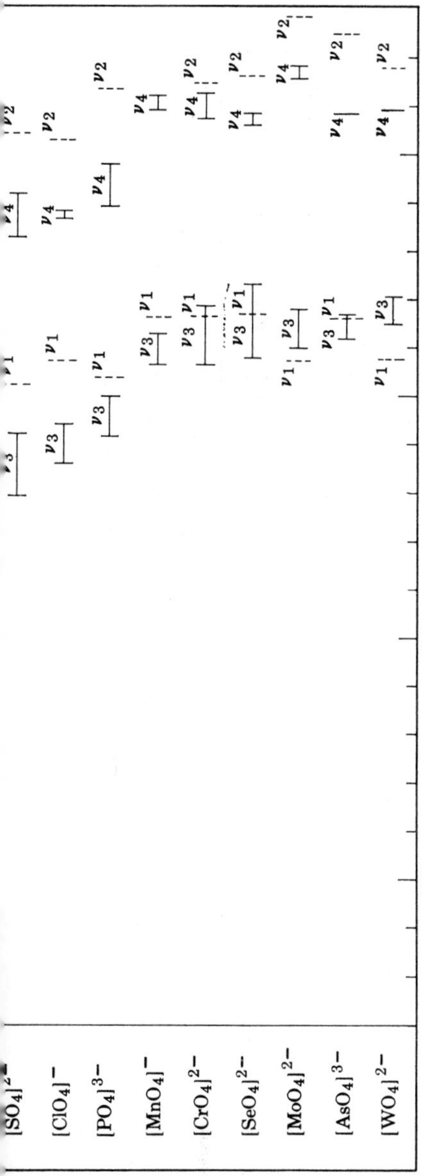

(*d*) Characteristic frequencies of some inorganic ions
(Broken lines indicate Raman active vibrations)

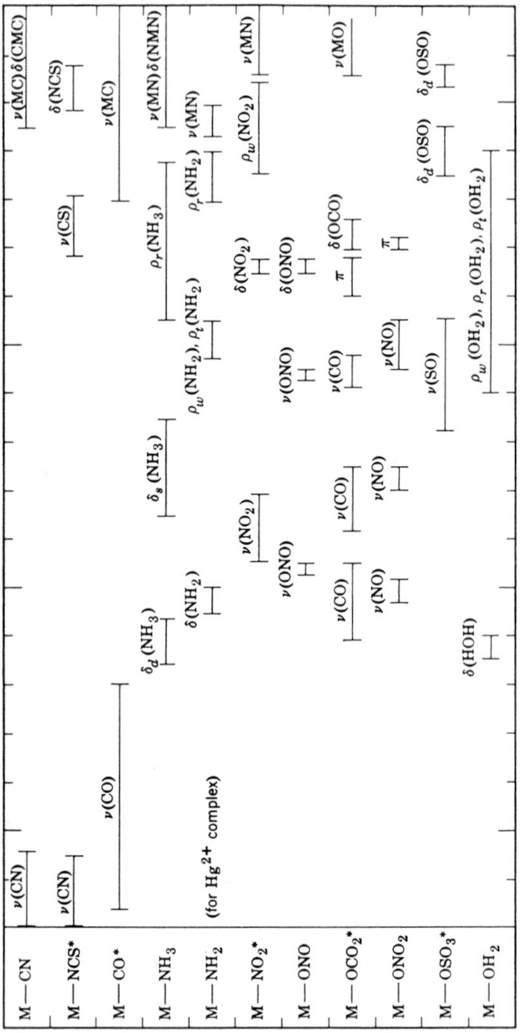

(*e*) Characteristic frequencies of metal complexes having simple ligands

(Frequency ranges include bidentate and bridged complexes for the ligands marked by an asterisk)

AUTHOR INDEX

SUBJECT INDEX

The compounds are listed alphabetically under the first element appearing in the chemical formulas as conventionally written, with the following exceptions: (1) For certain inorganic species (mainly oxy-acids and their ions), chemical formulas have been rearranged to place the central element first. For example, H_2O, H_2SO_4 and $[H_2PO_4]^-$ are written OH_2, $SO_2(OH)_2$ and $[PO_2(OH)_2]^-$, respectively. Cross references are given in ambiguous cases. (2) Compounds containing complex anions are listed under the central element of the anion (with the cation omitted). For example, $Na_3[Co(NO_2)_6]$ is listed under Co.

Isotopic compounds, except D (deuterium) and T (tritium) compounds, are not listed.

X and R are used to represent a series of halogen and alkyl compounds of the same type, respectively.

Boldface page numbers refer to figures.